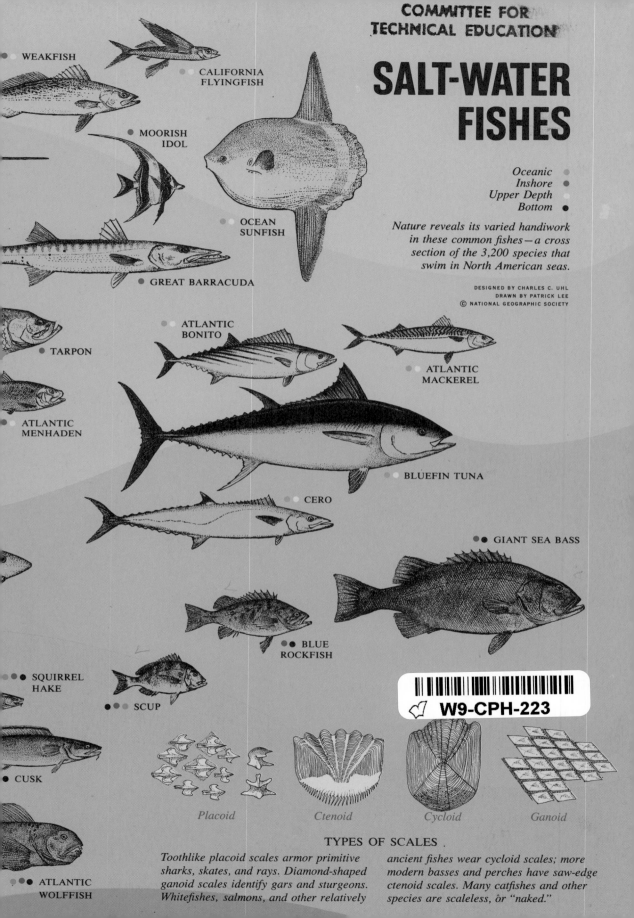

SALT-WATER FISHES

Oceanic ●
Inshore ●
Upper Depth ●
Bottom ●

*Nature reveals its varied handiwork
in these common fishes—a cross
section of the 3,200 species that
swim in North American seas.*

DESIGNED BY CHARLES C. UHL
DRAWN BY PATRICK LEE
© NATIONAL GEOGRAPHIC SOCIETY

WEAKFISH

CALIFORNIA
FLYINGFISH

MOORISH
IDOL

OCEAN
SUNFISH

GREAT BARRACUDA

TARPON

ATLANTIC
BONITO

ATLANTIC
MACKEREL

ATLANTIC
MENHADEN

BLUEFIN TUNA

CERO

GIANT SEA BASS

BLUE
ROCKFISH

SQUIRREL
HAKE

SCUP

CUSK

ATLANTIC
WOLFFISH

Placoid   *Ctenoid*   *Cycloid*   *Ganoid*

TYPES OF SCALES

*Toothlike placoid scales armor primitive
sharks, skates, and rays. Diamond-shaped
ganoid scales identify gars and sturgeons.
Whitefishes, salmons, and other relatively*
*ancient fishes wear cycloid scales; more
modern basses and perches have saw-edge
ctenoid scales. Many catfishes and other
species are scaleless, or "naked."*

19TH-CENTURY NEW ENGLAND WEATHERVANE
COURTESY NATIONAL GALLERY OF ART

WONDROUS WORLD OF FISHES

NATIONAL GEOGRAPHIC SOCIETY
WASHINGTON, D. C.

WONDROUS WORLD

OF FISHES

Published by
THE NATIONAL GEOGRAPHIC SOCIETY

MELVIN M. PAYNE, *President*

MELVILLE BELL GROSVENOR, *Editor-in-Chief*

FREDERICK G. VOSBURGH, *Editor*

1508

Staff for enlarged edition

Editor and Art Director
LEONARD J. GRANT

Associate Editors
JULES B. BILLARD, THOMAS Y. CANBY

Design and Production
HOWARD E. PAINE, CHARLES C. UHL,
  JOHN L. McINTOSH

Illustrations
ANDREW POGGENPOHL, WALTER A. WEBER

Research
GEORGE CROSSETTE, NEWTON V. BLAKESLEE,
  BETTE J. GOSS

Engraving and Printing
WILLIAM W. SMITH, JOHN R. METCALFE

Index
DOROTHY M. CORSON

Scientific Consultant
LEONARD P. SCHULTZ
Former Curator, Division of Fishes
Smithsonian Institution

_____

A volume in the
National Geographic Society's
Natural Science Library
MERLE E. SEVERY, *Chief, Book Service*

First edition: 100,000 copies
New enlarged edition, first printing: 50,000 copies
Library of Congress Catalog Card No. 71-91441

SPADEFISH (JACKET AND TITLE PAGE) BY JERRY GREENBERG
HADDOCK (OPPOSITE) BY DEAN CONGER, NATIONAL GEOGRAPHIC STAFF
RAINBOW TROUT (PAGE 6) BY TREAT DAVIDSON

Foreword

I HAVE OFTEN THOUGHT I should like to go on the banks of Newfoundland and fish with a telephone," Alexander Graham Bell, my grandfather, remarked when he was experimenting with hydrophones for the Navy early in World War I. "If you were to send the transmitter down among the codfish with the bait, perhaps you would find something to hear."

His suggestion that fish might communicate drew snickers then. But—as you will discover in *Wondrous World of Fishes*—marine creatures make a great racket, perhaps even "talk" to each other. Their noise was no laughing matter during sonar's development in World War II, when Navy men had to learn the difference between fish sounds and those of enemy submarines.

Few of us have eavesdropped on undersea conversations, but nearly everyone has had memorable experiences with fish. My earliest came on Nova Scotia's Aspy Bay, when I joined a harpooner in his dory for a thrilling "Nantucket sleigh ride" behind a 500-pound swordfish. It was in Nova Scotia, too, that F. W. "Casey" Baldwin, Grandfather Bell's Canadian associate, taught me the fine art of flyfishing. I would fidget while Casey waited to see which insects the fish rose to take. Then he would painstakingly fashion a fly to match.

Bored with such perfection, I slunk off one day with worms and cane pole. Jubilantly I returned with a string of trout—to be severely reproved for my unsporting method. But I suspect Casey was secretly proud of my new-found enthusiasm for a sport that attracts more than a third of the Nation's adults.

The array of photographs and fresh scientific data presented in *Wondrous World of Fishes* would have amazed Casey. For example, some 50 species bear new common or scientific names adopted by a committee of U. S. and Canadian ichthyologists only a few days before this enlarged edition went to press.

Four decades ago, when NATIONAL GEOGRAPHIC published the world's first undersea color photographs, Society cameramen had to ignite a raft of magnesium powder to light each exposure—nearly blowing themselves up in the process. Today photographers casually probe reef and wreck. Fishes even 5½ miles down lose their privacy—snapped with electronic flash cameras designed by Dr. Harold E. Edgerton of M.I.T. under a Society grant.

Bold, Society-sponsored explorations of Jacques-Yves Cousteau, Edwin A. Link, and others bring mushrooming knowledge of the sea. We tapped these sources, and many more. We combed, too, the Society's vast archives for photographs and text, making possible this remarkable volume at modest cost.

In distilling this ocean of material, we received the expert guidance of Dr. Leonard P. Schultz, distinguished former curator of the Smithsonian Institution's Division of Fishes. NATIONAL GEOGRAPHIC staff members worked meticulously—artist Walter Weber even kept a catfish in his bathtub to ensure accurate sketching. Across the resulting pages of this enlarged edition parade more than 375 underwater creatures from Newfoundland's streams to Hawaii's reefs. I invite you to explore this wondrous world of fishes.

Melville Bell Grosvenor

Contents

BECAUSE I'm an ichthyologist, a man whose business is knowing fishes, I get a lot of calls from fishermen. Not unnaturally, they want a proved scientific way to catch the big trout and bass.

I do my best. I tell them what the fish eats and where he ought to be, and I wish them luck. Also, I take pains to warn them that I'm a fisherman myself, and that I do not seem to do any better than anyone else. And if I think they can take it, I tell them that the best angler with rod and bait I know of is a fish.

Though some of my callers think I'm joking, I'm not. The incredible anglerfish has a fishing pole built right into its head, as I'm willing to explain if my callers are willing to listen. Actually this angler's rod is the front spine of the dorsal fin. Nature separated it from the rest of the fin, perched it atop the snout, and fashioned it into a slender rod. From its tip hangs the bait— a little blob of muscle which the anglerfish wiggles like a worm.

The angler waits, immobile except for the tantalizing bait. An inquisitive fish approaches, weighing the risk of a nibble. Nearer it draws, slowly, suspiciously. . . .

Then like lightning the angler opens its mouth and sucks in. And the victim finds itself in the angler's stomach.

Fishes that fish are a surprising idea, but no more surprising than some of the other things these wonderful animals do.

For example, fishes have voices and use them freely. The "silent" sea is clamorous with their calls. When the U. S. Navy developed a sensitive hearing device to detect the noise of submarines, operators had to learn to screen out the sounds of fishes be-

CHAPTER ONE

By LEONARD P. SCHULTZ, Ph.D.
Former Curator, Division of Fishes,
Smithsonian Institution, Washington, D. C.

Fishes and How They Live

Beneath the surface of America's waters, fishes spin nightgowns, use fishing poles, court like bashful lovers, rear young in their mouths

STILETTO FANGS *and gaping jaws rank the saber-toothed viperfish among the world's most fearsome-looking animals—until a child's hand puts him in perspective (right). As do myriad other creatures of the sunless depths,* Chauliodus sloani *generates cold light similar to the firefly's. Unlike most of North America's 4,000 species of salt- and fresh-water fishes, it migrates vertically, each morning descending a mile or so, bobbing up nights to within a quarter mile of the surface.*

fore they could work the equipment properly. Even now Navy sonarmen must guard against misinterpreting readings.

In my own scientific probing, using earphones that relay sounds from 30 feet underwater, I have heard fishes squeak, toot, grunt, and make musical whistling noises. Fishermen on Chesapeake Bay need no phones to hear the croak of the croaker or the grunt of the spot—especially when the fish swallows the hook. The sluggish toadfish, which nests on the bay bottom in old jars and cans, is particularly vocal. Both sexes make a harsh grunting sound, and the male also trills a musical boat-whistle call, probably to entice a female toadfish into his hideaway to spawn.

Fishes have even solved the problem of sleeping with their eyes open—a necessary feat since they do not have eyelids to close. Not all fish sleep, but many do. They sleep lying down, erect on the bottom, buried in the sand, or suspended in the water.

As dusk settles over the Bahamas you can watch the tropical queen triggerfish pick out a nice bed of rock or sand. It patrols the area until dark, savagely chasing away intruders. Then at nightfall, the fish tucks in, comfortably on its side.

The American striped parrotfish sleeps in a nightgown—probably as protection from predators. Leaning against coral or shells, the fish secretes a filmy mucous envelope around itself. Two openings permit water to enter the mouth and leave the gills, so that the fish can respire. Shine a light on it, or wait until sunrise, and the parrotfish quickly swims out of the nightgown.

These are just a few of the unbelievably strange ways of fishes. They are talented creatures, as you can see, but before I discuss their other abilities, I must answer a basic question: What is a fish?

We ichthyologists say that a fish is a vertebrate—backboned—animal that lives in

BRACED AGAINST THE BREAKERS, *a fisherman pulls in a 22-pound striped bass at Montauk Point, Long Island. Bluefish, weakfish, marlin, and swordfish also draw New York City anglers.*
ROBERT F. SISSON, NATIONAL GEOGRAPHIC STAFF

11

the water and respires by means of gills. But nature, never a slave to a rule, takes immediate exception. The lungfishes of Africa and South America respire with both lungs and gills. The sharks, skates, rays, lampreys, and hagfishes live in water and respire through gills as a fish should, but their backbones are not made of bone. Indeed the only bonelike parts of these odd fishes are the teeth of the sharks, skates, and rays. Their body frames are formed of cartilage.

These cartilaginous fishes are of a primitive type, little changed from the dim-past evolutionary days before fish ancestors developed backbones. Even the more complex salmon harks back to this era, as you can tell when you eat its backbone which is canned along with the flesh.

Marine animals such as the whale and porpoise look like fishes, but are not. They are mammals, as we humans are. They have lungs and warm blood, and they suckle their young. This is a long way from our cold-blooded, egg-laying fish which may as easily devour as tend its young. Another difference between fish and aquatic mammal: Whereas fish swim with a side-to-side movement of the tail, whales and porpoises work their horizontal caudal fins up and down.

The fish is more than flesh and bones; it reacts and adapts to its environment. It builds nests, cares for its young, defends its territory, and fights for its mate. Its brain is highly developed; its body represents one of nature's most streamlined creations.

You find fishes nearly everywhere there is water: in the oceans that cover 71 percent of the globe, in most rivers, and streams and lakes and ponds.

Some are mountain dwellers like our western golden trout, which live in streams more than a mile and a half above sea level. Others dwell in caves and abysses: Texas' blind catfish swims in pitch-dark wells nearly 2,000 feet deep. Sailfish frolic at the ocean surface; saber-toothed viperfish and gulper eels prowl a mile down; still deeper, eyeless fishes mingle with those that see.

U. S. Navy bathyscaph divers descended nearly seven miles in the Mariana Trench off Guam, and what did they find at the bottom? In the beam of their searchlight squirmed a solelike fish, swimming in "the eternal night which was its domain."

The world's fish population runs to the uncountable trillions. Even the number of known *kinds* of fishes staggers the imagination: about 32,000, two-thirds in salt water, one-third in fresh. Compare this with the 8,900 kinds of birds, 6,000 mammals, 2,500 amphibians, and 6,500 reptiles, and you will see that fishes comprise more than half the vertebrate animal species on earth.

The fish population of just the regions with which this book deals is immense. About 3,200 kinds of fishes swim in the salt water surrounding North America. Some 800 species live in the continent's streams and lakes. Hawaii has another 585.

The coasts, streams, and lakes of North America teemed with fish in 1607 when the *Godspeed, Discovery,* and *Susan Constant* stood into Hampton Roads to found Jamestown. Nearby Chesapeake Bay offered one of the Nation's most productive fishing basins. Quickly the colonists learned to locate schools of protein-rich menhaden by searching for gulls feeding—a guidepost sea fishermen have always followed.

James I of England, debating whether to permit freedom-seeking Pilgrims to sail for the New World, gave the royal approval when told they would go as fishermen. "'Twas the Apostles' own calling," said the pious monarch, and the Pilgrims boarded the *Mayflower.*

Fishing kept the colonists from starving on Massachusetts' "stern and rock-bound coast." Cod, big and meaty, nosed close to shore. Before long, New England fishing boats swarmed on the cod-rich Grand Banks off Newfoundland, and the young colony had its first industry.

Fishermen played a major role in America's growth. In the Revolution they provided manpower and ships for the Nation's fledgling navy. Indomitable fishermen from Marblehead, Massachusetts, rescued Washington's army after the battle of Long Island, and ferried it across the Delaware to surprise the Hessians at Trenton. Yankee fishermen accumulated capital that fostered

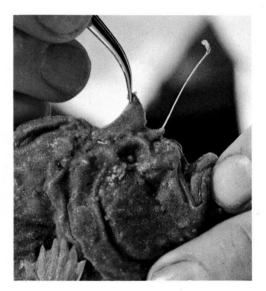

SPECIMENS SURROUND *the author, Dr. Leonard P. Schultz, as he examines an anglerfish at the Smithsonian Institution in Washington, D.C., home of one of the world's finest fish collections. Dr. Schultz served as curator of the museum's Division of Fishes for 28 years. Foreground jars contain alcohol-preserved characins from South America; those on shelf hold conger eels.*

A squat anglerfish (Antennarius chironectes) *at right carries a built-in fishing pole and pendent bait to entice victims. The ocellated frogfish angler* (A. ocellatus) *opens a huge mouth to gulp an aquarium dweller attracted by the lure (below). Here pole and bait—the modified first spine of the dorsal fin —relax above its snout. When not fishing, the angler tucks the pole between its eyes. Females of deep-sea species sport an added attraction: luminescent bait to decoy prey in the dark.*

later New England industries. As traders and whalers they carried the American flag to the far corners of the world.

The colonists and later pioneers found the American Indian a skilled fisherman. Red men jigged with barbless hooks of bone, wood, thorns, and bird talons. They set traps and weirs across woodland rivers, speared fish through holes chopped in Great Lakes ice, and fished with bow and arrow at mountain pools.

Among Pacific slope Indians, fish ranked as the chief item of food and trade. They dried eulachon, an oily smelt, and burned it as a candle. They used wicker baskets to dip vast quantities of migrating salmon. The importance of fishing to these tribes continues into our own period. When a dam in the 1950's inundated Columbia River sites where Indians had taken salmon for centuries, Congress granted nearly $27 million to compensate the tribes.

The Nation's fisheries burgeoned through the 19th century and into the 20th. Today's fishermen are as daring as the old Marble-headers, but many face hard times. Always rugged individualists, they are slow to organize for tackling fisheries' problems. New boats and modernization of old ones are expensive, yet a law—passed in 1792—prevents use of cheaper boats built abroad.

Thus our largely antiquated trawler fleet fishes the Grand Banks beside the Soviet Union's steel fishing boats and huge factory ships that fillet and freeze the catch on board. Our Pacific tuna vessels, despite vigorous modernization, struggle to compete with the gleaming ships of Japan, a perennial leader in the harvest of fishes. Peru, Russia, Red China, and Norway also catch more than our total take of five billion pounds a year.

But improvements are being made. More and more, science goes to sea with fishermen. Pacific tuna fleets spot schools by helicopter and sonar, then catch them with huge nets. Depth sounders locate shoals and underwater shelves where fish congregate. Underwater television helps in the testing of new equipment—and can give fishermen

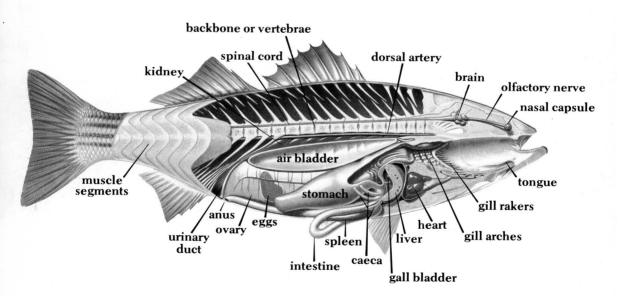

FISH INTERIOR *resembles man's, with its brain and nervous system, heart and circulatory vessels, mouth and digestive arrangement, and skeleton. But respiration sets the fish apart. Taking water into its mouth, the fish strains it through gill rakers, then passes it between gill arches and over the gills, which are lined with tiny blood vessels. The latter absorb dissolved oxygen. The air bladder serves as a hearing aid, as a vibrator for making noises, and helps to equalize the fish's weight with that of water. Fingerlike caeca, probably aiding in digestion, correspond to the human appendix. Large liver—in sharks at least 10 percent of the total fish—often abounds with vitamin D. Muscle segments are the flesh we eat.*

a true picture of what the fish are doing. Special submarines carry observers into the fishes' own realm.

New devices and studies will no doubt fill in some important blanks in the biography of the fish. But the main story is already clear. We ichthyologists can give some satisfying, and surprising, answers to questions laymen often ask: How big can a fish grow? How long can a fish live? Such queries lead us into fascinating studies.

Take the matter of the fish's growth. Between 16 and 20 years we humans stop growing upward (and often start growing outward). Growth of a fish never stops. It slows abruptly at sexual maturity, but the fish generally gets a little longer and a little thicker every year. Usually a female will outweigh a male of equal age.

The largest living fish recorded was a 45-foot whale shark taken off Florida in 1912. Estimated weight: 20 tons. The basking shark, second largest, may reach 35 feet. A quarter of the basker's weight is liver, and a single liver has yielded 200 gallons of vitamin-rich oil. Oddly, both the basker and whale shark—like the world's largest mammal, the whale—attain their huge size on a diet of plankton, tiny creatures of the sea.

The disklike ocean sunfish, a pudgy fellow of the world seas, grows in height more than he does in length. A 10-foot specimen measured 13 feet up and down and weighed some 4,400 pounds. The batlike manta ray reaches a width of more than 20 feet and may weigh more than a ton.

The Columbia River yielded probably the largest fresh-water fish caught in North America—a white sturgeon twelve and a half feet long. Its 1,285-pound body contained 125 pounds of roe—an impressive haul of caviar. Alligator gars, second largest of our fresh-water fishes, reach 12 feet.

Along the shores of Chesapeake Bay I have found fossilized white shark teeth perhaps twenty-five million years old that measured six and a quarter inches across. A California white shark, reportedly 30 feet long, had teeth that measured two inches. If the teeth of fossil sharks, like living ones, were

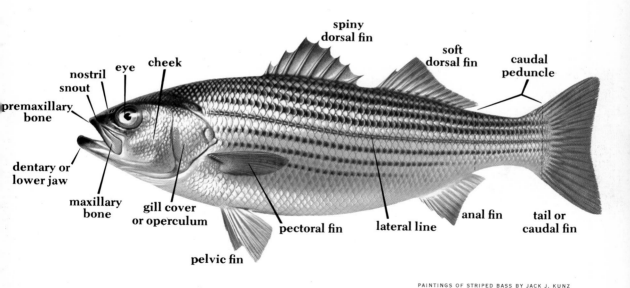

PAINTINGS OF STRIPED BASS BY JACK J. KUNZ

FISH EXTERIOR, *covered with scaly armor, forms one of nature's most streamlined creations. Swimming by undulating the body from side to side, some fishes can outrace a nuclear submarine. Fins help in maneuvering. To turn, the creature sticks out a pectoral fin, flips its tail, and pivots. To stop, it flares out pelvics and pectorals as brakes. If one fish nibbles off another's fins, they quickly regenerate, as do lost scales. Fish have no outer ear but can hear: Sound waves strike the skull, which transmits vibrations to an inner ear. Fish taste, touch, smell, see—and have a sixth sense in the lateral line running along each side of the body. It houses organs that detect low-frequency vibrations unnoticed by the ear.*

15

FROM HERMAN MOLL'S MAP OF NORTH AMERICA, C. 1710, LIBRARY OF CONGRESS

18TH-CENTURY FISHERY *processes cod, a colonial staple, on a bleak Newfoundland shore. Bundled-up fisherman (left) holds baited hook; men on ship fish from suspended barrels. Unloaded from a boat, cod are dressed, salted, washed, then dried on a platform. A press extracts "ye oyl from ye Cods Livers." Honoring the lifesaving food and source of wealth, Massachusetts legislators hung a "representation of a Cod Fish," carved from pine, in the State House (below).*

BATES LITTLEHALES (OPPOSITE), AND ROBERT F. SISSON, BOTH NATIONAL GEOGRAPHIC STAFF

in proportion to length, the white sharks of that remote age may have grown more than 60 feet long and weighed more than 100,000 pounds. This probably represents the ultimate in fish growth.

Most of the common fishes have a short life compared to ours. Some are merely annuals like the petunias in your garden. Members of the family Cyprinodontidae of Africa and South America mature during the rainy season in temporary streams and pools. As the water recedes they lay eggs in the mud, then die. When new rains moisten the mud, the eggs hatch, and the fry emerge for their single season on earth.

The old New York Aquarium, predecessor of the modern complex at Coney Island, kept records of life spans. A striped bass lived there 20 years. Whitefish reached 15; largemouth bass, 11; muskellunge, crappie, rock bass, and yellow perch, 10.

Considering the trillions hatched, relatively few fishes die of old age. Tagging studies reveal that natural mortality and fishing destroy 70 percent of the fish population each year. Thus of a million hatchlings 300,000 survive the first year, 90,000 the second, 2,430 the fifth, 65 the eighth. Only half a dozen survive their tenth year.

We owe much of our knowledge of the growth and age of fishes to records inscribed on their scales. These form a tailored, flexible suit of armor that the fish and his ancestors have worn through the nearly half billion years they have existed. The ichthyologist has learned to decipher scales much as a forester reads the rings of a tree.

Like the tree, the scale grows concentric rings as fish and scale mature. In summer, when water warms and food is abundant, the fish grows quickly. The rings form far apart. In autumn, growth slows and the rings become closer. Counting the clusters of closely placed rings, or annuli, scientists can estimate the fish's age.

The scale will also identify the species of fish, just as a fingerprint identifies its owner. And sometimes the same legal complications result. Once I received a telephone call from a representative of the U. S. Food and Drug Administration.

BARBLESS BONE FISHHOOKS *snagged food for Alabama cave dwellers thousands of years before Christ. Ingenious two-piece hook, once lashed at the bottom to form a V, spread wider when the fish struck—planting itself more firmly. A little more grinding on the slotted deer bone (right) would have finished a single-piece hook. A National Geographic– Smithsonian Institution expedition unearthed the artifacts in Alabama's Russell Cave. The Society gave the site to the Federal Government in 1960 for a National Monument.*

"Can you identify the kind of Pacific coast salmon if I bring you a fillet to examine?" the official asked.

"Yes," I said, "if the scales are on it."

He soon appeared at my laboratory with some frozen salmon steaks, scales and all. I placed the scales under a microscope. They told me that they came from a pink salmon, and I showed the official the structural marks that proved it.

IN FROM THE HERRING HARVEST, *fishing boats
tie up at the Bay of Fundy island of Grand Manan.
Part of the catch goes into cans as sardines; part
cures in smokehouses, permeating the island with
an appetizing scent. A coating washed from the
scales, called pearl essence, makes costume
jewelry. Bright-colored buoys (foreground) mark
lobster pots when dropped offshore. Dead
fish lure the crustaceans into traps. Like nearby
Maine, Grand Manan is noted for lobster.*

W. D. VAUGHN (CENTER) AND WILLARD PRICE

WHITE-BELLIED FLOUNDERS *come aboard a Nova Scotia dragger; more wait to be hoisted. Fishermen use a Danish seine—a long net that rings an area of sea floor and corrals the fish when drawn shut. One haul often yields more than 5,000 pounds of bottom feeders. Large-mesh net lets small fish wriggle through—to grow and be taken another year.*

BOATS TIGHTEN *a purse seine around Gulf of Mexico menhaden, valued for oil and as animal feed (above). Chanting crewmen pull them in (left). Low-flying planes locate the huge, shadowlike schools. The U. S. menhaden catch, more than a billion pounds yearly, is four times that of either tuna or salmon, which vie for second place.*

KNEE-DEEP *in salmon, an Alaska netter crams a seiner's hold. Fishing rivals oil as the state's top industry.*

HOOKS HIT *the fish-churned Pacific and—wham! tuna strike. Men catapult the fish into bins on deck; barbless hooks slip from mouths, and lines snap back for more. Live sardines, strewn overboard by the chummer, excite tuna until they frenziedly seize feathered lures. To handle big fish, four bamboo poles bend as a single rig (opposite). A good day may yield 30 tons. Tuna boats sail from San Diego and San Pedro year round, roaming south to Peru.*

Then he explained his curiosity. The U. S. Army had bought thousands of pounds of coho salmon steaks. But the fish company had delivered pink salmon, which sells for a lower price.

My detective work aided legal proceedings that led to confiscation of the shipment.

The skin that anchors the scales contains pigments that enable some fishes to change color like a chameleon. The pigments, in thousands of cells called chromatophores, may be red, orange, yellow, green, blue, brown, silvery, or black.

Whenever the fish wishes, he can expand some color cells and contract others. Swimming over a black bottom, the fish expands the black cells. Thus camouflaged from enemies, he stalks his prey unseen.

To test the adroitness of that quick-change artist, the flounder, scientists placed one first over checkerboard patterns, then over polka dots. They found that in no time the flounder's upper side resembled a blotchy oblong checkerboard or an oversized polka-dot tie. The fish's eyes tell him what colors to mimic. Blindfolded, he cannot change to match his environment.

Not long ago I watched a fish use his color cells to create a different kind of camouflage. When not in motion, he wore vertical stripes which blended with growths of coral and weed in the background. When he

JOHN H. TASHJIAN (ABOVE), E.W. GUDGER (INSET), AND TREAT DAVIDSON

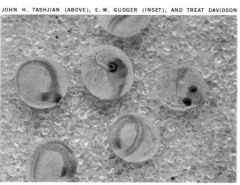

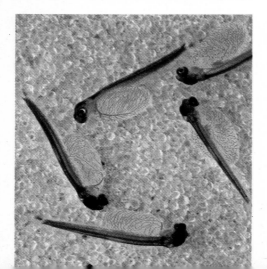

EGGS MAKE A MOUTHFUL *for Atlantic catfishes of the family Ariidae. Sea cats (Arius felis,* top pair*) and gafftopsail catfish (Bagre marinus,* inset*) carry eggs for a month and hatchlings another 10 days, all the while eating nothing themselves.*

*Brook trout are born more prosaically. Mother lays as many as 4,000 eggs on gravel, and in 45 days they are ready to hatch (*left, enlarged four times*). Fry (*lower, two hours old*) feed on yolk sacs until able to forage.*

PORPOISE BABY, *photographed at the moment of birth at Marineland of Florida, enters the world able to swim; mother snaps the umbilical cord with a twisting jerk of her body. A mammal, not a fish, the porpoise nurses offspring for nearly a year.*

22

swam, he changed to horizontal stripes, becoming a hard-to-see blur of movement.

Fishes even don different dress as daylight fades to darkness. Their changing patterns show in remarkable photographs (page 152) made by a research team off the Florida Keys. The group's studies on protective coloration were sponsored by the National Geographic Society and the University of Miami's Institute of Marine Sciences.

In most of his internal workings, the fish differs little from ourselves. It is his respiration that sets him apart. Like us, he requires oxygen, but he must get it from the relatively small amount of air that dissolves in water.

The fish takes in water through the mouth and pumps it back through strainers called gill rakers, which sift out floating food particles and foreign matter. Then the water runs over the gills proper—four to nine paired rows of feathery filaments, each loaded with tiny blood capillaries. These absorb the dissolved oxygen.

When you see an aquarium fish constantly opening and closing his mouth, he is pumping water back through his gills—he is respiring. The nostrils play no part in this; they are used only for smelling.

Some kinds of fishes require more oxygen than others, and this affects their choice of waters. Brook trout prefer northern

Blue whale, world's largest animal, feeds on zooplankton.

1 Sea's cycle of life begins with phytoplankton (algae and plant-animals), here highly magnified. Using the sun's life-giving power, these minute organisms combine water, carbon dioxide, and minerals into carbohydrates, proteins, and fats. They serve as the ocean's basic foodstuff.

6 Chemicals from decomposition well up to the sunlight zone and replenish the life cycle.

5 Plant and animal debris rains down on the ocean floor, there to nourish bottom dwellers and to decay.

Portuguese man-of-war entangles fish in its tentacles.

2 Zooplankton (microscopic animals) feed on phytoplankton.

3 Herring and other fish, by the hundreds of millions, feed on minute zooplankton, here highly magnified.

4 Tuna and other predators eat smaller fish and in turn fall prey to sharks and killer whales.

Life cycle of the sea

ROBERT C. MAGIS   NATIONAL GEOGRAPHIC STAFF ARTIST

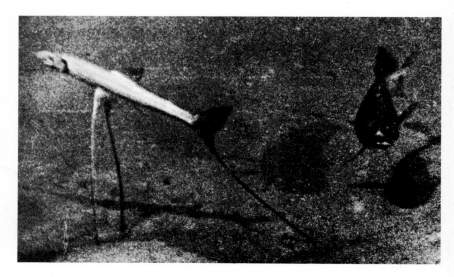

FINS SERVE AS STILTS *for* Benthosaurus, *which stands and hops on the sea floor more than a mile down. Prior to observation from a deep-diving bathyscaph in 1957, scientists—studying dredged up specimens—had guessed that the long fins served only as feelers. A "double-tailed" bottom dweller,* Haloporphyrus, *cruises at right; its shadow shows the split caudal fin.*

Eel-like Halosaurus *(below) hovers over the abyssal ooze, its tail undulating in the current. Bulbous eye of a dogfish (lower photograph) eerily reflects the searchlight's glare. Oversize eyes are common to deep-water denizens.*

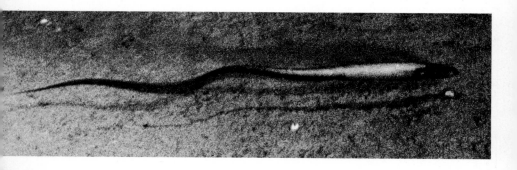

BATHYSCAPH—*a steel gondola slung beneath a cigar-shaped craft filled with gasoline for buoyancy—opened the sea's blackest depths to man in the 1950's. Here the artist shows it dropping some 5,500 feet into Setúbal canyon off Portugal. In it Lt. Comdr. Georges S. Houot watched graceful jellyfish and torrents of plankton drift past his gondola porthole as he descended. At the bottom his searchlights illuminated a surrealistic rock garden of plantlike gorgonians and pennatulids. In this and other pioneering dives, Houot used electronic cameras designed by Dr. Harold E. Edgerton, Massachusetts Institute of Technology, whose research was aided by National Geographic grants. On the sea floor, Houot photographed the weird fishes opposite as they paraded by.*

PAINTING BY MICHAEL RAMUS

streams because cold water retains more dissolved oxygen than warm water. Carp, requiring less oxygen, live comfortably in warm ponds and sluggish streams. In particularly stagnant waters they suck in the oxygen-rich surface film which has been in direct contact with air. Goldfish survive in simple unaerated fishbowls because they too suck in the surface water.

Most fishes suffocate in air. The tarpon compromises. To augment the oxygen supplied by the gills, he gulps surface air into a lunglike chamber behind his head.

This chamber, called the air bladder, may have served fishes as a lung in past ages, allowing them to adapt to shifts of the earth's waters that left them high and dry.

The air bladder survives in most fishes, but few respire with it. They use the bladder in other ways. Some slowly inflate or deflate it to adjust their density to that of the water, so that they will not rise or sink. They also use the bladder as a resonant receiver of sounds. And some fishes, like the voluble croaker, vibrate the air bladder to produce their own sounds.

In the lungfishes the air bladder still serves its original purpose. Partly because of it, lungfishes can survive year-long dry seasons in a cocoon completely out of water. The kidney also plays an important part in this phenomenon, keeping the lungfish from drying out. The kidney continues to dispose

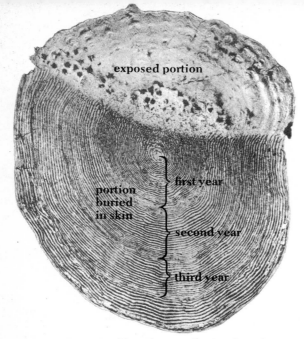

exposed portion

portion
buried
in skin

first year

second year

third year

FISH SCALE, *like a human fingerprint, gives clues about its owner. Three clusters of rings, called annuli, mark this salmon scale (enlarged 15 times) as from a four-year-old fish. Wide white bands show periods of quick growth, thin ones lean times.*

Skin layers turn purple when dye penetrates the cross section of a sailfin molly (below, magnified about 100 times). Epidermis atop scales houses slime sacs whose secretions protect fish from parasites, waterproof it— and make it slip from the hand. A fish at birth has its full quota of scales; as it grows, they grow proportionately.

of urea, but in doing so it zealously sees that a minimum of body fluid escapes.

A few fishes, such as salmon, can move freely between salt water and fresh, and here too the kidney makes the difference.

Salmon hatch and spend their youth in fresh-water streams, then swim down to mature in the ocean. When they reach salt water, they face the problem of osmosis— the tendency of one liquid to flow into another more dense when the two are separated by a semipermeable membrane.

When the salmon enters the sea he encounters a saltier medium than the fresh water he left. Thus his body fluids, formerly conditioned to fresh water, tend to seep by osmosis into the denser salt water. Unchecked, this seepage would dry the salmon out. The kidney and salt-secreting cells in the gills come to the rescue by retarding the disposal of body fluids.

When the sea-conditioned adult salmon returns to less dense fresh water, the reverse seepage tends to occur. But again the kidney balances things, helping keep salty body fluids from soaking up fresh water, and upriver goes the salmon to spawn.

It seems to be the law of the sea that the more responsible parents are, the fewer young they will have. Salmon and other fishes which protect their eggs by making

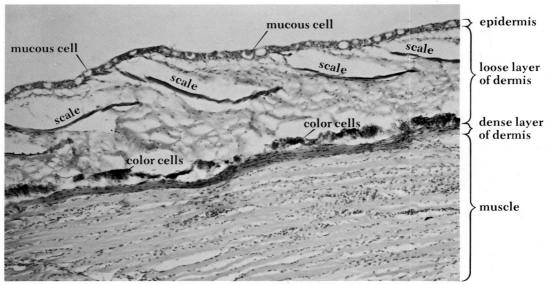

mucous cell — epidermis

mucous cell

scale

loose layer of dermis

scale

scale

scale

color cells

dense layer of dermis

color cells

muscle

SILVER HATCHETFISH, *a monster in the background drawing, assumes true size in the palm of Eda Zahl, wife of a National Geographic senior editor (author of chapter 18). Light-producing photophores on the underside of* Argyropelecus hemigymnus *glow like embers (below, enlarged 10 times). Each is backed by reflectors that train light into the water. Other deep-sea dwellers sport pink, white, purple, and blue light organs. Common equipment for fishes in dark depths, they may lure prey, repel enemies, signal friends, or light the way like lanterns. Luminescent bacteria and interacting enzymes generate the glow. Hatchetfish's tail resembles the handle of a hatchet, its body the head.*

29

LEPROUS SKIN *and frondlike fins of the sargassumfish make it nearly invisible in tropical Atlantic vegetation where it climbs about on its pectorals. Open water reveals its disguise and the fishing-pole snout that identifies* Histrio histrio *as one of the anglerfishes.*

SHAPELESS STONEFISH, *a bump in shallows of the Indian and Pacific Oceans, packs the most poisonous venom of any fish. To step on* Synanceja verrucosa's *dorsal spines can bring death in hours.*

Fish Carry a Bagful of Tricks for Eluding Enemies

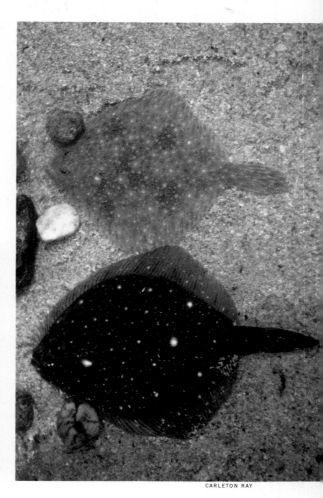

CARLETON RAY

a nest in a stream bed lay relatively few eggs—perhaps 3,000 to 30,000. Fishes that show less concern for their offspring, or tend to eat them, survive only by laying hundreds of thousands of eggs, or more. A haphazard parent like the cod may produce nine million eggs. If all the eggs of every cod resulted in offspring and these in turn reproduced at the same rate, it would take only a few years for the ocean basins literally to overflow.

Sea catfish, good parents, lay few eggs—and a lucky thing for the male. For six weeks he protects the eggs and babies by carrying them in his mouth. A relative, the gafftopsail catfish, has been observed to carry 55 eggs in his mouth, each three-quarters of an inch in diameter! Unable to eat during this period of exemplary behavior, male catfishes become extremely thin.

One of the most amazing spawning patterns is that of the grunion. Every two weeks from March to August, at the high spring tides, grunion congregate along the sand beaches of southern California. Right after the turn of a tide, they ride the waves onto the sloping beach. Quickly the female wriggles her tail a few inches into the sand and lays her eggs. A male at once fertilizes them. Then the grunion catch the next wave and

PAUL A. ZAHL, NATIONAL GEOGRAPHIC STAFF (ABOVE), AND JOHN H. GERARD

FANGS BURIED *in its prey, a fisher spider sucks the juices from a minnow (opposite, enlarged about three times). The spider climbs down plant stems into the water to seize a fish with its legs, injects its deadly venom, then drags the lifeless body up to its web to feed.*

UNWARY SILVERSIDE *becomes a sea anemone's meal. Paralyzed by tiny hypodermics in the waving tentacles, the fish will be engulfed —then later disgorged as a lump of bones and scales. This anemone species, an inch and a half across, lives on rocks in the Mediterranean.*

return to sea, leaving the eggs ashore, undisturbed by the receding tide.

The grunion eggs mature in the sand. In two weeks the spring tide returns, loosening the sand and uncovering the eggs. Once free in the water, they hatch like popping corn, and the young in their turn ride the receding waves to sea.

Sea catfishes and grunion reproduce oviparously—the female lays the eggs and the male instantly fertilizes them externally. Most fishes produce their young this way.

A few are viviparous, like humans. Surf fishes such as the blue perch, for example, fertilize the eggs internally, and the female carries the embryos, supplying them nourishment from her own body fluids. The vicious-looking sand tiger shark works a macabre variation on this system. The largest embryo becomes a prenatal cannibal, devouring smaller embryos and successive eggs as fast as the parent produces them.

The mating habits and family life of fishes vary from extreme indifference to what would seem overconcern. Herring could hardly care less about a mate. Congregating in great schools, males and females deposit countless eggs and clouds of milt and swim on. Parental care is nonexistent.

The little bitterling foists off parental responsibilities on others. First the male finds a suitable fresh-water mussel. Then

the female lays her eggs in the mussel's gill chamber, and the male releases his milt. Afterwards the parents swim away, leaving to the passive mussel the job of hatching the orphan bitterlings.

Trout act with more affection. They pair off and court, and the female scoops out a nest in the river bottom for the eggs. Here, however, the bond usually ends. Parents go their separate ways, and the eggs are left to their fate.

The coy male of the grunt sculpin resists matrimony to the utmost. When a female is ready to spawn, she pursues her mate until she corners him in a crevice. Blocking his escape, she lays 150 eggs. Only when he has fertilized them is the male allowed to resume his celibate ways.

Jewelfish of aquarium fame show remarkable devotion. The male, brightly colored in spawning season, selects a nesting place, then vigorously fends off other males. A ready-to-spawn female approaches; the gallant male takes her in. Days before egg laying, the couple frolic in courtship.

The jewelfish guard the eggs until they hatch, chasing away intruders. Then they carry the helpless young in their mouths from place to place. When the fry start swimming, the grown-up jewelfish ride herd protectively, catching strays in their mouths and spitting them back into the family

32

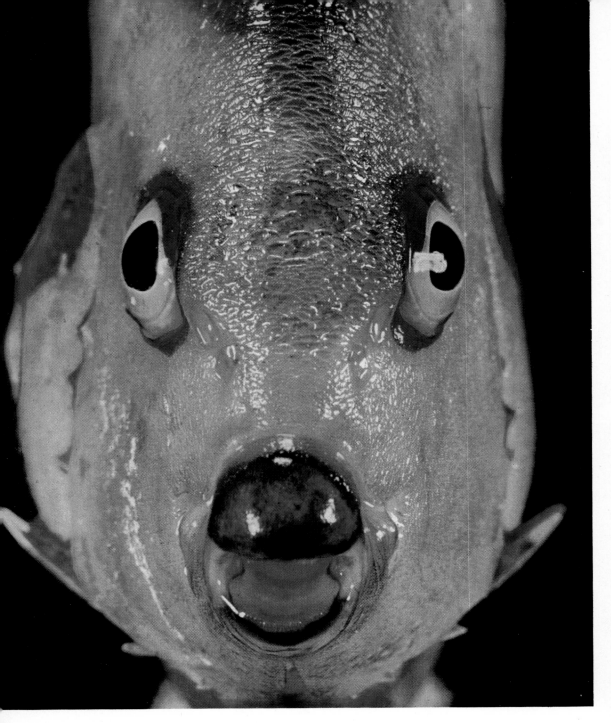

PAINTED-CLOWN FACE *of a blue angelfish bears a tiny mouth that limits its owner to nibbling invertebrates and vegetation. Many fishes, voracious flesh eaters, have tooth-studded jaws. Teeth seize but do not chew; fish swallow victims whole or rip them into manageable chunks. For dainty eaters such as the vegetarians, nature provides grinding-mill teeth in the pharynx. Between meals the pharynx locks shut, protecting the stomach from a constant flow of sea water that would dilute the digestive juices.*

Slim body of the angelfish serves admirably for a life among rocks and reefs of the tropics, enabling it to flit through narrow crevices. Spiny barbs can inflict painful wounds.

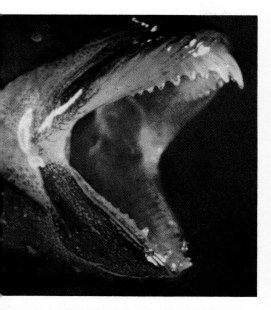

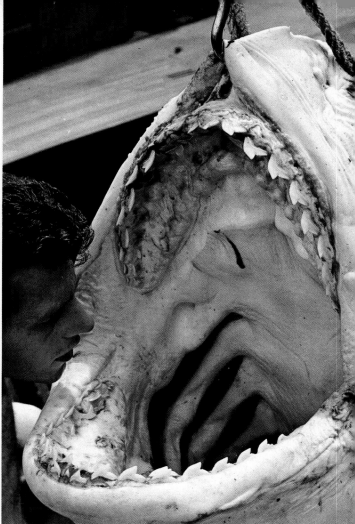

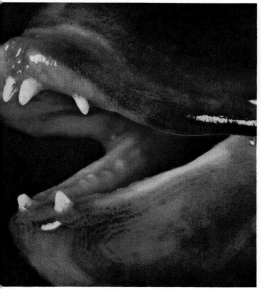

OTIS IMBODEN (ABOVE) AND PAUL A. ZAHL, BOTH NATIONAL GEOGRAPHIC STAFF

HEAD-DWARFING MAW *of the tiger shark, one of the sea's fiercest man eaters, carries a bony arsenal. As outer teeth wear or fall out, inner rows move forward.*

Canine teeth mark the bluehead (left, above) and thick lips the hogfish; each is a species of wrasse. Their throats contain grinders for crushing mollusks.

Ripsaw teeth of a needlefish clamp a sergeant major (below). The staring predator sneaks his beak alongside a victim, then whirls and snaps. To turn his catch lengthwise for swallowing, he keeps releasing and seizing it until he has jockeyed it into position.

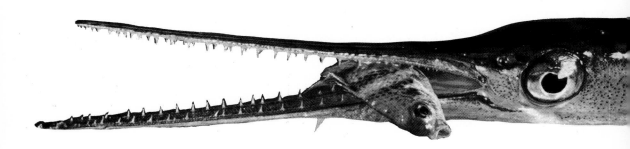

LIVING FOSSIL, *hauled flopping onto a South African trawler in 1938, astounded scientists. They had believed coelacanths extinct at least fifty million years. Preserved five-foot specimen shows stalklike pectoral and pelvic fins with which it probably crept over ocean bottom—and which suggest the legs of land animals. More coelacanths have since been caught off South Africa's east coast. Opposite: Fossilized* Mioplosus, *possibly an ancestor of the Atlantic coast's white perch, choked on a herring forebear sixty million years ago in waters that covered southeast Wyoming. Lake-bottom ooze that became rock of the Rockies preserved the tragedy.*

group. Only when the young have gone off on their own do the mother and father consider parting. And often the devoted couple stays together to rear another family.

The most loyal husband among the fishes is an ugly anglerfish that dwells deep in the sea. Living in ocean darkness among a none too numerous species, the male angler has no easy task to find a female. So, to make one meeting last, he bites into his mate's body—ten times larger than his—and hangs on the rest of his life. He receives nourishment from her blood vessels, and his mouth degenerates, soon fusing with her flesh. He becomes literally "one with her." For the rest of his life, he will be always on hand to fertilize the female's eggs.

The social behavior of fishes is not limited to courtship and family life. Like men and many animals, they tend to form groups. No doubt schooling is a protective device—a safety-in-numbers instinct. Herring sometimes run in masses estimated at three billion individuals. Rainbow trout have been photographed schooling in a precision rank-and-file formation—a little fish army on

parade. Vast congregations of menhaden, feeding on plankton, darken Atlantic and Gulf coast waters like cloud shadows as they swim in perfect unison.

A fascinating instance of social fish behavior takes place at fish "cleaner stations" scattered along our coasts. There fishes congregate while other fishes or shrimp remove parasites from their bodies and mouths. In one small area—near Catalina Island off California—researchers discovered more than 50 stations where pile perch, senoritas, and shrimp clean jack mackerel, garibaldi, and other fishes.

No matter that jack mackerel normally delight in eating pile perch; the perch unconcernedly enter and cleanse the mackerel's mouth and gills. The fish have declared a truce to their mutual advantage: the mackerel gets cleaned and the perch enjoys a parasite lunch.

To determine the significance of all this, scientists removed the cleaner fishes and shrimp from several stations. At first the other fish came anyway to be cleaned. But in a week their numbers dropped sharply; in

two weeks even more. Those that remained developed sores, fuzzy blotches, and ravaged fins.

The remora, or diskfish, eats at the same table with sharks and other large fishes. Nature has fashioned the remora's dorsal fin into a marvelous suction disk with which it clings to a fish's side. When the host makes a kill, the remora lets go and gobbles up leftovers. Then it clamps on again to ride to the next meal.

I have heard stories of Pacific islanders using remoras to catch turtles. Tying a line to a live three-foot remora, they let it swim out to a turtle. Quickly it fastens its disk to the reptile's shell. Then the islanders pull in remora, turtle, and all.

One of nature's greatest opportunists is the pilotfish, which swims in the cushion of water that moving sharks, whales, and ships push ahead of them.

Mariners long credited the pilot with leading lost swimmers and off-course ship captains to safety. That was the basis for naming him *Naucrates ductor*—"leader of the ship master." Now we know that the pilotfish travels ahead of ships or sharks to take advantage of the easier swimming in the "water pocket" there—and to dart out to pick up scraps of food.

Scientists, watching fishes bolt their food, long wondered whether they could taste it. Experiments indicate that the sense of taste exists, although in certain fishes it is weak. The fish's tongue, an inflexible cartilaginous blob in the bottom of his mouth, contains taste buds which detect sourness, saltiness, bitterness, and—in some species —sweetness.

Catfishes that dwell in muddy waters cannot find food with their eyes; many have eyes that scarcely function. Instead they have whiskers, or barbels, that are covered with sensitive taste buds. Dragged over the bottom like minesweeping gear, they serve as food detectors.

Most of the fish's other senses are keener than his taste.

Smell is highly developed among some fishes, especially the predators. It occurs in the paired dead-end nostrils in the snout, where sensitive receptors detect molecules

37

YELLOW POISON *cascades down a Michigan stream where lampreys spawn. Harmless to food fishes, the larvicide kills baby lampreys before they descend tributaries to prey on Great Lakes fishes.*

of foreign matter that the water washes in.

Fishermen catch croakers and spot in murky waters in which the bait is invisible. They succeed because the fish can smell a tiny piece of bloodworm on the angler's hook at surprising distances.

Let a few molecules of fresh blood enter the nostrils of the shark; at once he swims from side to side across the spoor of diluted blood, homing in on the hapless victim. In water heavily impregnated with blood, sharks sometimes go into a feeding frenzy, slashing even at each other.

To prove that a shark follows his nose, scientists have plugged both nostrils with cotton. They found that a shark had to be close to food, so that his eyes could take

over, before he would make his savage lunge.

That some fishes have a sharp eye will be attested by trout fishermen who have watched a leaping rainbow take a fly before it touches water. More often the fish, staring out on the world with bulging eyes, has been regarded as dismally nearsighted. Modern research, however, indicates that some fishes, perhaps many of them, enjoy the trout's acute vision.

When we want to see distant objects, eye muscles flatten our lenses to focus long-distance light rays. The fish lacks muscles to do this, and his lens is too firm to be flattened easily. When he wants to see at a distance (100 feet is pretty far), a muscle pulls his lens closer to the retina, just as we

MURDEROUS TEETH *stud the ugly mouth of the sea lamprey, scourge of sea and lake fish. With suction-cup lips, it tenaciously grips a victim (human thumb at upper right). Then 112 to 125 horny teeth bore in, and* Petromyzon marinus *gorges on blood. Lampreys may grow as much as three feet long. Rainbow trout below, hosts to the parasites, are doomed. Man himself unleashed the lamprey in the Great Lakes. Until 1829 Niagara Falls had barred the ocean predator from Lake Erie and waters west. Then Canada opened the Welland Canal, and the lamprey followed westering ships. It strewed the Lakes with dead whitefish and lake trout. By the 1950's the annual commercial catch had plunged from 18 million pounds to almost nothing.*

Today conservationists, treating streams where lampreys spawn, are revitalizing this fishing in the Lakes.

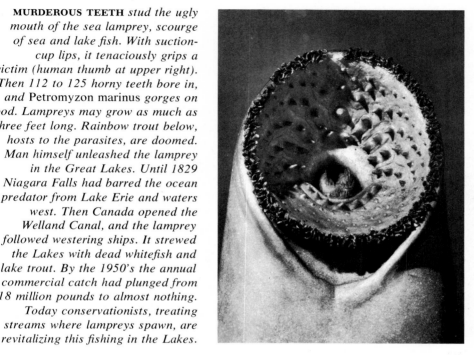

ANDREW H. BROWN, NATIONAL GEOGRAPHIC STAFF, AMERICAN MUSEUM OF NATURAL HISTORY (ABOVE), WISCONSIN CONSERVATION DEPT. (RIGHT)

extend a camera's focus by moving the lens closer to the film.

One difficulty for the fish is that light travels poorly in a liquid. Even in clear water darkness pervades less than half a mile down. Submerged objects which look dim to us a few yards away probably look that way to the fish too.

However, the fish doubtless sees underwater better than we do. This is because nature gave him spherical lenses, built to focus light rays in the thicker medium of water.

Most fishes have eyes set wide apart, one on each side of the head, and that is the way the flounder and halibut start life. But before they grow an inch long their eyes wander curiously. One eye, in halibut usually the left, begins migrating to the other side of the head. At the same time the fish, which had been swimming upright, begins to lean. The eye continues moving, the fish continues leaning. In a few days the roving eye has moved nearly 120 degrees to join the other one, and the fish swims with his eyeless side parallel to the bottom.

Most fish hear acutely, in spite of the absence of external ears. Because sound travels much better in water than in air, a fish does not need humanlike ears to collect sound waves, nor does it need ear drums to pass them along. Instead, sound waves strike the flesh and bone of the head. These relay the sounds to inner ears which pass the message to the brain.

The human ear picks up vibrations ranging from about 20 to 25,000 a second. The goldfish has a range that reaches up to 3,480, and some fishes go to at least 7,000. Goldfish might hear the thunder

THE CHASE: *Menaced by a starfish, an orangethroat pikeblenny (Chaenopsis alepidota) ducks tailfirst into a tubeworm's former home. A defiant look takes little courage: The pursuer speeds but six inches a minute. The starfish, an invertebrate, usually hunts less agile oysters, prying open shells with suction cups that line its arms.*

40

of an approaching storm, or a piano's middle C (261.7 vibrations). But they would unwittingly ignore a coloratura soprano who reaches high C at 4,186 vibrations a second.

The fish's sense of touch is much like ours. Sensitive nerve endings, lodged in the skin, relay touch sensations to the brain.

The fish has a sixth sense—something of a cross between touch and hearing. It resides in the fish's lateral line—the stripe that runs down each side from the gill cover to the tail.

The lateral line is rich in sensitive nerves whose main function is to detect low-frequency vibrations unnoticed by the ear. The nerves *feel* sounds—the footfalls of a fisherman on the bank, an insect dropping in the water, the motions of an injured fish. Once I watched a jack stalk a wounded squirrelfish that swam erratically on a reef ledge. Though unable to see the injured fish hidden by the ledge, the jack moved in unerringly. Probably the water disturbed by the squirrelfish registered on the jack's lateral line, leading him to the kill.

Do fish feel pain? Because humans experience it, and because fish avoid danger and predators, we think that they experience it too. Many fishermen believe otherwise. Because they have released a fish and quickly retaken it on the same hook, they say the fish has no sense of pain—or very little. The fishermen have a point.

Humans have three senses, beyond the traditional five, for which they seldom give themselves credit: equilib-

THE CATCH. *Pike fingerlings, kissing cousins of nearly identical size, end their friendship in a single gulp. The victor's eyes and stomach bulge; the victim's tail still protrudes. In the fish world's rapacious cycle of eat and be eaten, big fishes devour little ones, brothers gobble brothers, and parents turn on their young.*

41

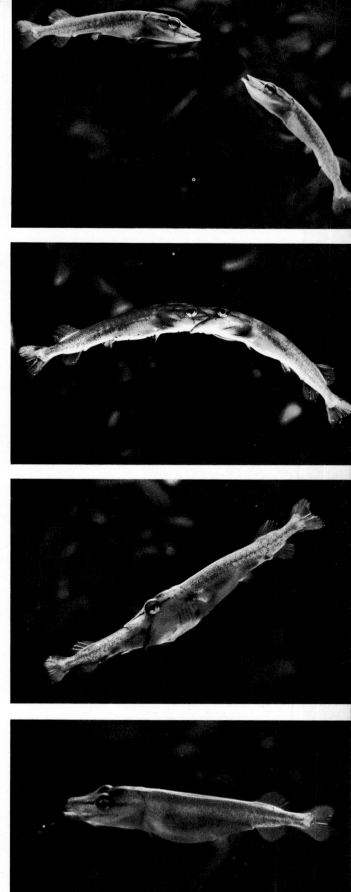

FORMIDABLE MOUTH *of a squirrelfish gapes wide—not to gulp a meal but to get its teeth tidied. On rocks and reefs in the sea, certain creatures set up "cleaning stations" where other fishes come to have them pick off parasites, gnaw away unhealthy tissue, rid fins and gills and even eye surfaces of bacterial infections. Often the pickers work inside the jaws of their customers, as does this cleaner wrasse* (Labroides dimidiatus). *They get a meal and—usually—immunity from their predator hosts. Eyes and chattering call give the squirrelfish its name.*

Yellow pigmy angelfish holds still for attention from another cleaner wrasse (above). Many cleaning fish wear bright colors, perhaps to advertise their profession. Pile perch, senoritas, and occasionally shrimps and crabs perform scavenger services.

Evil moray eel (below) humbly allows a banded coral shrimp to pick its teeth. The shrimp bears a green egg mass on its abdomen.

WALTER A. STARCK II (BELOW) AND DOUGLAS FAULKNER

rium, temperature detection, and kinesthesia—this last, the awareness of the position of an arm or leg without looking to see which way it's pointing. The fish has at least two of these. An equilibrium gauge in his ear, as in ours, tells him he is swimming right side up or tilted. He feels temperature changes through the nerve endings and possibly the lateral line. And, judging by how the flyingfish extends his "wings" and the walking gurnard places his "legs," fishes have the kinesthetic sense also.

The fish swims with his entire body as well as his fins. Along his length, overlapping like giant scales, run flakelike segments of muscle that make up the fish's flesh—the part we eat. To swim, the fish contracts successive muscle segments on one side, bending his tail region to that side. Then he quickly contracts the muscles on the other side, straightening the tail and pushing it against the water. Because the water resists being pushed backward, the fish shoots forward. Back and forth the tail swishes, pushing against the water to propel the fish ahead. A snake moves across rock somewhat in this manner.

The fish's tail fin plays a major role in forward locomotion. The other fins act as stabilizers and delicate controls for maneuvering. It is in precision actions—the accurate leap of the trout, the absolute motionlessness of the pike in ambush—that the fish uses all of his fins to the utmost.

An athlete, dashing a hundred yards in our airy world, makes 23 miles an hour at best. Fishes, twisting through the dense medium of water (800 times denser than air), can do nearly twice that well. Observations show that dolphin attain 23 miles an hour and barracuda 27.6, while mighty blue marlin can probably hit 40 miles an hour in spurts. That grand gamester the largemouth bass is a fighter but not a racer; his top speed seems to be some 12 miles an hour.

Fishes not only swim; they fly, burrow, walk, jump, and scoot by jet propulsion.

Flyingfishes of tropical seas have fascinated men for centuries. Four hundred and fifty years ago the chronicler of Magellan's voyage round the world noted that they "fly more than a crossbow shot, as long as their wings are wet." Other fish, the seafarer added fancifully, follow the shadow of the flyingfish and devour it when it descends—"a thing marvelous and agreeable to see."

Does the flyingfish flap its "wings" like a bird or merely plane like a glider? We know now that the fish lacks muscles to move the wings up and down. High-speed motion pictures of airborne flyingfish prove they merely glide.

I studied these fish in the Marshall Islands of the Pacific, watching them leap

LUIS MARDEN, NATIONAL GEOGRAPHIC STAFF, AND A. M. AWL (INSET)

SLUMBERING FISH *lie like fallen leaves in a flash camera view of a Bahama reef (left). A rainbow parrotfish (above), staring vacantly in Florida waters, drowses unaware of a diver's hands. Some species sleep buried completely in sand or tucked in abandoned shells. Lacking eyelids, fish nap with eyes open, apparently undisturbed by visual messages to the brain.*

FILMY NIGHTGOWN *wraps a dozing striped parrotfish (below). At dusk it secretes the mucous covering, probably to ward off predators. Each morning it swims out of its shroud. Holes let water in for respiration.*

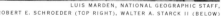

LUIS MARDEN, NATIONAL GEOGRAPHIC STAFF,
ROBERT E. SCHROEDER (TOP RIGHT), WALTER A. STARCK II (BELOW)

FOUR-EYED *fish of Central America peers through ingenious "bifocals" (opposite). Nature gives each eye of* Anableps dowi *a single egg-shaped lens adapted to scan both air and water for food or enemies. The small end, with its short axis, focuses light rays traveling through air; thicker lower portion provides a longer axis for the extra light-bending power needed to focus underwater images.*

Most fishes do well without tear glands and eyelids, since water cleans the eyes. Anableps, *gazing into the air, could use eyelids. Lacking them, it periodically submerges to freshen its lenses.*

SCIENTISTS TAG *a bluefin tuna, hoping whoever catches it will return the marker. Thus Woods Hole Oceanographic Institution traces the tuna's long-mysterious migrations, aided by a research grant from the National Geographic Society. Spotters on the "tuna tower" locate the quarry. Plastic barb (lower left), jabbed into fish, anchors a yellow streamer which tells of return address and $5 reward. One bluefin, tagged in the Bahamas, turned up 50 days later off Norway.*

from the water at speeds up to 35 miles an hour and glide for 20 seconds. They have been clocked aloft for 42 seconds, soaring 50 feet high in flights of hundreds of feet.

An unrelated species, the four-inch flying characin of South America, gives the appearance of flying, nimbly arching several feet into the air. Aquarists report that it flaps its pectoral fins so fast that they make a buzzing sound. Aquarium owners are often grieved to find their flying characin dead on the floor several feet from an uncovered tank.

A fish which burrows may sound peculiar, but this talent may save its life. A frightened mudminnow plunges headfirst into a soft bottom. The snake eel, one of several fishes that swim backward as easily as forward, retreats tailfirst into sand. Certain wrasses, flatfishes, and skates wriggle into sand or mud to conceal themselves. The stingray, on the other hand, burrows in search of clams and other food.

Walking fishes, such as the gurnards, strut across the ocean bottom on enlarged and separated rays of the pectoral fins which serve as legs. The mudskipper of the Indian and Pacific Oceans walks on mudflats after the tide ebbs, moving with such agility that it outmaneuvers man.

Jumping apparently can be an act of pure fish pleasure; tarpon and sailfish often seem to leap for no visible reason. More commonly, fish acrobats seek to evade an enemy or shake a hook.

A light will attract many fishes like a magnet and they will leap for it. Once in Bikini Lagoon in the Pacific I drew a flashlight beam slowly across the surface. Needlefishes and halfbeaks leaped in the rays like steeplechasers. I watched them fascinated, but I was also a bit wary. A three-foot needlefish once speared a man through the neck; another pierced the nose of a woman, leaving part of its beak imbedded.

Many a fish probably owes his quick-starting action to jet propulsion. He takes water in the mouth, then suddenly squirts it out through the gills. The backward force of the jet stream propels him forward. This device is used by the flounder, who shoots a stream through his underside gill to vault from the bottom.

When a fish is on the move he is usually fleeing a predator or pursuing something to eat. His manner of eating is as full of surprises as his modes of locomotion. For one thing, the fish's mouthful of teeth, often formidable, is seldom used for chewing. The job of the teeth is to seize a victim, cut it into manageable chunks, or grip it until the fish can swallow it whole.

Certain fishes, such as the vegetarians, do chew, but not in their mouths. Nature has provided them with grinding mills—pharyngeal teeth—well down in the throat. The mills have fearsome power. The parrotfish, nibbling vegetation from reefs, crunches off fragments of coral—and crushes them in his throat. He later ejects the pulverized coral as a fine cloud.

Do fishes drink? Fresh-water ones, a little; they swallow a small amount of water with their food. We drink partly to provide moisture for perspiration, which evaporates to cool our bodies. The fresh-water fish, always the temperature of the surrounding water, does not "drink like a fish."

Salt-water fishes are heavier drinkers. They do not perspire, but they must cope with osmosis. Because they live in a salty medium, their body fluids tend to escape by osmosis into the denser water. To counteract this, they drink large amounts of sea water, some of which the blood absorbs to maintain its salt content.

One of the favorite foods of fish is other fish. They also eat shellfish, insects, snails, worms, water plants, crustaceans such as lobsters and crayfish, and tiny floating plant and animal life known as plankton.

Though fish normally eat incredible quantities of food, they can exist for incredible periods without eating. The lungfish may estivate for a year wrapped in a ball of mud, living off his own tissues. In a controlled test a 13.2-ounce lungfish "ate" three ounces of himself during a six-month sleep. Just as impressive are Pacific salmon, which stop eating when they enter fresh water to spawn. Some labor 2,000 miles up the Yukon River of Alaska and Canada. Despite distance and effort, they still do not eat.

One of the worst overeaters is the loathsome hagfish. The hagfish rasps a hole in the side of a haddock or cod—preferably one that has been hooked—and disappears inside. In a few hours it can consume body juices equal to more than three times its weight, leaving the victim literally a "bag of skin and bones."

Another big eater is the imposing but indolent giant grouper, or jewfish. One day at Florida's Marineland a captive 500-pounder fixed a doleful eye on a 50-pound stingray. In a gulp he swallowed all but the tail. For two days, while the grouper's stomach digested that mammoth mouthful, the stingray's tail dangled from his mouth.

In his natural habitat a fish often has little chance to become a glutton. An acre of water, like an acre of garden, produces only so much food and thus supports only so many fish. Sometimes anglers catch trout or bass whose heads look abnormally large. Actually it is the body that is abnormally small, stunted by malnutrition while the skull has continued growing.

Some years ago I was called to Montana to investigate a once excellent trout lake whose population had declined sharply over the preceding 10 years. The decline coincided with a planting of pumpkinseed sunfish. My research team set a few gill nets. In each 50-foot section we soon had more than 200 runty sunfish about three-and-a-half inches long.

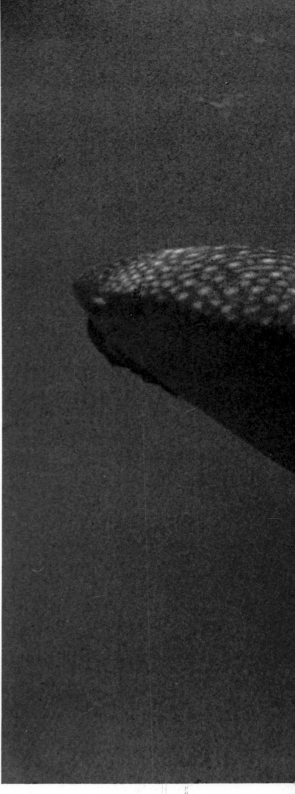

HUMAN HITCHHIKER *rides a docile whale shark, earth's largest fish, as it lumbers through Australian waters. The 35-foot behemoth wears a beard of remoras (left), which cling with*

suction-disk dorsal fins as they wait to dine on leftovers. With a cavernous mouth almost as broad as its head, the whale shark gulps down great loads of small fish and plankton. Though straddling a shark or hanging on to its tail may be exhilarating, the Shark Research Panel of the American Institute of Biological Sciences labels the sport "dangerous and foolhardy."

49

That told the story. The aggressive pumpkinseeds had exterminated the game fishes and now were eating each other out of house and home.

Improved fishing methods also have cut fish populations. But far more destructive is the impact of civilization on the fish's habitat. The felling of shading forests raises water temperatures. Erosion brings silt that ruins gravel bottoms for nesting. Dams block spawning migrations. Wastes from factories and homes pollute streams. Insecticides poison waters or wipe out a link in nature's food chain.

Already six species of small North American stream fishes are extinct. Thirteen more are threatened, among them a favorite of anglers, the sleek, hard-fighting grayling.

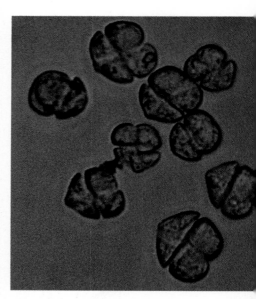

WINDROW OF DEAD FISH *bobs between clea waters of the Gulf of Mexico and polluted area called "red tide." Florida conservation boat samples the toxic region for scientists t study. Population explosions of tiny sea life (the dinoflagellate* Gymnodinum breve, *abov magnified 500 times) cause the discoloration The organisms' nerve-killing poison paralyze. fish. A century ago Charles Darwin describe a red tide off Chile as "great bands of mudd water" aswarm with "minute animalculae darting about and often exploding."*

The danger brought by insecticides came home to me a few years ago. Stinging fire ants had invaded the Gulf states. Airplanes attacked, dusting huge areas with a chemical poison. They took pains to keep it out of streams. But rains came, washing a minute dilution into these waters. In ten days nearly every fish they held was dead.

In experiments to provide havens for fishes, scientists do what might sound ridiculous if it did not work. They dump old automobile bodies on to barren sea bottom. Like sunken ships, these wrecks encourage plant life, afford small fishes places to hide, and draw big fishes in pursuit of little fishes.

A year after dropping 20 old cars off California, census takers found the wrecks had attracted between 10,000 and 24,000 fish. Steel bodies disintegrate, however, and scientists at the University of Miami, with a grant from the National Geographic So-ciety, are studying artificial reefs built of coral limestone dredged from canals.

Fish by the hundreds of millions are raised in the more than 500 state and federal hatcheries that dot the Nation. Rearing salmon, trout, bass, bluegill, and catfish, the hatcheries stock commercial fisheries, farm ponds, sportsmen's lakes and streams. Such innovations as fortified foods steadily increase the ability of hatchery-reared fingerlings to fend for themselves in the wild.

Today millions of Americans operate their own hatcheries. They are not large; a 15-gallon tank ranks above average. And they are not particularly practical, breeding such frivolous fishes as angelfishes, Siamese fighting fishes, red tuxedo platys. But the operators do not mind. These home aquariums bring hours of delight, and give a first-hand introduction to the ever-fascinating ways of that marvelous creation, the fish.

MEN HUNT FOR RADIOISOTOPES *to keep the Columbia River safe for fishes and for people who eat them. A plutonium plant at Hanford, Washington, cools its reactors with Columbia water and returns it—slightly radioactive—to the river. Caught fish reveal activity far below danger level. Experiments indicate that fishes can stand much greater doses of radiation than man.*

B. ANTHONY STEWART, NATIONAL GEOGRAPHIC STAFF, AND M. WOODBRIDGE WILLIAMS (OPPOSITE)

FISHING FOR FUN

*Sizzling fish, scented smoke, ravenous appetites —
these crown a perfect day for Izaak Walton's
"Brothers of the Angle." Oblivious of distance,
weather, and time, they pursue the wily game fishes.*

CHAPTER TWO   By LUIS MARDEN
Chief, National Geographic Foreign Staff

Angling in the United States

The thrill of a strike, the beauty of nature, and the urge for solitude lure 60 million fishermen a year to brook, lake, and ocean.

THE FISHERMAN leaned back against the oak tree and stretched his legs contentedly. In the meadow behind him bees droned through the summer heat. From the crook of his arm the cane pole slanted over the muddy river, and the red-and-white float under its tip lay motionless as though embedded in opaque glass.

55

Idly the fisherman wondered if the impaled pink worm, invisible below the surface, was still wriggling attractively. Then the float disappeared. Seizing the pole in both hands, the fisherman pointed the butt toward the water and backed up the slope, his cane curving in a deep parabola.

The red waters parted and a struggling yellow fish—a five-pound mudcat—flopped against the grass. Holding it carefully to avoid the sharp spines in its fins, the fisherman removed the hook, then strung a line through the gills. He wiped his hands on his blue jeans, gathered up pole and fish, and walked across the meadow. Already he could hear the frying pan sizzle and taste the catfish's succulent white flesh.

Five hundred miles away, another angler fished a mountain stream. Beneath alders and hemlocks the rushing torrent tumbled over boulders and gravel beds. The angler stood waist deep where the stream made a sharp turn at the base of a rock wall, shattering in a burst of spray and rebounding in white-flecked whorls and eddies.

The angler tied a small gray-brown dry fly to his hair-fine leader as the icy stream swirled around waders that reached nearly to his armpits. Under the waders, his many-pocketed fishing jacket bulged with tackle. Six countries besides his own had contributed to that equipment: rod bamboo from China, cork for the rod grip from Portugal, the leader's silkworm gut from Spain, the line guide's agate from Madagascar, the fly reel from England, and hooks from Norway.

The fisherman began false casts upstream, his rod rhythmically switching back and forth, the reel buzzing intermittently as he lengthened the line in the air without permitting it to touch the water. When about 40 feet were out, he put a bit more wrist power into the forward cast, then stopped the rod sharply just above the horizontal. The line rolled out, the leader straightened, and the little fly hesitated, then dropped softly into an eddy behind a boulder.

A fly fisherman sees with his mind and instinct as well as with his eyes. It seemed to the angler that he could distinguish each fiber of the fly's feather ruff as it floated, wings cocked in an insouciant V. At last he saw the expected dimple, snapped his rod tip up, and was fast to a good trout.

The rod bent and the line ripped through the water as the fish shot round the pool. Stripping in line slowly, the angler brought the trout close. Then he guided it over the lip of his landing net. Grasping the lower jaw between thumb and forefinger, he carefully unhooked the bedraggled fly from the corner of the brook trout's mouth, and held up his 11-inch prize so that the sunlight gleamed on the red-spotted sides, white-edged orange fins, and moss-agate back of the most beautiful fish that swims.

The angler rinsed his fly in the stream, then squeezed it dry between folds of facial tissue. Wading ashore, he rested his rod against a low hemlock branch, and filled his pipe. It was the beginning of a good day.

These two men were hundreds of miles apart in distance and fishing method, yet each in his own manner followed the great American sport. Between the two extremes there are all kinds, degrees, and grades of fishermen—60 million of them from one end of the country to the other.

What makes this recreation so popular with more than a third of the Nation's adult population? One reason is that no other continent on earth has so great a variety of game fish as North America. Some 220 sport species swim in every imaginable type of water: cold mountain torrents, deep blue lakes, slow lowland rivers, tropical palm-fringed creeks, and thousands of miles of ocean shoreline. All these the automobile and the airplane bring close to the American angler's rod.

Angling in the United States is a diversion that can be followed by almost anyone, almost anywhere. The fisherman may outfit himself for a dollar, or he may use a $200 fly rod or an $800 deep-sea reel. And what fisherman does not love the delightful gadgetry of angling? There are so many wonderful things to play with! So many that tackle making is big business. In 1968 anglers spent the impressive total of 400 million dollars for a bewildering array of practical equipment and pretty gadgets, from hooks

SMALLMOUTH BASS OPENS WIDE *to engulf a bucktail lure. The fish's ferocity in attacking prey produces the smashing strikes admired by fishermen. Widely distributed, the smallmouth ranks among North America's hardest-fighting game fishes. It is also one of the most intelligent, concluded photographer Elgin Ciampi, who took this picture while testing the ability of game species to distinguish artificial lures from real food.*

57

REMINISCENT OF HUCK AND TOM, *youngsters maneuver over a fishing hole on a Michigan pond.*

to big-game reels, and from floating hollow nylon lines to instruments for predicting fish feeding time by barometric pressure. Not all the bright-colored flies and lures seen in the shops catch fish, but all of them seem to catch fishermen.

Someone has truly said that fishing takes one to the best places at the best times of year. The angler sees the first yellow-green spring flush of the waterside willows, uncovers the first violets, and watches the evening dance of mayflies; he casts his lure to the edge of lily pads where white blossoms unfold to the summer morning; he matches his fly to the burning colors of autumn. In winter the ice fisherman skating over the frozen lake may glimpse the tracery of bare black branches against the sky.

Millions find in fishing a relief and refreshment from the pressures and hurry of everyday life. For the true fisherman, there is no competitive feeling on the water; he fishes for himself alone, his only opponent the fish. As "that undervaluer of money," Sir Henry Wotton, said, fishing is to the angler

"a rest to his mind, a cheerer of his spirits, a diverter of sadness, a calmer of unquiet thoughts, a moderator of passions, and a procurer of contentedness."

And the modern writer George Orwell called fishing "the opposite of war."

Yet the first settlers of this country found little time for sport fishing. They fished for the pot, and netted and speared fish by day and by torchlight, just as they carelessly shot the deer and turkey that abounded. Fish, like game, seemed inexhaustible. Every spring the rivers filled with hordes of migrating fishes swimming in from the sea to spawn—herring, shad, salmon. Practically every East Coast river held its stock of the noble salmon. The Connecticut received an enormous annual run, and even the Hudson knew the leaping silver fish.

When with increasing population came dams and water pollution, the sensitive salmon were the first to go, but the hardier shad have, incredibly, persisted to this day in the Hudson, and each spring a remnant of the once-great hordes returns to swim past the skyscrapers of New York to cleaner spawning grounds upstream.

In those days, every stream and rill on the northeast coast contained the most American of fish, the brook trout. Let quibblers say he is not a trout, but a char (a little matter of the mouth's bone structure), but the countless anglers who have seen him flash in a pool know better. He is a trout.

By the middle of the 18th century, rod fishing for trout was fairly widely practiced. Tackle came from England or was built here on the old models. Rods were formidable weapons of solid wood, 15 to 18 feet long, usually fashioned of ash, hickory, or lancewood, in three or four sections. The butt, shaped like a billiard cue, was sometimes hollowed out for storing the other sections.

Though the reel had been mentioned in English angling literature as early as 1651 and was in use in China by the 13th century, most American fishers fixed their braided horsehair line directly to the rod's tip.

Not until about 1830 did Americans do much fishing with the fly. Then they used a brass winch to hold the horsehair line that tapered to one or two hairs carrying a "leash"

POCKET SPINNING ROD *for the traveler-sportsman fits in a passport-size case. Its ten pieces assemble into a four-foot, four-inch rod using flexible, fiberglass ferrules for springy action. Here the author casts with the Phillipson-made rod on the Potomac at Washington, D. C.*

FISH FOR A FLYROD, *the exquisite golden trout, bantam member of a distinguished family, inhabits crystal waters high in the Sierra.*

LUIS MARDEN (ABOVE) AND JAMES E. RUSSELL,
BOTH NATIONAL GEOGRAPHIC STAFF

of three flies. The flies followed the classic patterns used in England for centuries. The first book in English on angling, dated 1496, lists twelve flies; ten of these patterns are still in use today.

Angling is easily the most literary of the sports. The literature of angling is ancient and a collection at Harvard University contains more than 10,000 titles. By far the largest number of fishing books were written in English beginning with the above-mentioned *Treatyse of Fysshynge with an Angle*, printed at Westminster by Caxton's successor, Wynkyn de Worde.

Ever since, angling and fine bookmaking have gone together, and some of the volumes on fishing are among the finest examples of the printer's art. Such books are frequently of a high literary order. The best contain essays on the joys of angling and lyric descriptions of the countryside, and voice the reflections of the contemplative angler. It is not for the outmoded fishing instruction that Izaak Walton's *Compleat Angler* has gone through some 300 printings since it first appeared in 1653.

The first useful American fishing manual was published in 1845; from then on, fishing books appeared in the United States with increasing frequency.

Some of the bags of fish taken in those early days seem incredible now. An angler counted it a poor day if he took less than 30 or 40 fish, and catches of 100 trout were not uncommon.

As the population grew, the lumberman's ax rang louder in the thick virgin forests of America. The shading and water-retaining trees disappeared, river temperatures rose, and silt from farm land washed into the streams. Large settlements dumped waste into the rivers, and pollution helped to depopulate the water of trout.

While fishermen in the Northeast fished for trout, pickerel, perch, and salmon, southern anglers caught bluegills, crappie, catfish, and another kind of "trout," as southerners called the black bass.

This great American game fish first became known to science in 1802, when the French naturalist Lacépède published a de-

scription based on drawings and a preserved specimen sent from the vicinity of Charleston, South Carolina. Unfortunately for scientific accuracy, the specimen had a mutilated dorsal fin, from which some spines had been torn. From this, Lacépède named the new genus *Micropterus*—small fin—though anyone who has ever caught a bass knows it has a large—and prickly—dorsal.

Originally the black bass inhabited all of the United States east of the Rocky Mountains except New England and the Middle Atlantic seaboard. There were two major species, smallmouth and largemouth, with the smallmouth inhabiting clear, rocky-bottomed streams and lakes, and the large-

RIVER DOVE, *meandering through hills of central England, felt the wet fly of Izaak Walton. As a guest of Charles Cotton, who wrote a supplement to Walton's* Compleat Angler, *he fished here for brown trout (below) that still draw anglers. U. S. browns came from Europe. English anglers sight the quarry, then "fish the fish"; Americans, whose rushing brooks conceal their trout, "fish the water." Much of Dove Dale, the limestone glen carved by the Dove and dividing Derbyshire and Staffordshire, is preserved as a shrine by England's National Trust.*

mouth favoring shallower, weedier waters.

The earliest bass fishers fished as many still do, with a long "pole" and live minnows, crayfish, or worms. But the fast rushes and spectacular leaps of the hooked bass suggested tackle with more scope, and by 1810 George Snyder, a watchmaker of Paris, Kentucky, had made the first Kentucky multiplying reel. This reel had a wide spool that was quadruple multiplying—it revolved four times for each turn of the handle. The angler wound his bait nearly to the rod tip, and on the cast the weight of the bait took line directly from the fast-spinning reel.

Other watchmakers soon followed Snyder's lead, among them the famous early makers Milam and Meek, and the Kentucky reel was rapidly refined until it became the finest bait-fishing reel in the world.

The early multipliers, of polished German silver with hand-cut gears, ivory handles, and agate or garnet bearings, ran as smoothly as the watches their makers turned out. Occasionally one was fashioned of solid silver. Sometimes, instead of the purring click that warned when a fish was taking out line, makers fitted little bells that on one reel at least were tuned to musical fifths!

Such reels were not cheap; they cost $50 or more in days when a dollar was a potent unit of currency, but they lasted for several lifetimes. Many are still in use today.

As trout fishing fell off, bass fishing grew more important, and the bass was introduced into other parts of the country. The hardy game fish took hold almost wherever planted, and multiplied rapidly.

The Potomac River and adjacent water systems in Virginia and Maryland, originally empty of bass, offer a striking example of the fish's adaptability. In 1853, 30 bass were carried in the water tank of a locomotive from Wheeling, West Virginia, to Cumberland, Maryland, and placed in a canal connecting with the Potomac. In a few years' time, this small planting had increased so prodigiously that the Potomac, Shenandoah, and neighboring streams afforded some of the best smallmouth bass fishing to be had.

Before 1870 anglers fished for black bass with rods 12 to 16 feet long. In the seven-

ties James Alexander Henshall began to publish articles on the black bass, about which he made the famous statement "Inch for inch and pound for pound, the gamest fish that swims." Dr. Henshall advocated a "short" single-handed rod of eight feet three inches, for use with the Kentucky reel.

This rod, like most others, whether for bait or fly, was made of solid wood, although a revolutionary method of rod building had already appeared in the United States. In 1845, Samuel Philippe, a gunsmith of Easton, Pennsylvania, made a rod of bamboo split into strips, planed to shape, and glued into a solid unit. Split-bamboo construction seems to have been first employed in England, but Philippe was the first to make such a rod independently in America.

Philippe's first rods were made up of three strips, but they would not cast true, so he changed to four-strip construction, making a rod square in cross section. The most common modern construction, six strips in hexagonal cross section, was brought to perfection about 1870 by Hiram Leonard of Bangor, Maine. The name of Leonard on a rod is like that of Stradivarius on a violin. Thomas and Payne, who worked in Leonard's shop, later set up on their own and became equally celebrated. These three names form the triad of great U. S. pioneer rodmakers, though others equally skilled have followed in a tradition that has made American split-bamboo rods the world's best.

To make the hexagonal split-bamboo rod, builders took a whole culm, or cane, of bamboo, split it into halves, quarters, and eighths, cut out the partitions that wall off the hollow tubes at the joints, filed off the outer nodes, then with a hand plane shaped narrow tapering strips into equilateral triangles in cross section. Glued together, the strips made one tough, springy stick.

Few modern rodmakers still plane the strips by hand. Milling machines now turn out strips to micrometric tolerances, though in other steps of the process the best rods are still largely the product of hand work.

Until 1834 most American fishing was done with live bait or artificial flies, but in that year there appeared an entirely new

COHO BONANZA *rewards fishermen on Lake Michigan. A boy and his catch attract a camera's eye; in the background bob some of the hundreds of salmon boats that dot the lake on weekends in spring and summer. A wader nets a 23-pound coho in the Little Manistee River, one of the lake's major spawning streams. Stocking the Great Lakes with cohos—West Coast salmon that spend much of their lives at sea—began in 1966 when Michigan released 850,000 fingerlings into streams feeding Lakes Michigan and Superior. Migrating downstream, the salmon thrived phenomenally on the lakes' hordes of alewives, and established breeding populations. Today many other states experiment with cohos.*

lure that accounted for phenomenal catches. The story goes that Julio Buel, while eating his lunch on the shores of a Vermont lake, dropped a spoon into the water. As it sank, turning from side to side and catching the light, a large fish struck at it. Buel saw the light, too, and on his return home soldered a hook to the bowl of a tablespoon. So was the "spoon bait" born, a lure that has become standard for salt-water trolling and for fishing in general round the world.

Americans of those days used a surprisingly full assortment of tackle for so new a country. The *American Angler's Guide* of 1857 could write that "with the exception of artificial baits, all articles of tackle made in this country are equal, if not superior, to those of England; and if the Angler can procure the American, he should patriotically avoid anything else."

The author should have excepted hooks. These were then, as now, to a large extent imported. The *Treatyse* of 1496 gives detailed directions for making hooks from needles—by heating and bending, slicing barbs in the points, and retempering by

MEMBERS OF THE ANGLERS' CLUB *of New York lunch at their quarters above Fraunces Tavern, the Manhattan inn where George Washington bade farewell to his officers after the Revolution. Meeting place for many of America's most skilled anglers, the club was founded in 1906 to "cultivate and practice the art of scientific angling." An Atlantic salmon adorns the wall; a document signed by Izaak Walton hangs to left. Member Theodore Gordon, who owned the fly box above, launched dry-fly fishing in the United States in the early 1900's. Below, author Luis Marden (right) and member Robert DeVilbiss examine a fly rod made a century ago by Samuel Philippe, father of split cane rods in America.*

quenching in water. But even before Walton's time hooks could be had ready-made.

English fishhook manufacture grew directly from the needle-making industry, and through the years English makers learned knacks that enabled them to produce fine hooks very cheaply. Today England and Norway nearly monopolize the world's fishhook industry, England specializing in sport-fishing hooks and Norway making hooks mainly for commercial fishing. However, domestic makers supply almost all the U. S. demand for bait and lure single hooks.

As for the artificial baits mentioned in the *Angler's Guide,* English anglers used minnows of oiled and painted silk, as well as a metal minnow fitted with fins that caused it to spin around the wire trace on which it was threaded. Fishing with the "Devon" minnow, called spinning as opposed to fly fishing, was done with a long two-handed rod and a free-running reel.

In the United States an accident similar to that attending the birth of the spoon lure brought an entirely new type of artificial bait into being. One summer day in 1898, James Heddon sat on the banks of clear, slow-flowing Dowagiac Creek in Michigan. He had been whittling a piece of wood, and now he tossed it into the stream and watched it float away. Suddenly there was a splashing eruption, and the stick disappeared, to bob up again in the agitated water. A bass had struck the piece of wood, then spat it out.

Profiting by this experience, Heddon whittled torpedo-shaped baits out by hand, fixed

65

a metal bottle cap over one end, and attached hooks. He fished the baits by casting them out and retrieving in jerks; the bottle-cap collar caused the bait to dart and wobble. He caught bass, big ones and many of them. Then Heddon set up in business, turning out the world's first topwater wooden minnows and later making diving and sinking models. Since then, American lures have been mainly wobblers; the British still prefer revolving baits.

To cast these "plugs," rods grew shorter, and eventually the single-handed five- or six-foot bait-casting rod as we know it evolved.

Only one more thing was needed to make the complete bait-casting outfit of today, and William Shakespeare, Jr., also of Michigan, brought that out in 1897—a level-wind device for the bait-casting reel. This consisted of a metal line guide that moved from side to side to spool the line in even coils as the bait was wound in. Plug casting with this midwestern short rod, level-wind reel, and silk line became the accepted method of fishing for bass.

Like pioneer trout fishers of the East, bass anglers of the early days took fantastic bags of fish. One writer records a catch of 214 to one rod in an afternoon. Happy days!

Fly fishermen angled for bass with floating cork and feather "bugs." They also found that bass would take a bright fly, and a whole family of gaudy new flies was developed. The unsophisticated brook trout of the northern wilderness had always taken a bright fancy fly readily, as well as imitations of natural insects.

By the eighties and nineties, the series of fancy flies for trout and bass had grown out of proportion to fish-getting qualities. Some people invented these lures, as they should more properly be called, to indulge their artistic whims, and named the new pattern for a friend or favorite fishing place.

A book published in 1892, *Favorite Flies and Their Histories,* shows, in exquisitely colored lithograph plates, most of the flies then in common use. Even then it is significant that the correspondents who sent in their lists of favorites from all round the country generally chose the soberer, more natural appearing flies as the most taking.

Today there are about 500 "standard" patterns tied in the United States, though any practical fisherman will usually use half a dozen at the most in his home area.

Peculiarly American "flies" that appeared later were the bucktails and streamers. Imitating a minnow rather than an insect, these tapering lures were tied of feathers or deer hair and were particularly effective for landlocked salmon in Maine lakes.

To replace the brook trout that was disappearing from many American streams, the brown trout was imported from Europe in 1884. The new arrivals throve in water no longer cold enough for the brook trout, but they were finicky feeders and harder to catch. Not for them the gaudy lures of the bass and brook trout; they would take only good imitations of natural insects.

As Americans moved west, the early fishing conditions and methods of the East were largely repeated. Pioneers, busy clearing land and making a living in the wilderness, fished for food and not for pleasure, until they too had secured the immediate future and could begin to angle for sport. In Middle West waters swam black bass; its relatives the sunfish, crappie, and bluegill; rock bass; the pike, similar to its European cousin; and the great solitary pike, the muskellunge.

The deforestation cycle repeated itself: The hardwood forests of Maine and the northeastern United States had long since been cut over, and now the men with calked boots and stagged-off trousers moved west, to fell the heavy woods of central Michigan. In the clear cold streams of this region dwelt the Michigan grayling, a salmonid fish with a huge dorsal fin. But he did not last long; sawdust coating the gravel spawning beds and voracious introduced trout soon decimated the ranks of this dainty fish, until today it is believed extinct. Related varieties —gold-flecked, purple tinged and eager to bite—survive in Montana and Alaska.

When settlers reached the Rocky Mountains, they found a whole series of new trouts—rainbows, cutthroats, and later the goldens—hard fighters and leapers, too, some of them. On the northwest Pacific

FIFTY-POUND BLUE CATFISH *loads a stringer on the Mississippi River, mainstream of catfish country.*

coast rivers were alive with five species of salmon. Unfortunately, though some salmon came to the spoon or spinner in salt or brackish water, most would not take a fly.

A Briton, investigating what is now British Columbia, advised his government to leave the region to the Americans because of his belief that "the salmon there will not rise to the fly."

Meanwhile, the principal game fish angled for in the Atlantic was the striped bass. Fishing stands, railed iron platforms, were set up on rocks and headlands along the coast, and anglers cast into the boiling waters for the sporting striped fish that often ran to 60 pounds or more.

In 1865 a sporting club was founded on Cuttyhunk Island off the Massachusetts coast. This little island had been the site of the first white settlement on the New England coast, when the English navigator Bartholomew Gosnold landed there—in 1602, eighteen years before the Pilgrims set foot on Plymouth Rock. The Cuttyhunk Club built 23 fishing stands around the island. Anglers employed a boy to "chum" the waters round the stand by throwing in bits of cut-up lobster. Today the bait would be worth more than the fish.

For this fishing, Capt. Lester Crandall, who had been manufacturing lines at Ashaway, Rhode Island, since 1824, made a hand-laid twisted linen line of small diameter, and soon fame of this light and strong line, ideally suited to salt water, spread far beyond the little island off the Massachusetts coast. "Cuttyhunk" line became the world's standard for deep-sea sport fishing, and so it remained until supplanted by nylon and Dacron after the second World War.

In 1879 and 1881, two plantings of striped bass were made in San Francisco Bay, introducing this game fish for the first time to Pacific waters. It multiplied beyond all expectations and today is found from Washington to the vicinity of Los Angeles. Round the San Francisco area, it is the pre-eminent surf casting fish. Along the West Coast, it is protected as a game fish, whereas on the Atlantic coast, its original home, commercial netters take a tremendous toll.

The building of the railways in Florida at the turn of the century opened that fabulous fisherman's wonderland to anglers. In Florida's inland and offshore waters swam more than 700 varieties of fish, one-sixth of the known fish fauna of North America.

The great silver herring, the tarpon, first caught on rod and reel in Florida's Indian River Inlet in 1884, became the focus of a new angling cult. Its devotees hotly disputed with salmon and bass enthusiasts the merits of tarpon as the supreme game fish.

Camps sprang up on both Florida coasts. Some were reached from railhead by stagecoach and sailboat. The fame of Florida fishing for tarpon, bonefish, snook, and other fishes spread, and anglers came even from England to try this new kind of fishing.

Florida was doubly blessed because the flat peninsula had scores of inland lakes that harbored some of the world's biggest largemouth bass in their brown-stained cypress waters. So large are these bronzebacks of Florida and nearby areas that the annual fishing contest of *Field & Stream* magazine has maintained a separate bass division for Florida and portions of adjacent states; otherwise, fishermen from these places always take first prize.

A major contribution to the art of sea angling had its beginning in 1896, when the first tuna caught on rod and reel was taken off Catalina Island on the California coast. Two years later, Charles Frederick Holder founded the Tuna Club on Catalina, and rules for tackle lengths and weights set by this club became the model for later attempts to regulate the new sport of big-game fishing for ocean giants such as tuna, swordfish, sailfish, and marlin.

The real flowering of big-game angling came with the invention, shortly before the first World War, of the slipping clutch reel.

WORLDS OF FISH AND FISHERMAN *appear simultaneously in this extraordinary picture of a hooked bonefish, taken off Yucatán by a camera with its lens half submerged. The angler's line at left draws in the lunging bonefish, called by devotees the gamest of American sport fishes.*

With this type of reel, a hooked fish could strip line directly from the slipping reel spool, the reel handle remaining stationary. An adjustable drag was added later so that the angler could put as much brake on the running fish as desired.

At the time Holder began his tuna fishing in 1898, reel handles spun like a buzz saw when a fish made a run, and the angler had only his thumb to use as a brake, a dangerous business with big fish.

From the fine old club at Catalina the sport of taking big deep-sea fish on rod and reel spread all over the world. The center in our country today is in Florida and adjacent Bahamian waters, where every year thousands of anglers take giant tuna, sailfish, white and blue marlin, wahoo, and other roamers of the open sea. Many world records have been made in the Gulf Stream off the minuscule islands of Bimini, just east of Miami.

Just before the first World War, the dry fly came to this country from England. From time to time early angling literature said something about fishing a fly on the surface, but the first mention of the dry or floating fly as we know it was in Pulman's *Angler's Vade Mecum*, published in England in 1851. In this delicate style of fishing, a floating fly was cast upstream and allowed to float down over the feeding fish like a natural insect. The method received its great impetus when England's F. M. Halford began in 1886 to publish his series of monumental books on the new art.

Halford evolved a whole school of dry-fly angling, with a full set of flies, meticulously tied to imitate exactly the species of flies found on the crystalline slow-moving chalk streams of southern England.

These famous Hampshire streams, such as the Test and Itchen, well up through the chalk subsoil and flow, limpid and gin-clear, through lush water meadows. Thick beds of weeds and water plants grow in these rivers, and form a haven for a rich growth of insects, shrimp, and other trout foods.

In such streams, brown trout grow fat and choosy, feeding only when a definite hatch of insects is on. The slow current permits the trout to inspect the fly in a leisurely manner, and the angler has to be skilled in his presentation. His fly must be an excellent imitation of the natural ephemerid to deceive these sophisticated fish, which, it is often said, "know Latin and Greek."

American conditions were different. Our streams were for the most part fast brawling rivers, dashing down over rocks and boulders at such a pace that the trout had to make up his mind quickly or the morsel of food was snatched away. Thus it was argued that the dry fly would not do for the rough American waters, but in 1914, George M. L. La Branche, one of the few really great anglers America has produced, wrote an epoch-making book, *The Dry Fly and Fast Water*, that opened the eyes of Americans to the possibilities of superior sport on their water, and the rage was on.

The English fisherman fished only the rise, casting a fly to the individual feeding fish; within the first two or three casts, he either caught the fish or "put it down," so that it stopped feeding. La Branche taught the American dry-fly fisherman to fish the water, since in the absence of heavy hatches of flies, there were fewer natural rises.

So the American cast constantly and kept his fly on the water, floating it as La

VOLKMAR WENTZEL, NATIONAL GEOGRAPHIC STAFF

DEFT HANDS *wind line guides onto fiberglass bait-casting rods; keen eyes check their alignment. Rods on upper rack are made from solid cylinders of glass. More costly tubular rods woven of fine glass fibers—3,000 yards could be drawn from a child's marble—weigh less and offer better action. Glass resists breakage and humidity. Lower left: A fly tier wraps strands of goose, ostrich, and mallard feathers on a McGinty, one of some 150 flies she will fashion in a day. Finished McGinty (lower right), imitating a bumblebee, stands ready for the trout stream.*

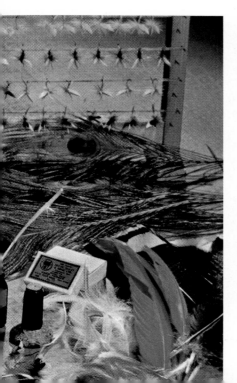

71

Branche had taught, even though for a few feet only, in every likely lie that might hold a trout. For such fishing the dry fly had to be tied of the stiffest of cock hackles, waterproofed with oil or wax, so that it would remain afloat in broken water.

Following the English pattern, there sprang up an American school of purists who fished with nothing but the dry fly, even when conditions were not appropriate, and who looked upon any other kind of angling as little short of poaching. These fanatics surrounded the method with an aura of mystery and difficulty, whereas, dry-fly fishing, once the elements have been mastered, is one of the easiest styles of fly fishing.

In England this fishing snobbery began to die out after G. E. M. Skues brought out his works on nymph fishing (using a sunk imitation of the nymph or larval stage of the aquatic insects), and gradually the narrow attitude lessened on this side of the Atlantic too. So that today, while admittedly the dry fly is the most delicate and sporting way yet devised to take fish, few anglers would deny that there are other methods just as taking and nearly as pleasurable.

Dry-fly fishing brought about a revolution in rod design too. Fly rods grew shorter, stiffer, and "quicker" because of the need to dry the fly by making constant false casts and to drive it upstream against a breeze. The need for a faster-actioned rod caused rod builders to modify their tapers and to abandon the old Calcutta cane entirely, using instead the stiffer Tonkin bamboo from southern China.

Originally, split-bamboo rods had been built of Calcutta cane, supposedly from India or Burma. How and why the newer material, first tried about 50 years ago, came to

FLINGING DIAMOND DROPLETS, *an eastern brook trout lunges for a damsel fly lure. Another, more wary, returns empty-mouthed, one eye peering back at the rejected fly.*

To freeze trout in their leap—nearly 20 feet a second—the photographers beamed an electric eye below the hookless lure. Interrupting the beam with their acrobatics, the fish tripped the camera shutter and a speed light set to flash at 1/5000 of a second.

be called Tonkin is anyone's guess; it does not come from the region of that name in North Viet Nam, but from a small area on the border of Kwangtung and Kwangsi Provinces in China.

Still another typically American item of tackle appeared increasingly from the nineties onward: the steel fishing rod. Earliest attempts to make rods of this metal consisted of rolling sheet steel into a tube. Later, rods were manufactured from fencing foil blades, and finally there appeared the drawn seamless steel tube. Excellent rods made of steel, solid and tubular, were sold in enormous quantities, particularly for bait-casting and light salt-water fishing. The material was a bit heavy and harsh for really satisfactory light fly rods.

With the passage of years, advances in technology placed many new materials and devices in the hands of American anglers. In 1939, the Du Pont company introduced a new synthetic fiber to the world. At first used to make women's stockings and to replace bristles in toothbrushes, nylon—waterproof and wear resistant—soon found its way into the manufacture of fishing lines and leaders. In the latter field it virtually drove silkworm gut from the market.

In fly fishing it is the heavy line, and not the weightless lure, that is cast. The double taper flyline, with a heavy belly tapering to fine points at each end, had been in use for years. With a double taper a long line is more easily and delicately cast and the fly lands lightly. American tournament casters, ever striving for greater distance, conceived the idea of building a thick heavy section of line near

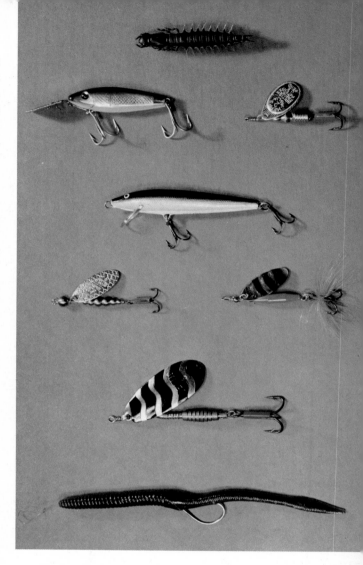

WINNING SPINNING LURES: *Most tackle boxes belonging to the legions of spinning-gear fans hold a sampling of these taking lures. From top, left to right, they are the rubber hellgrammite, MirOlure diving minnow, Mepps spinner, Rapala minnow, C. P. Swing spinner, Abu-Reflex spinner, Celtic spinner, and Creme plastic worm. Flexible plastics, such as used in the Burke Flex-Plug Pop Top minnow (below), give lures a lifelike feel to biting fish.*

PLUGS, SPOONS, AND SPINNERS *simulate minnows; they may also provoke attack by angering the fish or arousing its curiosity. Fresh-water lures above take bass, pickerel, pike, walleye, yellow perch, and sunfishes. In the left column, from top, are the Midget Runt, Tiny Tadpole, Lucky 13 threadline lure, and Bass Oreno. Middle column: Silver Minnow (best with pork rind), Paul Bunyan 66 fly with spinner, and Weezel spoon with bucktail. Right: Chugger Spook, River Runt, Dardevle, and Flatfish. When cast or trolled, the plugs wobble and dive or dart from side to side.*

74

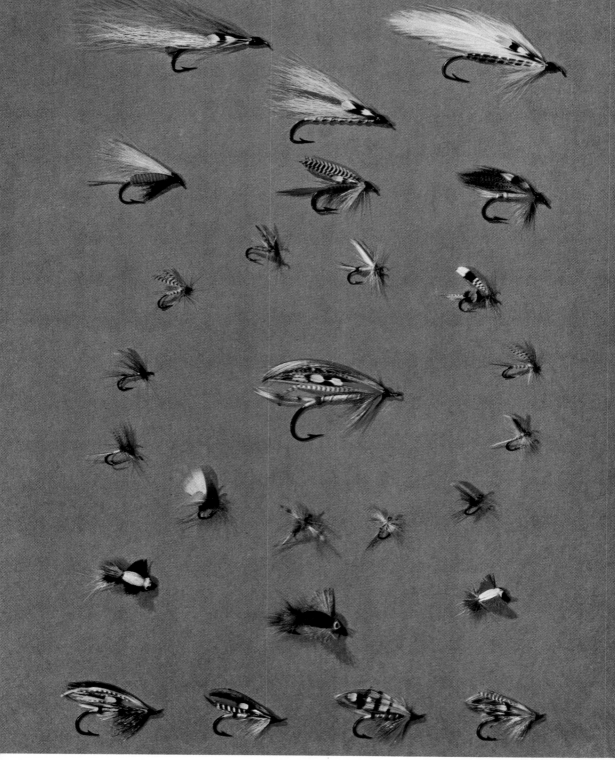

FLY PATTERNS *number in the thousands, but an angler usually swears by a few favorites. Three streamers at top look like minnows to New England trout and landlocked salmon. Second row has Pacific steelhead flies. Wet trout flies form top half of circle, dry ones the bottom. Next three are bass bugs. Flies at bottom and center take Atlantic salmon. Some 1,750 years ago a Roman told how Macedonians "fasten red wool around a hook, and fit ... two feathers which grew under a cock's wattles ... the fish ... enjoys a bitter repast." Their fly probably resembled today's streamers.*

ARMY OF ANGLERS *invades the rocky Potomac near the Nation's Capital in a spring assault on migrating herring and hickory shad. Herring ignore lures and must be snagged; shad take spoons. Distant rowboat fleet tries for perch. Opposite: No, these anglers are not fishing in the Reflecting Pool at Washington's Lincoln Memorial; they are perfecting casting technique.*

the end; in casting, this weight pulled the lighter line after it. Thus was developed the "torpedo" head or tadpole taper. Multiple taper lines with seven or more tapers woven into them have been designed, following careful study of their action in casting. With such lines the world's record cast has consistently lengthened.

Shortly before the second World War, a form of angling new to this continent arrived from Europe. Called threadlining by the British, who originated it a generation ago, and light casting by the French, who are its most ardent and advanced present-day exponents, the method falls somewhere between fly fishing and bait casting. The original threadline rods are usually of split bamboo, seven to seven and one-half feet long, fitted with a reel that differs from all other fishing reels in that the drum, fixed parallel to the axis of the rod, does not revolve. Instead, the light nylon monofilament line slips off the open end in loose

coils as the lure is cast, much as sewing thread might slip off the end of a spool. Thus there is no fast revolving spool to overrun and cause backlash, the tight tangle known to all bait casters that occurs when the angler's thumb allows the spool to run faster than the outgoing line.

With such equipment it is possible to cast much lighter lures than with bait-casting tackle; the usual lure is a small weighted revolving spoon.

Americans call such angling "spinning," although in England, where the term originated, spinning (from the revolving Devon minnow) refers to all forms of bait casting, as opposed to fly fishing.

Today the threadline rod has moved to first place as the universal fishing tool, for with it one can fish bait and cast spinners, artificial minnows, and even dry flies. Because of the nearly invisible line, it is like fishing with a 150-foot leader. Threadlining has a place on big waters, for bass, pike,

WINTER ANGLER *lands a whitefish on a snowy bank of the Snake River at Jackson Hole in Wyoming. Mountain whitefish* (Prosopium williamsoni) *can be taken in winter when trout are out of season. Popular lure is an artificial nymph imitating the larval stone fly that lives in the gravelly river. Whitefish below have been soaked in brine and cured with alder smoke.*

panfish, and even trout, but it can nearly depopulate small streams since it is so easy to use under all conditions.

The fixed-spool reel has almost completely supplanted the classic bait-casting reel, and larger versions of it are used for surf casting and even deep water trolling.

Fishing-rod makers constantly seek ways to make rods stiffer and stronger without increasing weight. A long time ago someone found out that by heating bamboo it could be stiffened and, incidentally, turned a handsome brown shade, lighter or darker according to the amount of heat treatment.

In 1942 the Orvis Company of Vermont developed a method of impregnating bamboo with Bakelite or other plastic. Split-bamboo rods so processed were stronger and stiffer than rods of untreated bamboo.

The Shakespeare Company revolutionized rod-making in 1946 by introducing the

glass fishing rod to the world. Incredible as it seemed at first, this usually brittle but tough substance appears to be the ideal material for fishing rods.

The Shakespeare rods are built of long fibers of glass wound around a mandrel. The fibers are next wrapped in cellophane tape, fused by heat into a homogeneous tube, and the mandrel withdrawn. Such construction approximated the structure of bamboo, nature's glass, with its hard fibers enbedded in softer pith. Other makers build glass rods by wrapping a length of woven glass fabric round a mandrel and fusing it.

Glass has many unquestioned advantages for fishing rods: It is unaffected by moisture, it is exceedingly flexible and tough, being almost impossible to break in normal use, and it rarely takes a permanent bend or "set." Yet, though nearly all bait-casting rods and threadline spinning rods in this

country are now made of glass, some fly rod enthusiasts have never fully accepted it. They say that nothing approaches the sweet, "nervous" feel of a split-bamboo rod from the hands of one of the best makers.

A recent development may give glass rods an even better action than jointed bamboo. In 1964 the Fenwick Rod Company of California patented a way to eliminate the metal ferrules of a joined rod.

A one-piece bamboo rod has a better action than one made of several sections. This is because there are no stiff spots where the metal ferrules interrupt the curve of the rod under stress. Yet a one-piece, eight- or nine-foot rod is awkward to transport. The Fenwick invention eliminates the metal. Instead, each section of the tubular glass rod slips into the slightly larger joint next to it. The result: a continuous curve when casting that feels very much like a one-piece rod.

Other rod makers now use similar methods of joining the glass sections. Thus it is now theoretically possible to build rods of almost any number of joints, as in the popular travelers' rods that come apart to stow in a small space. One company, Phillipson of Denver, even makes a ten-piece rod that—case and all—fits in a breast pocket.

No other angler in the world today is so well equipped as the American fisherman. His split-bamboo and glass rods have been refined and perfected to a high degree, growing lighter through the years until today they average about half the weight of the traditional British rods. His bait-casting reels, while lacking the polish and bejeweled hand finish of the early Kentucky masterpieces, cast far better than did those early prototypes, thanks mainly to light aluminum alloy spools that sharply reduce backlashes. Most fixed-spool spinning reels, however, are imported from Europe. And the best fly reels still come from England. U. S.-made salmon rods are single-handed and light, as the American fishes small water or from a boat, rarely having need to cover large rivers from the bank, as in Britain. And no other country can approach the quality and design of American big-game deep-sea tackle.

With all this equipment, what do most Americans fish for? Most popular by far are the so-called panfish—bluegill, crappie, sunfish, yellow perch, rock bass, and calico bass. Sixty to eighty percent of American anglers, according to the region, fish for these or catfish with poles and live bait.

Next most angled-for fish would probably be the bass, largemouth first, then smallmouth, with walleyes, pike, and pickerel following. Then would come the trout and landlocked salmon, with the muskellunge in solitary majesty at the end. In some areas as many as one-fourth of all fishermen may use artificial fly or bait-casting lures of one kind or another for these game fishes.

Fly fishing for trout is strongest in the New England states, Pennsylvania, Michigan, the Rocky Mountain states, and in some West Coast areas. Nearly all states have some fly fishing, and in Florida fishermen take bonefish, tarpon, red drum, and other sea fish on the fly.

Bait casting is done nearly everywhere, but the short rod and multiplying reel now flourish best in the southern and southwestern states, where warm waters permit fish to feed the year round, and growth is correspondingly more rapid. There bass and panfish grow to legal size in half the time needed in colder northern waters. Bait-casting enthusiasts in Florida even use bass tackle to take tarpon of up to 100 pounds.

In 1968 there were more than 60 million sport fishermen in the United States. This means that at least one-third of the total population of 12 years old or over went fishing at least once during the year. Although the population is mounting at an alarming rate, the number of anglers increases 2½ times as fast. Yet fishing waters have not magically expanded correspondingly, nor has the fish population taken a spurt to match.

Little virgin water remains within the bounds of the continental United States. The automobile and its attendant network of roads, and the airplane, have opened up the last wilderness areas. In few other countries can the fisherman pack up his tackle and drive two hundred miles or more to his fishing place and return the same day. Never in the history of angling has so much fishing water been available to so many.

This extreme mobility of the fishing population poses a serious conservation problem. In other, older countries, streams, lakes, and coasts feel fishing pressure only from local inhabitants. The American fisherman has a continent at his disposal, which is wonderful—while it lasts.

In some places, fishing, through wise scientific management, is better than it ever was. But such spots are few; on the whole, fishing has declined through deforestation, water pollution, introduction of competing species, and overfishing. The take is decreasing, with the average now estimated as less than one fish per fishing hour. Forward-looking tackle manufacturers have given considerable thought to the possibility that before too long they may be making tackle to catch something that no longer exists.

What then is the future of angling in the United States? Fish conservationists are not too pessimistic. But they say that people will not awaken to the need for stronger conservation measures until they actually begin to feel the pinch of poor fishing. In other words, fishing will have to get worse before it can get better.

There is no simple road to better fishing. The old idea of stocking hatchery-reared fish to be caught by anglers within a few days is a poor and partial answer. And it is too expensive. Today a hatchery trout placed in a stream costs the state more than the

MAN WRESTLES MARLIN *on the deck of the* Ramona *during the annual Deep Sea Fishing Rodeo staged by Mobile, Alabama. Angler Mickey O'Brien reeled in the powerful white marlin; companion Tommy Taul boats it. Rodeo fishermen vie for $15,000 in prizes.*

BILL SHROUT

80

license fee paid by the angler who catches the trout. Because of this, trout fishermen in some places must pay a higher license fee than other anglers.

Smaller bag limits and closed seasons do not now, as they once did, seem to be the whole answer. Indeed, in some large southern waters it may be better to permit year-round angling—to reduce the stock and so increase size and quality of the fish.

Fish conservationists have discovered that an acre of water, like an acre of land, can produce only a certain amount of animal life. Generally speaking, the figure is about 100 pounds of fish per acre. Hook and line fishermen take only about half the "standing crop" in big waters like lakes, while in a small, heavily fished trout stream, a substantial portion of the larger fish are taken out by anglers each season.

Man the Changer is the only animal that consistently alters his environment. A classic example of man's meddling with nature, as well as a spectacular instance of what imagination and scientific management can do to improve fishing, is furnished by those inland seas called the Great Lakes of North America, the largest bodies of fresh water in the world.

When the Welland Canal went into service in 1829, it bypassed Niagara Falls and so opened a gateway between the chain of lakes and the sea. Because of the enormous extent of the Great Lakes, no change was noted in the fish life for many years. But an unseen and repellent predator had swum in from the sea: the sea lamprey, an eel-like primitive fish with a rasping sucker mouth (page 39). By the late 1940's, they teemed in the Great Lakes and populations of food and game fish fell off alarmingly. Commercial fishermen went out of business, and fisheries biologists began an intensive search for a way to control the predator.

In 1951, after six years of dogged effort during which 6,000 toxic compounds were tried, government biologists achieved a technical miracle: they found a chemical that would kill lamprey larvae in spawning streams without harming desirable fish. Within ten years, lamprey population had been slashed by 80 percent.

The balance of nature is a delicate thing. Change or remove one vital bit of the intri-

BLUEFISH TROLLERS, *hauling on handlines, hit the jackpot off Highlands, New Jersey, a century ago. Today power cruisers take anglers over the same waters and find the blues still biting. When feeding,* Pomatomus saltatrix *strikes furiously at almost any lure, providing sport for boat fishermen and surfcasters from New England to Florida.*

ANKLE-DEEP *shallows in the Gulf of Mexico yield a pair of red drum to the spinning tackle of writer-fisherman Byron W. Dalrymple. He slogs across flats off Texas, where scrappy* Sciaenops ocellata *grubs for shellfish in water barely deep enough for maneuvering. Tail spot identifies the drum, often called channel bass by Atlantic coast surfcasters and redfish in the Gulf.*

cate interdependence of plant and animal life and the whole structure begins to sway and shift; sometimes it collapses with a rush, like a log jam from which the key log has been extracted. So it was in the Great Lakes: When the lampreys reduced the stock of lake trout and other foragers almost to nothing, the alewife, a small herring-like fish that had also slipped in from the sea, increased explosively. In recent years alewives have almost entirely supplanted the native food and game fishes of Lakes Michigan and Huron, becoming a dismaying 99 percent of the fish population of both lakes.

Alewives so crowded the lakes that they literally ate and breathed themselves into mass suicide by depleting the store of plankton and oxygen. In 1967 alone one *billion* alewives died in Lake Michigan. The dead fish covered the surface, clogged city water intakes, and rotted in windrows on the shore.

In 1966, the Michigan Department of Conservation, to convert the mass of living alewives into game and food fish, imported coho salmon from the Pacific coast. Fisheries men chose the coho because it is a fast-growing, wide-ranging forager. Thus, if coho

did successfully establish themselves in the lakes they would roam the depths and shallows seeking food, unlike the relatively sedentary trout and bass.

The big question was: Could the coho spend its entire life in fresh water? In its original habitat the coho is anadromous, spending most of its life in the ocean, returning to its native stream to spawn. Biologists, relying on evidence that the salmon was originally a fresh-water fish that adapted to the sea in geologically recent times, decided to take the chance. The results have astonished scientists and delighted anglers.

Of the one million coho eggs brought from Oregon, 850,000 hatched and survived to be planted as six-inch fish in Lake Superior and Lake Michigan streams. Not minding the lack of salt, the small fish swam down into the inland seas of the big lakes and began to feed on the gargantuan feast of alewives. That autumn anglers caught the first coho on hook and line off the mouths of the parent streams. Fishermen took two thousand fish averaging three pounds; one fish taken from this, Michigan's historic first salmon run, weighed over seven pounds. This fish, growing fat and heavy on the

MORE FISHERMEN THAN FISH *mark opening day at Saxton Falls on the Musconetcong River in New Jersey. Jumble of lines underscores a nationwide problem: Our enormous number of anglers—some 60 million—is expected to double by the year 2000, but fishing facilities are not expanding as rapidly and in some areas are vanishing. Exhaustive studies made by the National Outdoor Recreation Resources Review Commission, headed by National Geographic Trustee Laurance S. Rockefeller, resulted in these recommendations: reduction of water pollution, greater access to privately owned streams and ponds, the impounding of more water for fishing areas, and public acquisition of stream banks, lake shores, and beaches.*

seemingly inexhaustible store of alewives, went from one ounce to seven pounds in only four months. It had added *a pound a week* during part of the summer.

The coho has a three- to five-year life cycle and by 1968 anglers trolling in open water from 1,000 boats took more than 100,000 fish. They averaged from eight to ten pounds, but fifteen-pound fish were not unusual, and one exceeded 22 pounds.

Most important, the coho has returned to its parent streams to spawn, proving definitely and dramatically that it can carry out its entire life cycle in fresh water.

Michigan's sensationally successful experiment has shown that science and careful management can indeed provide better fishing for more people, but it is only a beginning.

With a rapidly increasing population, the United States is no longer a pioneer nation, where unlimited wild lands abounding in fish and game lie just over the horizon. To provide better fishing for everybody, there must be a combination of water improvement, stocking, closer regulation, and an increase in fishing water.

The use of water reservoirs as fishing places was long overlooked in this country of past abundance. But it is significant that some of the largest trout caught each year in the British Isles come from the water supply of a great industrial city. We are coming to realize that reservoirs, with careful management, can furnish superlative fishing to large numbers.

Hand in hand with these things goes the education of the fisherman. Fewer and fewer Americans cling to the primitive belief that a man must bring home a huge string of fish to prove he is a good fisherman. Everyone goes fishing to catch fish, but most anglers realize that sooner or later the catching becomes less certain unless common sense and intelligent management are combined. American fishermen today are determined that the future shall hold not only good fishing, but better fishing for everybody. "And if the angler take fish; surely then is there no man merrier than he is in his spirit."

CHAPTER THREE

By THOMAS J. ABERCROMBIE
National Geographic Staff

Ice Fishing's Frigid Charms

The cold, lonely chore of hungry Eskimos becomes the winter sport of thousands on the northern lakes

I T'LL WEIGH 11 pounds easy," said Frank Gudridge (opposite). His catch, a walleye two minutes out of water when I took the picture, had frozen as stiff as a baseball bat in the 25-below-zero cold at Minnesota's Mille Lacs Lake.

Mr. Gudridge, bare-fingered, threaded another minnow on his hook, broke the thin ice over his fishing hole, and lowered his line. Only then did he draw on his mitts.

"There are plenty more like this one right under your feet," he told me.

All around us parka-clad fishermen were cutting holes through the 32-inch-thick ice, then pushing heated shanties overtop. What is the lure, I asked, that draws these zealots from their cozy fireplaces at home.

"Fishing is the best sport," an old-timer explained. "Why let winter stop you?"

Improved clothing and tackle prime the ice-fishing boom. Stores offer candle-heated minnow buckets, motor-driven ice drills, and electrically heated stockings. Devices called tip-ups automatically signal a strike by popping up a red flag, enabling the fisherman to monitor two holes at once.

When the ice thickens, temporary towns spring up on many lakes. "Perchville," a shanty village on Lake Huron's Tawas Bay, has its own mayor, who sets up city hall at "Perch Street" and "Pike Avenue."

To make these photographs, I motored through the ice-fishing belt in Michigan, Wisconsin, and Minnesota. Using a snowmobile sled, I breezed across frozen lakes. With Aqua-Lung and camera, I dived into ice-covered depths and recorded a perch's view of fishermen.

PRONE ANGLER *scans a lake's dim depths for pike; head and arms shut out distracting light.*

87

ICE-FISHING CONTEST *draws five to six thousand enthusiasts each year onto White Bear Lake near St. Paul, Minnesota. I don't know how the ice supports them; here the crowd spills outside the four-leaf clover design of the 4-H clubs. At the contest I attended, one fisherman*

prophesied, "No fish in its right mind would swim within a thousand yards of this mob."
Evidence supported him: The largest catch weighed less than three pounds. I saw a toddler
of 2½ on the ice and talked with a 97-year-old who kept his live bait in a pocket flask.

A PIKE *looms into view; a second later the razor-sharp, five-tined spear impaled it.*

Dangling a minnow bait from his jig stick, the fisherman sits in his dark house on a Minnesota lake. Windows are omitted because the black interior enables him to see into the depths.

The photographer's flash illuminates this dramatic scene. The shot took hours of patient waiting.

In many ice shacks card games go on endlessly by lantern light. Bottled-gas stoves produce summer temperatures, and radios drown out the moaning wind.

FROZEN STIFF, *a 98-pound lake sturgeon leaves Winnebago on a spearman's shoulder. Smoked sturgeon flesh ranks as a delicacy. A female this size may hold half a bushel of roe. The fence posts mark the man's lake-front home.*

FROM ONE OF THESE CABINS
on Lake Winnebago, Wisconsin,
came a cheery voice: "How
about a cup of coffee?"

Inside, I found neighbors
barging in and out. Before
spring thaw, they said, they
would drag away the 2,000
shacks of their village.

One courageous soul
insisted on facing the
elements. Bundled head to
foot, he carries a spud, or
chisel, to chop ice.

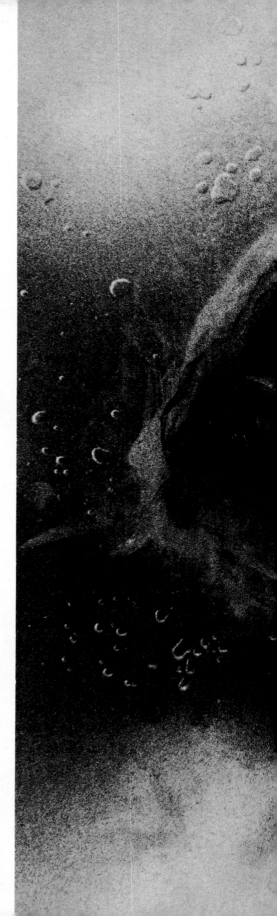

I WENT UNDER THE ICE *twice—I think now I must have been crazy. Despite insulating suits, the cold was sheer horror. Below, I wince in a Wisconsin lake as my face mask is adjusted. I photographed a fish's view of ice fishermen (opposite) from 20 feet down in Lake Huron. A fellow diver (above) spears a bony little carp—all we caught. Dark spots show pockets of our breath trapped by ice.*

92

WINNER, CATCH, AND CUP. *Jimmy Tobin's
2-pound 12-ounce bass topped all other fish
in a tourney on White Bear Lake. He won a
$500 boat-motor-trailer combination.*

PICKET FENCE *of frozen walleyes, a family's weekend catch, stands in the snow of Mille Lacs Lake, Minnesota (left). Trailer dwellers drove onto the ice, cut holes, then watched their lines from indoors. Not the diehard above: I photographed him in numbing cold as he neared the 50-perch limit of Tawas Bay, Michigan. Snowmobile (below) whisked me 60 miles an hour over Lake Minnetonka, Minnesota.*

CHAPTER FOUR

By VAN CAMPEN HEILNER
Vice President, International
Game Fish Association

The Lordly Tarpon — Angler's Delight

Big, abundant, and chock full of fight, he is the "silver king" of America's big game fish

M Y FIRST TARPON weighed only 20 pounds, but if he had weighed 200 my excitement and delight could not have been greater.

Nor could he have engraved my memory more indelibly. A moonlight night, the ghostly arches of the Florida Keys viaduct, the putt-putt of the tiny launch that carried me crosswise to the rushing tide; then the strike and the flash of silver, dripping diamonds of spray from his flanks as he catapulted into the air again, and again, and yet again.

A lot of water has flowed through those arches since then and many a tarpon has leaped at the end of my line. Each has been a memorable thrill.

I remember one blazing hot afternoon toward the end of March on the vast banks off the southern tip of Florida. The tide had turned to the flood, and from Sandy Key eastward to Snake Bight tarpon were rolling. The mullet were in, and the water was discolored a milky white.

As we slid across the flats in our little skiff, we could see the long dorsal plumes of tarpon wavering for an instant on the surface. The sun had just set in a ball of red fire as we started up a winding blue-green channel. I was fishing with an extra-light rod— four and a half ounces over all—that was more suitable for fresh-water gamesters.

We came to the end of the channel and turned to retrace our wake. Suddenly there was a swift surge on my line. I struck, and into the air bounded a tarpon.

I could hear the tinkle of the spoon as he thrashed his head from side to side to dislodge the hook. But it held, and this threw him into a frenzy of acrobatics.

The skiff drifted with the tide, and the fish continued its mad leaping. Half the time I did not know whether I had him on or not. But then the line would strain, and I knew the fight was not finished. The tackle was so light that I could not easily force the fighting, and it took more than half an hour to bring him alongside.

His terrific exertions had worn him out; we tipped the skiff down on one side and slid him in. He weighed 56 pounds and today adorns the walls of my studio. I count

WALTER A. WEBER, NATIONAL GEOGRAPHIC STAFF

WRITHING WITH RAGE, *a glistening hooked tarpon meets his reflection head-on.*

TARPON
Megalops atlantica

With bulldog jaws and body full of fury, the tarpon has brought so many anglers to Florida that it is regarded as one of the state's leading promoters. It abounds also in the Gulf of Mexico and Caribbean and visits north to Cape Cod. Relatively slow swimmers, tarpon owe their fame to their power and explosive leaps.

Heavily fished, tarpon multiply apace; a 142-pound female held an estimated 12 million eggs. Where these oversize herring spawn is a mystery; the best guess is in the Caribbean or Gulf. Instead of growing up, larval tarpon "grow down": Transparent fry shrink radically in length as they enter the juvenile stage. Unlike most fishes, tarpon use the air bladder for breathing, occasionally gulping air at the surface. Coarse and bony, their pinkish flesh finds a market only in Central America.

Characteristics: large silvery scales; single soft-rayed dorsal fin; bony plate under mouth. *Range:* North Carolina to Brazil, strays to Cape Cod; occurs both sides of Atlantic. *Weight:* rod and reel record 283 pounds. *Length:* to 8 feet.

97

ERUPTING FROM FLORIDA WATERS, *a tarpon gyrates wildly to throw the hook. Larger trophy (below) stretches as long as its six-foot captor, Dr. Melvin M. Payne, President of the National Geographic Society. The 105-pounder waged a grueling battle lasting more than two hours.*

him one of my proudest achievements with rod and line. For thrills aplenty, try the "silver king" on bait-casting tackle!

Another June day on the west coast of Florida we were still-fishing in a pass. Tarpon had been rolling all around us, but we could not tempt them to bite.

I was drowsing in my seat at the stern of the skiff when suddenly the line, which I had stripped from my reel and laid on one of the thwarts, started to uncoil and slide over the edge into the sea. For several seconds I watched, fascinated. When it had almost reached the end, I let it come taut and struck, once—twice. Immediately a tarpon shot skyward and the battle was on.

From then on, tarpon hit at everything. In a brief time we boated and released seven.

So it goes. A friend brought to boat 25 tarpon between sunup and sundown at Boca Grande, the famous Florida west coast resort of these mighty fish. Off Cuba we have hooked and jumped as many as 104 in one day, of course releasing them if uninjured.

The instant tarpon feel the hook they leap; about three out of every four throw the hook on the first jump. Those that do not throw it or break the line finally exhaust themselves with their acrobatics.

There are exceptions to this rule of bat-

STRAEA
NAPLES
FLA

VENICE TARPON CLUB (BELOW) AND A. W. AND JULIAN DIMOCK

FISHERMAN SCRAMBLES FOR SAFETY *as a hundred pounds of tarpon flips nearby; sometimes the frantic fish land in the boat, causing injury or capsizing the craft. Another silver king, fought to the finish (below), tips the skiff that will carry him ashore to be mounted.*

tle. One of the largest tarpon of which I have any record jumped only once during the entire fight. At the end, as the fish was almost to boat, a shark rushed up and bit it in two just behind the dorsal fin. The part remaining weighed more than 200 pounds and in all probability represented a world's record tarpon.

Sharks are a real problem. A fresh fish, if given a slack line, may outrun one, but for a tired fish there is little hope. In some sections of the world at certain times of the year it is practically impossible to land an unmutilated fish. I've watched fishermen protect their catch by firing a pistol at marauding sharks. Frequently they shoot off the wire leader by mistake, although if you tried to do it on purpose you would never succeed in a million years.

Generally tarpon run from 30 to 80 pounds; many trophies weigh 170.

These are large fish. A specimen of 200 pounds is exceptional. The present world's record was taken in Lake Maracaibo, Venezuela, in 1956. It tipped the beam at 283 pounds and measured seven feet, two and three-fifths inches. I have seen a mounted tarpon in New York's American Museum of Natural History,

details of capture unknown, which from appearances must also have been close to 300 pounds. This I should think is about the limit for the species.

I have a theory that as tarpon grow larger and older they lose some of their agility and more easily fall prey to sharks.

To the tarpon is due no small amount of credit for the development of Florida, though he is by no means confined to that peninsula. He is the original big game fish. Anglers came from the four corners of the earth in search of him long before sailfish, marlin, or tuna were heard of as game fish.

Tarpon probably spawn somewhere in the Caribbean area, possibly up brackish or fresh-water rivers. I have always felt, though I could never prove, that some must spawn up the rivers of the west coast of Florida; I have seen countless baby tarpon in these streams and in the ditches along the Tamiami Trail.

The tarpon is more or less common in summertime north to Long Island, New York, and south to Brazil. The northern wanderers are frequently caught in nets, infrequently by anglers. At Cape Hatteras, North Carolina, the fish are present throughout the warm months, no doubt because of the Gulf Stream about 10 miles offshore.

Most of the tarpon clubs are in Florida, though a number flourish in Texas and Mexico and there is a famous club in the Canal Zone. Here where the great Gatun Dam spans the Chagres River is to be found some of the finest tarpon fishing known.

For years tarpon defied efforts to transplant them to the Pacific coast. Even attempts to tow them through the Panama Canal alive in slatted, submerged pens met with failure. But anglers catch tarpon off the Balboa entrance; apparently the fish makes it to the Pacific coast on its own yet has not become established there.

ENRAGED by the barb in its bony mouth, a big tarpon surges up in a furious try to shake free. Three out of four times the initial leap succeeds. If the hook holds, the angler is pitted against one of fishing's hardest-fighting, most acrobatic gamesters.

The species also is plentiful in several places on the west coast of Africa, notably Angola and Nigeria.

The tarpon loves to frequent passes, channels, and cuts through the banks. There he lies in wait for whatever small fishes the tides will bring him. He can be caught either by trolling back and forth through the passes, or by still-fishing with crab or cut bait on the bottom. Time must be given for the tarpon to swallow the bait before setting the hook.

In Florida the best tarpon fishing occurs in May and June. Anglers often catch them earlier along the viaducts of the Overseas Highway to Key West and in the ship channel at Miami Beach. Then they seem to strike best at night.

I have seen the tarpon around Florida's Cape Sable lying in the shallows like shoals of bait. At Bimini in the Bahamas, about 55 miles across the Gulf Stream from Miami Beach, large numbers of 30- to 50-pounders lie on the bottom in the clear harbor water.

For several years I carried on exploratory work in the swamps and rivers of southern Cuba. This country could be reached only after arduous travel on horseback and afoot through almost impenetrable swamps. The rivers literally swarmed with tarpon which had never even seen man. They would strike at any moving object.

Quite frequently their first leap carried them high into tree limbs overhanging the water. Then they fell back with a great crashing and breaking of branches, leaving the angler's line a tangled mass.

Though none ever actually landed in our boat, several came mighty close to it. An 80-pound fish thrashing in a boat—it has happened—would certainly injure a fisherman if it struck him, and could kill him.

If you love angling and want spectacular sport, pack your tackle and make your plans next spring to slip down the coast to Florida, Texas, Mexico, Panama, or anywhere on the fringes of the Caribbean. There you may try your mettle on one of nature's grandest gifts to fishermen, that bow of flashing silver, that master of aerial acrobatics, the leaping tarpon.

CHAPTER FIVE

Windows on a Watery World

THE DRAMA OF LIFE in the sea, as rich as that on land but not so intimately known, kindles man's curiosity. And it accounts for the appeal of aquariums—showcase tank to giant outdoor bowl—that provide windows on a watery world.

Romans built ponds to raise fish for food, and ancient Chinese domesticated the carp for display. But the first public aquarium as we now know them opened at London's Regent Park in 1853, exhibiting fresh-water fishes. The first in the United States was at the Bureau of Fisheries in Washington, D. C., in 1888. Oceanariums, solving the difficult problem of large-scale presentation of salt-water species, began with Marineland of Florida, in 1938.

Now such centers dot the Nation, drawing throngs of sightseers and scientists. Hypnotized spectators gape at ponderous jewfish (left) or pack "porpoise stadiums" to cheer nature's brainy clowns. Marine biologists test shark repellents or probe the secrets of barnacles' powerful adhesive. The accompanying list locates major galleries.

CONEY ISLAND'S BOARDWALK *leads to the New York Aquarium, operated by the New York Zoological Society. In such centers, explains the society's board chairman Fairfield Osborn, people can satisfy "an innate craving to observe and enjoy the living things of nature."*

Major Aquariums of North America and Hawaii

Public exhibits of marine life offer varied fare to delight and instruct; some charge admission. Federal and state hatcheries also welcome visitors.

NORTHEAST

Boston, Massachusetts
 New England Aquarium

Chicago, Illinois
 John G. Shedd Aquarium

Cincinnati, Ohio
 Fleischmann Memorial Aquarium

Cleveland, Ohio
 Cleveland Aquarium

Detroit, Michigan
 Belle Isle Aquarium

Grand Rapids, Michigan
 John Ball Park Aquarium

New York, New York
 New York Aquarium

Niagara Falls, New York
 Aquarium of Niagara Falls, Inc.

Philadelphia, Pennsylvania
 Aquarama

Pittsburgh, Pennsylvania
 AquaZoo

Powell, Ohio
 Arthur C. Johnson Aquarium

Provincetown, Massachusetts
 Provincetown Marine Aquarium

Staten Island, New York
 Staten Island Zoo

Toledo, Ohio
 Toledo Zoological Gardens Aquarium

Washington, D. C.
 National Aquarium

Woods Hole, Massachusetts
 Aquarium of the Bureau of Commercial Fisheries

103

DOUGLAS FAULKNER (OPPOSITE) AND LILO HESS, THREE LIONS

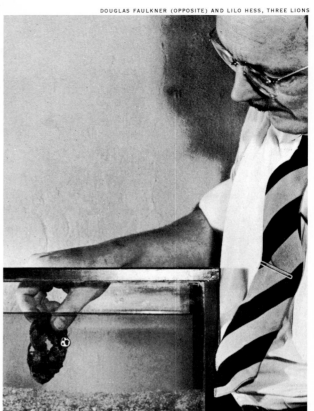

THIS AFRICAN MUD PIE *has a lungfish filler. Dr. Christopher W. Coates, director emeritus of the New York Aquarium, snips the grass binding, frees the curled-up fish, and dunks it. In 12 hours the blob becomes a shriveled suggestion (below) of an unlovely lungfish (bottom). Surface-breathing* Protopterus annectens *can live for more than a year out of water by using up its own tissue. It likes horsemeat but not company; two in a tank tear each other to pieces.*

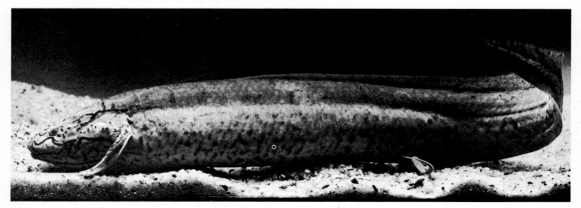

ELECTRIC EEL'S *discharge
at the New York Aquarium
lights a voltmeter, crackles in
a loud speaker, and makes a
little boy hold his ears. Living
batteries that generate direct
current make up half the
South American fish's tissue;
a full discharge can kill
a man. Even a six-inch*
Electrophorus electricus *can
produce 300 volts. Crooklike
copper electrode conducts
current to the meter from the
three-foot eel in the tank.*

SOUTHEAST

Fort Lauderdale, Florida
Ocean World, Inc.

Fort Walton Beach, Florida
Gulfarium

Islamorada, Florida
Theater of the Sea, Inc.

Key West, Florida
Key West Aquarium

Memphis, Tennessee
Overton Park Zoo and Aquarium

Miami, Florida
Miami Seaquarium
Hialeah Marine Aquarium

St. Augustine, Florida
Marineland of Florida

St. Petersburg, Florida
Aquatarium

NORTH CENTRAL

Guttenberg, Iowa
Guttenberg National Aquarium

Lake Ozark, Missouri
Missouri Aquarium

Milwaukee, Wisconsin
*Milwaukee County Zoological
Park*

Yankton, South Dakota
Gavins Point National Aquarium

SOUTH CENTRAL

Dallas, Texas
Dallas Aquarium

Fort Worth, Texas
James R. Record Aquarium

Galveston, Texas
Sea-Arama

Gulfport, Mississippi
Marine Life

New Orleans, Louisiana
Odenheimer Aquarium

San Antonio, Texas
Richard Friedrich Aquarium

NORTHWEST

Depoe Bay, Oregon
Depoe Bay Aquarium

Hoodsport, Washington
Hoodsport Submarine Aquarium

Newport, Oregon
Oregon Undersea Gardens

Seaside, Oregon
Seaside Aquarium

Seattle, Washington
Seattle Marine Aquarium

Tacoma, Washington
Point Defiance Aquarium

Westport, Washington
Westport Aquarium

SOUTHWEST AND HAWAII

Crescent City, California
Sea Wonders Alive

Eureka, California
Shipwreck Deep Sea Aquarium

Honolulu, Hawaii
Waikiki Aquarium

La Jolla, California
*T. Wayland Vaughan
Aquarium-Museum*

Makapuu Point, Oahu, Hawaii
Sea Life Park

Monterey, California
Wharf Aquarium

Morro Bay, California
Morro Bay Aquarium

Palos Verdes Estates, California
Marineland of the Pacific

Redwood City, California
Marine World

San Diego, California
Sea World

San Francisco, California
Steinhart Aquarium

Tucson, Arizona
*Arizona-Sonora Desert
Museum*

OTHER AQUARIUMS

Calgary, Alberta, Canada
Calgary Brewery Aquarium

Quebec City, Quebec,
Canada
Aquarium de Québec

Vancouver, British Columbia,
Canada
Vancouver Public Aquarium

Nassau, Bahamas
Seafloor Aquarium Limited

The Flatts, Bermuda
*Bermuda Government
Aquarium*

THREE-RING SEA CIRCUS *greets visitors at California's Marineland of the Pacific, near Los Angeles. At such oceanariums big fishes—if fed well—live compatibly with small fry in water carefully filtered to provide viewing clarity; normal ocean murkiness hampers vision at 20 feet. Portholes line Marineland's 500,000-gallon center tank, which displays 5,000 species. Sea lions and bottlenose dolphins frolic in the foreground arena. The circular stadium houses striped dolphins and trained whales, including Bimbo (right) who flashes a toothy smile at Melville Bell Grosvenor, Editor-in-Chief and Board Chairman of the National Geographic Society.*

106

CHAPTER SIX

Gallery of Marine Fishes ▶

GAME SPECIES

R ODS BUCKLED in the early 1900's as fishermen futilely hooked mighty bluefin tunas. A Canadian lost 41 straight, one after a heartbreaking 19-hour battle. Then author Zane Grey, with improved gear, conquered 700-pounders. More monsters fell to such angling giants as Ernest Hemingway, S. Kip Farrington, Jr., and Michael Lerner—and the grueling sport of big game fishing had arrived.

Not all marine game fish are deep sea giants. Light-tackle scrappers abound within casting range of pier and beach, or a quart of gas away by outboard. They bear out Hemingway's dictum that "Salt water fishing is a sport for everyone."

In a realm where mild exaggerations are not unknown, the International Game Fish Association keeps unassailable records on 49 species. Officials from France to Fiji scrutinize photographs of record-breakers, test lines that caught them, employ accredited weighmasters.

Many fishermen mount their catch. Others deposit it in frying pan or freezer. An increasing number free their fish, ensuring sport for other anglers who seek salt-water gamesters described on the following pages.

Jacks, Pompanos, and Dolphins

N EVER-SAY-DIE GAMENESS and lightning sprints of more than half a mile a minute earn anglers' respect for the jacks, pompanos, and dolphins. They come in a variety of sizes, shapes, and habitats. Little pompanos, their bodies deep as they are long, stay close to shores and reefs. Jacks, generally more elongated, prefer offshore banks and the open sea. Amberjacks, torpedo-shaped predators that exceed a hundred pounds, seldom enter shallows. Dolphins, fastest of all, roam wherever tasty flyingfishes lead.

The warm-water predators wear a divided dorsal fin and a deeply notched tail that usually denotes speed. Some exhibit bony plates along their slender caudal peduncle. The young usually school; adults move alone or in small groups. Jacks and pompanos belong to the family Carangidae; dolphins to Coryphaenidae.

DOLPHIN

Coryphaena hippurus

Arcing out of the water, a dolphin drops like a bomb on trolled lure and streaks for the horizon, tearing line from the screaming reel. It stops, leaps 10 feet, 20 feet, then bursts into wild runs. Boated at last, its iridescent flanks flash with shimmering blues, greens, and golds that fade at death like a passing sunset.

Dolphins have long fascinated man. Ancients adopted them in heraldry and Christian art as symbols of diligence, love, and swiftness. Poets have drawn imagery from their colors. Mariners wrapped them in legend.

Sprinting nearly 25 miles an hour, dolphins leave most fishes behind. They grow fast too: 1½-pounders introduced in Florida's Marine-

land reached 25 pounds in 4½ months. But in three years their furious life probably is spent.

Dolphins, or "dorados," race beneath airborne flyingfishes and gobble them as they land. Their diet includes sardines, anchovies, and mackerel. Baby dolphins fall prey to diving terns.

Anglers troll for dolphins near drifting objects and sea grasses with feathered jigs, spoons, rag baits, squid lures, plugs, and cut fish.

Mature dolphin bulls nearly double females in size and develop a characteristic high brow. The name dolphin confusingly includes members of the mammalian porpoise clan.

Characteristics: blunt head, tapered body, forked tail, long soft dorsal fin; brilliant blue-green coloring. *Range:* world-wide in warm seas. *Weight:* rod and reel record 85 pounds. *Length:* maximum 6 feet.

DOLPHIN

PAINTINGS BY HASHIME MURAYAMA

AMBERJACK (top) and YELLOW JACK

GREATER AMBERJACK
Seriola dumerili

Groups of 20- to 70-pound greater amberjacks patrol Texas shores and Florida reefs, seldom entering depths of less than 15 feet. Some follow the Gulf Stream north to Cape Hatteras, preying among wrecks that dot the "graveyard of the Atlantic." Swift and powerful, they are sought by ocean anglers wherever found.

Amberjacks excel as line cutters, deftly dropping over the side of a reef to use its edge as a knife. Hooked and brought alongside, their frantic last-minute thrashings often snap taut leaders. Fish brought to boat frequently attract other amberjacks into casting range.

The Atlantic coast harbors three other amberjacks, distinguished only by slight anatomical differences, *S. fasciata*, *S. rivoliana*, and *S. zonata*. Most fishermen lump all under the general name amberjack.

Characteristics: often a black stripe across the eye that may disappear with age, grayish-purple back, golden sheen overall; juveniles have bright golden bands which are lost with age. *Range:* Carolinas to Brazil, strays to Cape Cod; perhaps world-wide in warmer seas. *Weight:* rod and reel record 149 pounds. *Length:* to 6 feet.

YELLOW JACK
Caranx bartholomaei

Swift and restless hunters of the open sea, yellow jacks are the terror of smaller fishes, rushing and driving them in wild flight. But yellow jack young have their own enemies: Countless fry swarming off Florida's Dry Tortugas fall prey to screaming gulls.

A variety of baits—cut fish, spoons, feathered jigs, metal squids—will provoke a strike from the jacks. Some fishermen spot a feeding school as it churns the surface, steer upwind, and cast as the boat drifts down on the commotion.

Anglers understandably confuse the Atlantic jacks. Most frequently caught is the common jack, or crevalle *(C. hippos)*, a hard fighter that reaches 40 pounds. The almost identical horse-eye jack *(C. latus)* likes waters around islands. Bathers often see little bar jacks *(C. ruber)* scampering fearlessly after barracudas. The similar blue runner *(C. crysos)* is prized as bait for attracting larger gamefishes.

Characteristics: body deeper than the amberjack's; keel of bony plates, called scutes, on each side of the caudal peduncle. *Range:* tropical Atlantic rarely to Cape Cod. *Weight:* to 25 pounds. *Length:* to 3½ feet.

109

AFRICAN POMPANO
Alectis crinitis

Filamentous fins stream like contrails behind the young African pompano, or threadfin. On older fish they vanish. So different in appearance are the two that adults are often erroneously classed as a separate species called Cuban jack *(Hynnis cubensis).* Adults occur frequently about reefs, while young drift in the open sea. The tropical west coast harbors a nearly identical threadfin *(A. ciliaris).*

Characteristics: flowing dorsal and anal fins shortening with age; dark bars that dim on older fish. *Range:* adults, tropics north to Florida; young to Cape Cod. *Length:* to 3 feet.

FLORIDA POMPANO
Trachinotus carolinus

Skittish pompanos, rooting close inshore for mollusks and crustaceans, usually show anglers a tempting flank or caudal fin, then bolt. When fleeing they may skim over the waves on their sides like sailed paper plates. Successful anglers stalk them with light tackle and set the hook at first strike, knowing that pompanos hit once, then run for their lives.

Superb food, pompanos are usually prepared whole to utilize rich oils in the head.

Characteristics: yellowish head and belly; deep body; adults toothless. *Range:* Cape Cod to Brazil, centered in the Gulf of Mexico. *Weight:* maximum 8 pounds. *Length:* to 18 inches.

MIAMI SEAQUARIUM (BELOW), CARLETON RAY (TOP), AND RALSTON PRINCE

AFRICAN POMPANO

PERMIT

PERMIT
Trachinotus falcatus

Long-finned version of the pompano, the slightly smaller permit provides the same hard-running fight and good, if not equal, flavor. Sand fleas, crustaceans, and tiny fishes feed them; small plugs, spoons, and fish strips catch them. Anglers frequently call young specimens "round pompanos" and apply "permit" only to large adults, once thought to be a separate species.

Characteristics: silvery belly, bluish back; high dorsal and anal fins. *Range:* Cape Cod to Brazil. *Weight:* rod and reel record 50 pounds. *Length:* to 3½ feet.

111

YELLOWTAIL (top) and CHUB MACKEREL

YELLOWTAIL
Seriola dorsalis

Favorite fish of party boats that leave southern California ports, yellowtails will strike at live bait trolled 10 miles an hour, then run like a race horse in one of fishing's finest performances.

Wolf packs of yellowtails, driving prey, may churn the surface to a maelstrom. High on their menu: mackerel, sardines, smelts, anchovies.

In spring yellowtails school off San Diego. They arrive off Los Angeles a month later, then in autumn vanish from California. They breed at sea, milling on the surface in tight circles, streaming milt and roe.

Florida's "yellowtail" is a snapper (page 128).

Characteristics: brassy lateral stripe and tail fin; mackerel-like body. *Range:* Monterey Bay to Mexico. *Weight:* average 10 pounds, rod and reel record 111. *Length:* to 5 feet.

CHUB MACKEREL
Scomber japonicus

Anything from live bait to dry flies brings chub mackerel in a rush. At times they literally push each other aside in their eagerness to strike. They assure high sport on light tackle.

Huge schools sweep along the Pacific coast in summer and fall; in the Atlantic, chubs are less abundant. They may glut West Coast markets with a catch of 100 million pounds one year, then be relatively scarce the next. One theory holds that fry drift into regions where temperature changes cause mass death.

Chub mackerel eat crustaceans, squids, and small fishes. They make excellent food fish.

Characteristics: 20 to 30 wavy dark stripes on back; 5 or 6 finlets behind dorsal and anal fins. *Range:* temperate Pacific and Atlantic. *Weight:* to 3 or 4 pounds. *Length:* to 22½ inches.

112

Mackerels, Tunas, and Bonitos

TWO-POUND MACKEREL or half-ton tuna, the performance is magnificent: jolting strike, breakneck runs, stubborn undersea struggle that sets the angler aglow with excitement and admiration. Every physical feature of the family Scombridae contributes to strength and speed. Smooth tapering head, torpedo-shaped body, satiny skin, and tight-fitting gill covers minimize water resistance.

Thus equipped, the streamlined predators hunt down prey at up to 40 miles an hour, strip line from reels with awesome speed, and, in the case of large tuna, engage anglers for 12 hours and even more. Tunas, mackerels, and bonitos sprout twin dorsals and rows of finlets behind anal fins. They usually swim in schools that contain fish of similar size.

ATLANTIC MACKEREL
Scomber scombrus

In years of mackerel abundance a ship's lookout may spot 50 compact schools at once fleeting like clouds near the surface. A single school may stretch half a mile wide and as much as 20 miles long. But overnight mackerel vanish, presumably ducking deep. Their numbers may fluctuate from year to year, caused perhaps by mysterious destruction to spawn or fry.

Striking readily and fighting well, they offer boundless sport. Anglers catch 50, even 100 in a good day's trolling, baitcasting, or flyfishing.

Mackerel appear off Chesapeake Bay about April and arrive northward progressively later, often looking lean and underfed from winter. As they fatten on small fishes and quantities of plankton they are bombarded by predators— whales, porpoises, mackerel sharks, dogfish, tunas, bonitos, bluefish, striped bass, cod, squids, parasitic worms, diving sea birds. May to July they spawn wherever they are schooling, depositing up to half a million eggs near the surface. In September the great schools fade, to winter farther at sea or in deep water.

Characteristics: 23 to 33 dark dorsal stripes; fine scales that give the skin a satiny texture; usually 5 finlets, 2 small lateral keels on either side of caudal peduncle. *Range:* Labrador to Cape Hatteras; occurs both sides of Atlantic. *Weight:* to 7 pounds. *Length:* to 2 feet.

ATLANTIC MACKEREL

PAINTINGS BY HASHIME MURAYAMA

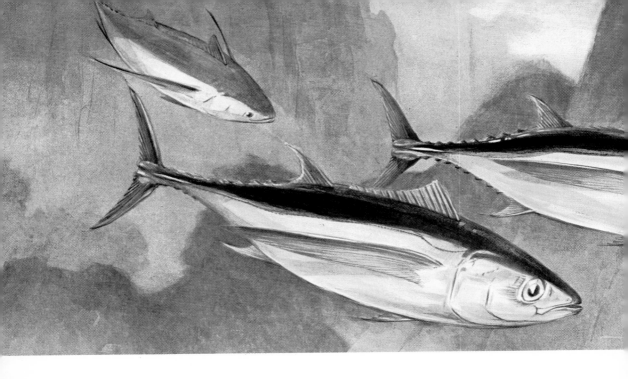

BLUEFIN TUNA
Thunnus thynnus

In spring the mighty bluefin, titan of tunas, arrives on both coasts lean and hungry. Schools splash noisily, gorging on herring, sauries, anchovies, mackerels, bonitos. Apparently never sleeping, the restless fish sweep northward. Unlike most fishes, their high metabolic rate maintains a body temperature warmer than the water's. Occasionally fang-toothed killer whales snap their backs or drive them aground in terror. Toward fall the bluefins vanish. Tuna appear to circle the Atlantic clockwise with ocean currents.

Hooked bluefins tow boats in miles-long "sleigh rides" and can take backbreaking hours to land—in one case 62. Fishermen find Pacific tuna more wary than Atlantic; anglers sometimes approach them with baits suspended from kites. Western Atlantic tuna are known to spawn in the Florida Straits and around the Bahamas, Pacific tuna in waters around the Philippines.

Characteristics: back deep blue or green; about 9 dorsal and anal finlets. *Range:* all warm and temperate seas. *Weight:* rod and reel record 977 pounds. *Length:* to 10 feet.

114

BLUEFIN TUNA

ALBACORE
Thunnus alalunga

Long-finned furies of the Pacific, albacores slam into trolled lures, streak like meteors for 25 to 50 yards, then carry the struggle to the depths. Anglers wait until the fish exhaust themselves before taking control.

Mysterious, wandering albacores are suspected of great migrations; tagged specimens have traveled the width of the Pacific. Normally found off the West Coast in warm months, they may unpredictably all but disappear, abounding at the same time off Japan and around Hawaii. They occur plentifully off southern Europe, sparsely off America's East Coast.

Albacores roam near the surface in loose schools. Fins fold into body grooves when they speed through the water, reducing drag. Best of the tunas for canning, they sell as "white meat tuna." West Coast commercial trollers land 40 to 50 million pounds annually.

Characteristics: long saberlike pectoral fins. *Range:* world-wide in warm seas. *Weight:* rod and reel record 69 pounds, reported to 80. *Length:* to 4 feet.

ALBACORE

YELLOWFIN TUNA
Thunnus albacares

Yellowfins rank as the United States' single most valuable food fish and as a favorite gamefish of southern California. About 150 million pounds, caught off Central and South America, cross California docks each year. Commercial fishermen are converting from hook and line to purse seiners that surround schools of giant thrashing yellowfins.

Yellowfin tuna migrate and spawn mysteriously. Several distinct, nonmingling populations apparently dot the Pacific. Often called Allison's tuna, yellowfins gain up to 60 pounds a year gobbling flyingfishes, sauries, sardines, and other small fishes. The stomach of one 34-inch yielded 21 squids. Overfishing threatens the yellowfin, and today's tuna fleets also seek the smaller, abundant skipjack tuna, sometimes called oceanic bonito *(Euthynnus pelamis).*

Characteristics: elongated, yellowish second dorsal and anal fins; yellow on sides that fades with death. *Range:* all warm seas. *Weight:* rod and reel record 269½ pounds, reported to 450. *Length:* to 8 feet.

PAINTINGS BY HASHIME MURAYAMA

YELLOWFIN TUNA

ATLANTIC BONITO
Sarda sarda

Fast and strong, Atlantic bonitos fight remarkably for their four to six pounds. Yet sportsmen and netters usually catch them unintentionally while seeking bigger Gulf Stream game.

Huge schools of bonitos roam the surface of the open Atlantic, splashing visibly as they leap in pursuit of their cousins the mackerels or after squids, alewives, and menhaden. They seize prey in large teeth that score trolled plugs or tear feathered lures to pieces. Boated, their brilliant blues die. They spawn in the spring, often are called skipjacks and horse mackerels.

Streamlined body and polished scales minimize bonitos' water resistance. Similar Pacific bonitos *(S. chiliensis)* yield more than 15 million pounds of fair food a year.

Characteristics: dark stripes running from dorsal finlets toward gills; 7 or 8 dorsal finlets, dorsal fins contiguous. *Range:* St. Lawrence River to Argentina; both sides of Atlantic. *Weight:* maximum 20 pounds. *Length:* to 3 feet.

WAHOO

WAHOO
Acanthocybium solanderi

A wahoo in the hand is worth many in the sea, for this slender mackerel makes the fastest, most challenging initial run of all game fishes. Light tackle users prevent line from being stripped by pursuing hooked fish at full throttle. Checked in the first wild dash, the wahoo offers a dazzling series of lunges, soundings, and 30-foot leaps.

Enormous shoals of wahoos have been reported off Bermuda, but the species abounds in few places. Wahoo about Florida swim solitarily off outer reefs and in blue water beyond. The sprinter's bony mouth calls for sharp hooks, and its razor teeth demand cautious handling. Wahoos are excellent cut into steaks. Hawaiians call them *ono*, Polynesian for tasty or sweet.

Mystery surrounds wahoo spawning; one of the smallest found, an eight-incher, came from a dolphin's stomach. Young fish and excited adults display dark vertical markings.

Characteristics: cigar-shaped body; 9 dorsal and anal finlets. *Range:* all tropical seas. *Weight:* average 20 pounds, rod and reel record 149. *Length:* to nearly 7 feet.

CERO
Scomberomorus regalis

Ceros appear in occasional large schools off Florida and the West Indies, where anglers esteem their extraordinary leaps and diners admire their oily, often pinkish flesh. Fishermen often confuse ceros with closely related Spanish mackerels; the species share such nicknames as Florida kingfish, cavalla, and sierra.

Ceros swim near the surface much of the time and show a definite preference for warm waters around outer reefs. In the Straits of Florida, a favorite area, they occur most plentifully between fall and spring.

Ceros, Spanish mackerel, and the similar great king mackerel *(S. cavalla)* spawn off shore in spring and summer. Their eggs—buoyant, nonadhesive, and transparent—hatch in a day. Ceros feed largely on smaller fishes and squids.

Characteristics: elongated tunalike body; longitudinal rows of yellowish dashlike marks, mostly below the lateral line; about 80 large conical jaw teeth. *Range:* Cape Cod to Brazil. *Weight:* average 5 to 10 pounds, maximum 35. *Length:* to 3½ feet.

SPANISH MACKEREL
Scomberomorus maculatus

Charter boat fishermen working the Florida reefs stare in wonderment when a Spanish mackerel streaks from the deep, snatches a trolled bait, and leaps ten feet out of the water before arcing downward to begin a furious fight. The similar king mackerel, which reaches 100 pounds, outdoes the Spanish. Blasting out of the sea, it rises a reported 20 to 25 feet.

Anglers tempt Spanish mackerel, cero, and king mackerel with trolled spoons, fish, squid, and strips cut from a fish's belly. Commercial fishermen, spotting Spanish mackerel schools from aircraft off east Florida and in the Gulf, land nearly 10 million pounds a year.

Slim fish of the open sea, Spanish mackerel venture inshore in summer, swimming leisurely alone or in small groups. Menhaden form a primary food. Like the tunas, Spanish mackerel and ceros have body slots that receive the fins.

Characteristics: yellow spots; 64 large conical teeth; keeled caudal peduncle. *Range:* Maine to Brazil; occurs both sides of Atlantic. *Weight:* average 2 pounds, to 25. *Length:* to 4 feet.

CERO (top pair) and SPANISH MACKEREL

ERL ROMAN (OPPOSITE) AND PAINTINGS BY HASHIME MURAYAMA

Sea Basses and Temperate Basses

FEW FAMILIES IN FISHDOM enjoy greater esteem among fishermen than the abundant sea basses (Serranidae) and the closely related temperate basses (Perichthyidae). Many family members attain great size; most show an eagerness to bite and fight. The 55 species of sea basses inhabiting U. S. shores differ from the temperate basses in minor anatomical features (see page 280) and in their disdain for fresh water. Chunky sea basses typically wait in ambush for prey, show an insatiable curiosity for moving objects, and when hooked try to wedge among reefs. The spring spawners generally school only when young.

RED GROUPER
Epinephelus morio

Always hungry, red groupers strike readily—but then nothing happens; they are not fighters. Endearing them to fishermen is an ability to live several hours out of water, keeping them from spoiling on the trip home. Confirmed bottom dwellers, red groupers inhabit moderately deep water around reefs. Though numerous, they hunt singly, vigorously pursuing mullets, grunts, and crustaceans. Scientists have discovered new crab and fish species in red grouper stomachs.

Characteristics: spines at front of dorsal fin, caudal straight-edged; sides auburn-blotched, changing to solid in excitement. *Range:* Virginia to Brazil, strays to Massachusetts. *Weight:* average 10 pounds, to 40. *Length:* to 3 feet.

NASSAU GROUPER
Epinephelus striatus

Kaleidoscopes of the fish world, Nassau groupers flick through eight distinct color changes in a single minute: mottled, off-white, gray-brown, and so on. One marking, a dark spot over the caudal peduncle, remains constant. Nassau groupers, or hamlets, abound near corals and gorgonian beds and are seldom seen elsewhere. They tame easily, and will even pick a diver's pockets baited with crawfish tails. Hooked, the tasty predators put up a stubborn fight.

Characteristics: body usually marked with blotches and four irregular vertical stripes, dark stripe from snout through eye to dorsal fin. *Range:* North Carolina to Brazil. *Weight:* average 10 pounds, to 50. *Length:* to 3½ feet.

GAG
Mycteroperca microlepis

Anglers on the Florida Keys find gags willing victims, sturdy fighters, and well worth converting into chowder.

Ranging occasionally in shallows, gags prefer deep water off reefs. There they feed on shrimp, crabs, and tropical forage fishes such as mullets and grunts. Typical of groupers and sea basses, gags lay eggs in the spring and travel independently.

Characteristics: tiny scales; brownish in deep water, lighter in shallows. *Range:* Maryland to the Gulf states and Brazil. *Weight:* average 4 pounds, to 50. *Length:* to 3 feet.

BLACK GROUPER
Mycteroperca bonaci

Outer banks and reefs, especially off Florida and the Gulf states, are favorite haunts of handsome black groupers. Wrecks, sunken snags, and bridge pilings also attract the predators as they seek out grunts and crustaceans. Black groupers hit hard at a baited hook and put up a long, strong fight that requires heavy tackle. Often called gray groupers, jewfish, or rockfish, black groupers quickly learn to flee spear fishermen. They make fair food fish.

Characteristics: sides olive to whitish with darker tones usually prevailing; tail slightly convex. *Range:* Florida to Brazil, rarely north to Massachusetts. *Weight:* to 100 pounds. *Length:* to 4 feet.

ROCK HIND

GIANT SEA BASS

GIANT SEA BASS
Stereolepis gigas

First comes a deceptively dainty nibble. Then the first mad rush, known to panic an experienced angler. Next, boat-pulling lunges that reduce the fisherman to exhaustion. At last the gaff hauls aboard a giant sea bass—perhaps 500 pounds of brute power with a mouth that could take in a man.

Largest of the temperate basses, this West Coast behemoth yields honors among U. S. basses to a Florida sea bass, the jewfish *(Epinephelus itajara),* known to reach 680 pounds.

Giant sea bass prowl Pacific coastal bottoms, often over kelp, hunting herring, bottom fishes, and crustaceans. Sneaking up, they drop open huge mouths and suck in prey with torrents of water. Fry little resemble parents; their shape is like a bluegill's, their color brick red.

Characteristics: separated dorsal fins; body blotchy brown or greenish. *Range:* Monterey Bay to Baja California. *Weight:* often 200 pounds, rod and reel record 563½. *Length:* to 7 feet.

121

STRIPED BASS
Morone saxatilis

Fished in pounding, face-stinging surf or beyond the breakers in a bobbing boat, striped bass enjoy a pre-eminence among surf fishermen of both coasts. Variously known as stripers, rockfish, or simply "rock," these temperate bass are invariably admired for their pleasing appearance, dogged strength, and delicious flavor.

Anadromous like salmon, the coast-dwellers migrate up streams until stopped by such barriers as the Potomac River's Great Falls. Females lay up to several million eggs. Chesapeake Bay, a vast bass-rearing pond, nurtures many that later swim to sea and fan out along the coast.

In the late 1800's some 400 young Atlantic stripers, carried in tanks, rode the rails west and splashed into a new home near San Francisco. Today their hard-fighting descendants, protected by law from commercial exploitation, provide a West-Coast sport-fishing bonanza.

Characteristics: divided dorsal; body olive to silvery, often gold-tinged, 7 or 8 dark lateral streaks. *Range:* St. Lawrence to Louisiana; introduced Columbia River to southern California and inland. *Weight:* rod and reel record 73 pounds, to 125. *Length:* exceeds 5 feet.

WEAKFISH
Cynoscion regalis

Probably more anglers seek weakfish—a member of the drum family and often called squeteagues and seatrout—than any other East Coast sport fish. "Weak" only in that the mouth and flesh are tender, the abundant battlers respond well to trolling, casting, and still-fishing—especially when tempted with shrimp and crab bait.

Found year round off the Carolinas, weakfish schools—swimming near the surface—arrive off the Middle Atlantic states in spring and stay until winter drives them into deep water. The nearly identical spotted seatrout (*C. nebulosus*) replaces weaks off Southern states.

Commercial fishermen generally land a few million pounds of each species; a single school of weakfish yielded 200,000 pounds. The New England catch, normally only a few hundred fish, at the turn of the century leaped briefly and inexplicably to the millions.

Only weakfish males make the strumming noise that identifies most drums.

Characteristics: high front dorsal; projecting lower jaw; freckled gray-brown back. *Range:* Florida to Nova Scotia. *Weight:* average 3 pounds, rod and reel record 19½. *Length:* to 3 feet.

STRIPED BASS (bottom pair) and WEAKFISH

Drums

WARM, TURBID BAYS and estuaries—waters easily accessible to fishermen—are favorite haunts of the metallic-looking drums (family Sciaenidae). Famous noisemakers, they beat stringlike muscles against a resonating air bladder and produce a drumming audible to boaters. Their message, if any, remains obscure, though they turn up the volume at spawning time. One genus, the swift kingfishes, lacks the air bladder but is believed to sound off by grinding the teeth.

Drums provide valuable food and good sport. Most of these carnivores lay drifting eggs, travel in schools or groups, wear a deeply notched dorsal fin, and grow large ear bones often prized as ornaments or "lucky-stones."

PAINTINGS BY WALTER A. WEBER, NATIONAL GEOGRAPHIC STAFF (BELOW) AND HASHIME MURAYAMA

RED DRUM (top) and BLACK DRUM

RED DRUM
Sciaenops ocellata

Red drums, found from New Jersey to Texas, swim beside striped bass, bluefish, and weakfish in an aquatic quartet dear to the hearts of surf fishermen. Shrimp-loving warriors of several names (page 83), they toy with bait, then wage a dogged underwater struggle. The predators spawn up to several million eggs, grow coarse and tasteless as they reach 15 pounds.

Characteristics: sides metallic, tinted coppery red; one or more tail spots. *Range:* Cape Cod to Mexico. *Weight:* rod and reel record 83 pounds. *Length:* to 4½ feet.

BLACK DRUM
Pogonias cromis

Stockier and more snub-nosed than their red cousins, black drums browse unhurriedly in coastal shallows, feeling with a chinful of barbels for oysters, crabs, and other bottom dwellers. In a family of vocalists they win top billing, often bursting forth with a throaty purring sound. Though powerful, black drums thrill anglers more with hugeness than hard fighting.

Characteristics: blunt snout, humped back, barbels. *Range:* Massachusetts to Argentina. *Weight:* rod and reel record 98½ pounds, reaches 146. *Length:* to 4½ feet.

123

SPOT
Leiostomus xanthurus

"Sinker bouncing"—dangling a bloodworm near the bottom from an anchored boat—is the approved way of capturing spots, one of the sea's tastiest panfish. Those caught in late summer and early fall taste best; spring spots incline to be thin and less flavorful, spent by wintertime spawning.

Unexplained population fluctuations reduce spots to a rarity in some years, produce hordes at other times. So many invaded New York harbor in 1925 that the Brooklyn Edison Company had to shut down its water-cooled steam condensers while crews shoveled out fish by the ton.

Commercial fishermen in the Norfolk area, where spots are a favorite food, lay haul seines from boats and then drag the nets to shore with land-placed electric winches. One haul netted 90,000 fish totaling 50,000 pounds. South Carolina netters land a large part of the nearly ten-million-pound annual catch.

Spots feed close inshore on tiny crustaceans, occasional mollusks, and worms. They enter brackish water and sometimes surprise anglers in rivers. New Englanders call them lafayettes.

Male spots make a weak drumming noise, the volume probably limited by a thin air bladder and feeble vibrating muscles.

Characteristics: dark shoulder spot, 12 to 15 oblique dark bars that fade with age; body bluish gray, often with a goldish tone. *Range:* Cape Cod to Texas. *Weight:* maximum 1½ pounds. *Length:* to 14 inches.

WHITE SEABASS (top) and CALIFORNIA COBINA

WHITE SEABASS
Cynoscion nobilis

Not a bass but a drum, the gamy white seabass makes up in fight and flavor what it lacks in numbers. The sought-after carnivores strike at spoons, flyingfish, and smelt jigged or trolled slowly close inshore.

Often called corbinas, white seabass spawn in spring and summer around kelp beds. They closely resemble the related Atlantic weakfish.

Characteristics: back blue to coppery, belly frosted silver; projecting lower jaw. *Range:* Alaska to Baja California. *Weight:* rod and reel record 83¾ pounds. *Length:* to 6 feet.

CALIFORNIA CORBINA
Menticirrhus undulatus

Valiant when hooked, delectable when served, California corbinas hold a cherished place among Golden State surf fishermen. Catching them presents a challenge: Instead of striking a bait they nibble it—and often detect the hook.

Swimming close inshore until their backs break the surface, the summer spawners forage by mouthing sand and sifting it for crustaceans.

Characteristics: single barbel, dark spots on scales that form wavy body lines. *Range:* Point Conception to Baja California. *Weight:* reported to 8½ pounds. *Length:* to 28 inches.

SPOT

ATLANTIC CROAKER

NORTHERN KINGFISH
Menticirrhus saxatilis

Venturing north only in summer, northern kingfish, or whiting, can be found on Carolina coasts year round except during cold snaps. Surf casters bait with shrimp and crab and seek the schoolers off sandy beaches. Southern anglers catch two nearly identical kingfishes, *M. americanus* and *M. littoralis*. All lack an air bladder for "drumming." Hatchlings, absorbing the yolk sac, float upside down.

Characteristics: chin barbel; S-shaped tail margin; long first dorsal spine. *Range:* Maine to Florida. *Weight:* to 2 pounds. *Length:* to 17 inches.

ATLANTIC CROAKER
Micropogon undulatus

Nowhere in sight one spring day, on the next croakers swarm in bays and estuaries. In fall they disappear again, to spawn 30 or 40 miles out at sea. Anglers catch the "hardheads" bottom fishing over oyster beds where croakers hunt worms, crustaceans, and mollusks. Both sexes drum noisily. Recent years have seen croakers decline drastically in Chesapeake Bay.

Characteristics: irregular brassy bars on silver-gray sides; small chin barbels. *Range:* Massachusetts to Mexico. *Weight:* rarely to 4 pounds. *Length:* to 20 inches.

NORTHERN KINGFISH

Snappers and Grunts

NAMES DESCRIBE FAMILY TRAITS of the snappers and grunts. Snappers, alert and crafty, have quick, snapping mouths that steal bait in a twinkling. Several of the grunts utter throaty noises, particularly in protesting capture. Grinding sharp pharyngeal teeth, they amplify the sound with an adjacent air bladder. Game fighters and superb food, snappers and grunts are panfish supreme of Florida and the Gulf.

North America's 16 snapper species (family Lutjanidae) and all but two of the 19 grunts (Pomadasyidae) are Atlantic fishes, commonest in Florida but venturing to New England. Most school, lay drifting eggs, feed nocturnally on small fishes and crustaceans, and inhabit reefs, tidal rivers, and mangrove swamps. Grunts run smaller than snappers, often sport fiery red-lined mouths.

RED SNAPPER (left) and MUTTON SNAPPER

WALTER A. WEBER

RED SNAPPER
Lutjanus campechanus

"One of the great fish of our country," proclaims master chef James A. Beard of the handsome red snapper (page 363). He speaks for legions of gourmets who gladly pay premium prices for the more than 12 million pounds of reds caught on hand lines each year.

Fond of 100- to 150-foot depths, Gulf reds crowd corals and other ledges known as "snapper banks." Ichthyologists isolate three confusingly similar snapper species: the Gulf red, unknown in the Caribbean; the Caribbean red (*L. purpureus*), which never ventures north of that sea; and the silk snapper (*L. vivanus*), found in both areas and easily identified by a yellow iris.

Characteristics: rose-red body and fins. *Range:* Yucatán to Hatteras. *Weight:* average 5 pounds, to 20. *Length:* reaches 3 feet.

MUTTON SNAPPER
Lutjanus analis

Reds, greens, yellows, and blues fuse with rare beauty in the tropical Atlantic "muttonfish." The snapper can change its body stripes—vertical to resemble plant stems while at rest, oblique while it swims. Young have blue-spotted scales.

Found at 20 feet and deeper over rocky bottoms, mutton snappers strike readily, fight well.

Eating snappers and other fishes of the West Indies and Central and South Pacific sometimes causes nerve poisoning called *ciguatera*. Spasms, loss of nails and hair, even paralysis result. Thermal sensations reverse: Hot soup seems cold to the mouth, ice cream warm.

Characteristics: black spot on each side; blue "eye shadow" beneath a fiery red eye. *Range:* Brazil to Florida; strays to Cape Cod. *Weight:* average 4 pounds, to 25. *Length:* to 27 inches.

RICHARD CHESHER (TOP); PAINTINGS BY WALTER A. WEBER, NATIONAL GEOGRAPHIC STAFF, AND HASHIME MURAYAMA

BLUESTRIPED GRUNT

BLUESTRIPED GRUNT
Haemulon sciurus

Bluestriped grunts, like gouramis, are kissing fish, pairs placing mouths together perhaps in courtship or in dispute of territory. By day dense schools skim coral bottoms, at night dispersing to forage. In the West Indies gamy grunts form important food. Anglers still-fish for them with small crustaceans.

Characteristics: blue and yellow stripes, inside of mouth scarlet. *Range:* Florida to Brazil. *Length:* average 12 to 18 inches.

MARGATE
Haemulon album

Handsome margates, often known as sailor's-choice, prefer labyrinthine homes among coral stacks, gorgonian patches, rocky areas, and shipwrecks. Game fighters and adroit bait stealers, they enter shallow water to feed, eating primarily invertebrates. These grunts school in early summer when spawning.

Characteristics: lateral brown stripes, often fading on adults. *Range:* Florida to Brazil. *Weight:* 2 pounds, to 12. *Length:* to 2 feet.

127

MARGATE

YELLOWTAIL SNAPPER
Ocyurus chrysurus

Yellowtails teem around the Florida Keys and count large in any catch of bottom fish. Anglers go after these fighters with light tackle and such natural foods as small fishes and crustaceans.

Alert, darting fish, yellowtails frequently defy snapper habit by traveling singly and venturing into deep, open water. More often they swirl in glittering schools about gorgonian thickets, reefs, shoals, lagoons, even in surf. Cold weather drives them offshore.

Characteristics: wide yellow lateral stripe that broadens to color a large forked tail; yellow spots above the stripe, yellow lines below. *Range:* Massachusetts to Brazil. *Weight:* average 1 pound, to 6. *Length:* to 2 feet.

STRIPED MARLIN

Billfishes

N^O ANGLING TROPHIES hold more exalted place than marlin, sailfish, and swordfish. They swim two-thirds of a mile a minute and fight so hard body heat may rise 12° F. They tailwalk in frantic efforts to throw the hook and "greyhound" in great bounding leaps. They ram boats, pierce three-inch planking. Billfishes grow immense. The title goes to a 1,560-pound specimen of the much-sought Pacific black marlin *(Makaira indica).*

The bill, round on marlins and sailfishes (family Istiophoridae) and flat on swordfish (Xiphiidae), slashes back and forth to stun schooling prey. Man knows little of their habits; only sailfish (page 177) have revealed their life history.

WHITE MARLIN

STRIPED MARLIN
Tetrapturus audax

Leap after spray-flinging leap wins striped marlin acclaim as one of the world's most exciting fishes. Beginning fishermen find the acrobatics have another virtue: They exhaust the billfish before human endurance fails.

Each March marlin in tremendous schools invade the Gulf of California. Three months later a vanguard reaches California. September sees marlin-hunting charter boats stream out of San Diego and other warm-water ports.

Striped marlin feed on small fishes and squids, clubbing prey with their bills. Spawning areas are unknown; one 154-pounder landed off Honolulu carried some 13,800,000 ripe eggs.

Characteristics: 10 to 17 pale bars. *Range:* California to Chile across Pacific and Indian Oceans. *Weight:* average 100 to 200 pounds, rod and reel record 465. *Length:* to 10½ feet.

WHITE MARLIN
Tetrapturus albidus

Wily as any fish that swims, trim white marlin will tantalizingly follow a trolled lure for miles, nudge it, even mouth it and spit it back. Captains alter boat speeds; feverish anglers pump the rod to wiggle the bait attractively. Hooked at last, the marlin explodes with all the aerial stunts of the larger billfishes.

From Texas to Canada, marlin arrive close inshore with warm weather. One of the greatest white marlin holes in the world is the Jack Spot, a patch of shoals off Ocean City, Maryland.

Swift predators, the white marlin and its larger relative the blue marlin *(Makaira nigricans)* can run down such racers as dolphins and bluefish.

Characteristics: blue back, white belly. *Range:* both sides tropical Atlantic, north to Canada. *Weight:* average 60 pounds, rod and reel record 161. *Length:* average 7 feet, to 9.

SWORDFISH

SWORDFISH
Xiphias gladius

Feeding singly or in pairs, swordfish range to depths of more than a thousand feet. Occasionally they surface with soaring leaps, in fun or to shake clinging remoras. A hooked "broadbill" may put up an hours-long fight—or charge and sink its sword in an angler's boat.

Commercial fishermen once sought the brutes only in summer when they surfaced in range of harpoons. Year-round fishing blossomed in 1962 with introduction of 3- to 15-mile-long lines suspended from buoys, floats, even inflated tire tubes. Up to 1,000 hooks, dangling on branch lines, may catch 125 fish in a night's haul. Thermometers find the 55° F.-or-warmer surface waters beneath which broadbills feed.

Fry, spawned in warm seas, grow a temporary sword on the lower jaw.

Characteristics: long flat bill; no pelvic fins. *Range:* from tropics to Nova Scotia and to Oregon. *Weight:* average 200 pounds, rod and reel record 1,182. *Length:* to 15 feet.

GREAT BARRACUDA

130

Other Common Species

BLUEFISH
Pomatomus saltatrix

Most bloodthirsty of ocean fishes, bluefish kill long after hunger is sated, leaving a wake of mangled prey. In 1935 hordes off Cape Hatteras strewed miles of beach with terrified menhaden and silversides and grounded themselves in ravenous pursuit. Some say feeding blues would skeletonize a swimmer. Even in a boat blues are dangerous, snapping meat-grinder jaws at oars, tackle, feet, fingers.

Churned water and diving gulls tell where blues are feasting. Surfcasters stalk them on foot.

Trollers circle a school and sometimes haul in fish until muscles ache.

Warm weather and north-moving prey bring bluefish off Florida in late winter, past the Carolinas in early spring, and to New England by June. Young enter harbors and estuaries. The commercial catch of four or five million pounds falls short of demand for the fine food fish. Blues are alone in the family Pomatomidae.

Characteristics: blue-green back; forked tail; short front dorsal. *Range:* world-wide in tropical and temperate water except central and eastern Pacific. *Weight:* rod and reel record 24¼ pounds. *Length:* to 45 inches.

GREAT BARRACUDA
Sphyraena barracuda

Insatiably curious, barracudas hauntingly trail skin divers with teeth bared and eyes fixed; they have even kept abreast of persons walking on shore. But they are not deliberate man-killers. Barracudas have amputated limbs and caused death through loss of blood—their rushing attack probably provoked by the glint of a belt buckle or the flash of an arm or leg.

Around the Florida Keys barracudas enter shallows in spring to spawn. Fry school; adults lurk solitarily like pikes. Other fishes skirt them respectfully, but lightning lunges pick off strays. Among the swiftest of fishes, barracudas kill compulsively, destroying more than they eat.

Not widely eaten in the United States, barracudas are tasty, though an occasional large one causes *ciguatera* (page 126). Sportsmen find them game fighters on light tackle. Californians fish the smaller Pacific barracuda (*S. argentea*).

Characteristics: large canine teeth; pikelike body except for second dorsal fin. *Range:* Florida to Brazil, strays to Massachusetts; nearly world-wide in tropics. *Weight:* average 5 pounds, rod and reel record 103¼. *Length:* to 8 feet.

JAMES W. LA TOURRETTE, MIAMI SEAQUARIUM

SNOOK

SNOOK
Centropomus undecimalis

Florida's boisterous snook rush into a series of leaps, runs, and dives that classify them as top contenders on light tackle. As a bonus to anglers they hug the shores of inlets and estuaries in easy range of fly rod and cane pole.

When snook are striking, which is almost every night as they feed, they hit most lures in the tackle box. Flicking the rod tip as the line is reeled in makes the lure more tempting.

Catching and handling snook calls for two cautions: Hooks tear easily from the fish's soft mouth, and the sharp rear edge of its cheek plate can badly lacerate a hand.

Snook occasionally ascend rivers to fresh water, and anglers catch them in Florida drainage canals. Usually, however, they course near the surface of mangrove swamps and estuaries, feeding hungrily on crustaceans and small fishes. Breeding habits are little known.

Characteristics: tan to greenish back, silvery sides, black lateral line extending onto tail fin; shovel-shaped head with long lower jaw; 2 dorsal fins. *Range:* Florida south, probably to South America. *Weight:* average 5 pounds, rod and reel record 52⅓. *Length:* to 55 inches.

COBIA

WALTER A. WEBER

COBIA
Rachycentron canadum

Sheer size entitles the cobia to respect: 50-pounders are not uncommon, 100-pounders have been caught. Add swiftness and brutish look, and little wonder cobias wax in popularity.

Cobias like to swim under floating objects, and almost any bait cast or trolled nearby may score. Other haunts include buoys, barges, break-waters, pilings, and wrecks. They feed both on bottom foods—crabs, crawfish, flounders—and on surface fishes such as menhaden.

Fine food fish, cobias swim off the Middle Atlantic states from spring to fall, arrive in lower Chesapeake Bay in June, and frequent Florida and the Gulf states year round. Their life history is a mystery.

Cobia nicknames include coalfish, crabeater, sergeant, and cabio. In Chesapeake Bay, they are black bonito. Found nearly world-wide in warm water, they represent the only species in the family Rachycentridae.

Characteristics: brownish back, silvery sides; projecting lower jaw; 8 low stout spines in place of front dorsal. *Range:* New Jersey to Argentina, found world-wide. *Weight:* average 10 pounds, rod and reel record 102. *Length:* to 70 inches.

BONEFISH
Albula vulpes

"Were bonefish to grow to the size of other game fishes," ventures angler-writer Van Campen Heilner, "nothing on earth . . . could hold them." Probably no other species so often draws the accolade: gamest fish that swims.

Bonefish advance over Florida flats with the incoming tide, dorsal and tail fins often protruding as they grub with piglike snouts for sand fleas, crabs, worms, and mollusks. One- to three-pounders school; larger fish travel alone or in pairs. At the least disturbance they scatter; thus anglers drop bait well in front and let the fish move over it. Hooked bonefish—often called ladyfish—make long, lightning surface runs that seem impossible for creatures their size.

Tasty but bony relatives of herring and tarpon, bonefish (family Albulidae) start life as transparent, ribbonlike larvae. At two or three inches they shrink by half and assume adult shape. Florida and Hawaii specimens dwarf those off southern California.

Characteristics: pearl color; small mouth; numerous small blunt teeth. *Range:* all warm seas. *Weight:* average 2 to 5 pounds, rod and reel record 19. *Length:* to 41½ inches.

133

COAST AND DEEP-SEA FISHES

The surf fisherman's rhythmic cast touches the edge of a teeming fish world—one that intrigues scientists, thrills those who seek beauty, fills the stomachs of millions.

R. E. LOUGHEED

Captains Courageous on the Grand Banks

ALL ALONE in their tiny craft, dorymen make for cod grounds off Greenland's forbidding fjords. The dories hold a ton of fish—a big day's catch on hook and line. Oars double as rudders; saplings serve as masts. The Cross of Christ on the homemade sail was stitched by a fisherman's wife (inset). A storm howling down Davis Strait will drive the hardy Portuguese seamen back to their mother ship.

Not even a decade after Columbus' first voyage of discovery Portuguese in sturdy sailing ships began crossing the Atlantic each spring to fish the Grand Banks off Newfoundland, 2,000 miles away. They fished with hook and line, filled their holds with cod, and raced home before the fierce northern winter.

Today, as then, a fleet of more than 60 Portuguese ships sets out each spring for the Grand Banks. Half a dozen of them still are sailing ships, equipped with diesel auxiliaries but dependent mainly on wind. And 3,000 fishermen still fish in their centuries-old way. Each morning on the Banks they sail from the parent ship in one-man dories and pit skill and luck against the sea.

Not too many springs ago I shipped out in the four-master *Argus,* queen of the sailing ships headed that year for the Banks.

I picked up the *Argus* in the broad River Tagus, where the fleet was assembling for the blessing. After the service the dorymen streamed aboard. I watched the good Portuguese get under way. Throaty calls of the sailors mingled with the clank of the anchor windlass and the creak of blocks as white sails piled aloft. As the schooner and her consorts passed out to sea, the spring wind sighed in the rigging.

Below in the *rancho,* as the forecastle of a Portuguese banker is called, the dorymen settled in among big bunks and a jumble of fishing gear. I noticed a gaunt, determined-looking man with a striking face. I learned that this was the First Fisher of the whole 137

ALAN VILLIERS

fleet. He caught a ton of cod a day. A ton a day by hook and line!

For some reason, sardines used for bait had temporarily deserted Portugal's coasts. And so we made toward St. John's in Newfoundland, to ship herring for bait.

I marveled at the *Argus:* a 696-ton steel schooner fitted with every useful modern device. The Portuguese are not old-fashioned; they stick to the schooner rig because it is ideal for fishing off the Banks, where a ship has to keep to sea over many weary months and a powered vessel might run out of fuel.

We made the Grand Banks and fished for cod for six cold and foggy weeks, while we waited for the summer sun to melt the ice in Davis Strait and clear the way to Greenland. But there was no sun and no summer either. What a place!

The *Argus* and her consorts just anchored on the Banks, choosing a place where the rocky bottom prevented the horde of trawlers from working because rocks ripped costly trawls. The Portuguese could go wherever the big fish were. The *Argus'* 53 dorymen went over the side at 4 o'clock every morning they possibly could, fog or fine—and it was rarely fine.

They'd streak away under their tiny oiled sails for the horizon, lay their long-lines, and fish all day. While the long-lines with their hundreds of hooks were down, they fished by hand with lead jiggers.

I went out with the dories. I had thought I was reasonably inured to the hardships of the sea. But fighting a great windjammer around Cape Horn is nothing to manning a dory on the Grand Banks.

Take a look at a dory first. It's nothing but a 14-foot open boat, flat-bottomed, built up of a few planks with no keel nor even a rudder. It looks all right for a quiet day on the Potomac. But there are few quiet days in spring on the Grand Banks, and fewer off Greenland.

My dory was yanked to the side of the rolling ship. I looked at the cruel sea and thought, "I'd rather stay in the *Argus*—she's small enough." But the 53 dorymen were looking on, and I had to go.

"Now!" yelled the men at the tackles, and let me go. With a swoosh and a smack on the sea, I was off.

It was savagely cold. I didn't see how I was going to work with my bare hands, though I had a 300-hook long-line to pay out when I reached a good place. A good place? How was I to know the difference? When the hull of the *Argus* was almost below the horizon, I thought I had gone far enough.

So I lowered my sail, threw out the little grapnel, and got the long-line laid on the bottom, across the current. There were about 35 fathoms of water. The long-line must be down three or four hours, so I fished with the jiggers, a line in each hand.

The wind began to sigh, and there was an ominous bank of nasty fog to windward. Here and there, as I rose to the crest of a sea, I could see a few other dories. I began to think that a lost dory would be mighty hard to find. I knew they were often lost.

Toward 9 a.m. I began to haul in my long-line. That took me two hours for I had no skill at the business. It got snarled. But the cod is a stupid and docile fish. Those on the hooks waited patiently until I hauled them up, even the 80-pounders.

By the luck of beginners, I had a fair enough haul—almost 50 fish. When I got them all in, my dory was about half full.

Ordinarily a doryman would stay out until his dory was full, or the *Argus* hoisted the recall flag. But I was not a doryman, and now I knew I never would be.

And that infernal fog *had* blown down. An arm of it was between me and the *Argus*. Suddenly I found myself alone on the sea.

"Don't ever panic," I had been told. "The panicked are dead."

My dory had a compass. Grimly I made off along the bearing that I'd had of the ship, and kept a smart lookout for other dories.

FORTY-THREE TIMES *in his 63 years this weathered mariner has left sunny Portugal to fish the cold Grand Banks. En route he takes the wheel of the* Argus. *On the Banks he will man a dory, as Portuguese have done since the early 1500's.*

A TWO-HOOKED JIGGER *snagged this Greenland cod. The elongated lead lure looks—to a cod, at least—like a herring. Lowered to the bottom and jerked up, it hooks the unwary fish from below. Little of the cod is wasted. Liver yields the famous oil. Even tongue and cheeks are eaten.*

A DORYMAN PULLS *a jigger-hooked cod from bleak Davis Strait off Greenland. The fisherman, warmed by a cocoon of oilskins, dangles a jig-line from each hand when not tending his 4,000-foot long-line. It runs through the pulley on the bow and spreads 1,000 baited hooks on the bottom. After three or four hours he pulls it in and—with luck—boats half a ton of cod. Already low in the water, the dory will hold another lineful of fish before it must return to the Argus, waiting on the horizon.*

    Dorymen wield two-pronged gaffs to fork their catch aboard the Argus (below). The captain (second from right at rail, in billed cap) estimates each load to reckon the fisherman's pay. Deck boys hold the dories alongside with long poles. Their load delivered, the men take on more bait and sail out again. They wind up a 20-hour day cleaning and salting the cod.

ALAN VILLIERS

I had a conch shell to blow, and I knew the fog signal *Argus* used. I blew it on my shell and waited for a reply. None came.

I blew again. What was that? An echo? It was a doryman sounding our signal.

Indistinct at first and almost unbelievable, I saw the triangle of a tiny sail harden in the surrounding murk. A dory! The First Fisher! I couldn't strike a better man.

"No good! No good!" he shouted. But he looked abominably cheerful, and fine big cod filled his dory to the gunwale.

That evening down in the rancho I found all hands cheerful enough. Nobody was lost. They were uncanny fog navigators.

The dorymen worked and worked, often 20 hours a day under the continuous midnight sun. They fished from 4 a.m., then cleaned and salted. Until our cavernous hold was filled, we would not head home.

The dorymen suffered tortures in the freezing air. Faces cracked, hands opened up, oilskins chafed their wrists. But the hardy fishermen were unhappy only when bad weather caused delays.

Off Greenland in Davis Strait, too, the fog was heavy, cold, and blinding. Once a doryman vanished. Then a gale blew for three days, and more fog came. But on the fifth day the weather cleared, and he came back smiling! He had to be hoisted in with his dory, for he was all but worn out. Yet he was fishing again later that day.

"I prayed," he told me. "I had to row plenty, to keep the dory head to sea. I ate the raw cod, and I drank the fog moisture wrung out of my woolen cap."

At last the day came when the captain reluctantly decided that we had cod enough, though not a full cargo, mark you!

For a hundred days we had eaten the midnight soup of codfish faces. The dorymen call it the "soup of sorrow," for they say that, once having eaten it, you are bound to return to the Banks again. A hundred days of the soup of sorrow were enough for me.

Yet it was not until we had sailed past the Danas Bank that the dorymen dared smile. Danas was the last large bank. The course now was southeast toward the Azores—the Azores, and sunshine, and good Portugal!

GALE ON THE WAY, *seamen stow the foresail of the barkentine* Gazela Primeiro, *last square-rigger to sail in Portugal's fishing*

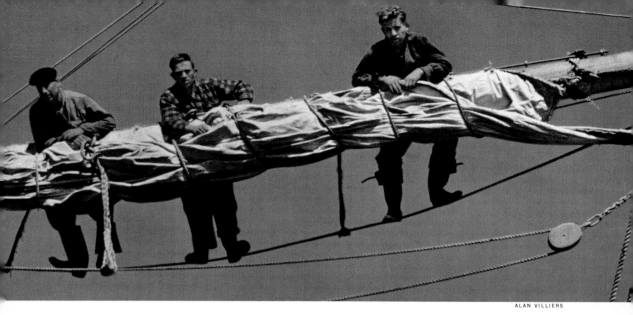

fleet. Easier-to-handle schooners like Argus *replaced them, just as motor ships now supplant schooners.* Argus' *sailors cling to nested dories as a comber crashes over the rail (below). In storms, helmsmen were lashed to the wheel; a hurricane sank one of the fleet's motor ships.*

CHAPTER EIGHT

By CHARLES M. BROOKFIELD

America's First Park in the Sea

A map appears here showing the Florida Keys region:

FLORIDA.

Joe Bay

Davis Cove · Tgout Cove

Eagle Key Pass

Gulf of Mexico

Miami · Miami Beach

Everglades National Park

Florida Bay

Dry Tortugas

Key West · Florida Keys

Pennekamp State Park

Atlantic Ocean

STATUTE MILES 0 — 60

Florida Bay

Swash Keys · Buttonwo Sound · Key Largo · Holiday Heig · Key Largo

Butternut Key

Bottle Key

Rock Harbor U.S.

Pigeon Key

Sunset Point · Point Cha

Hammer Point

Ramshorn Shoal

Overseas Highway

Long Point

Tavernier

Soundings in feet

STATUTE MILES

NAUTICAL MILES

MAP BY V. J. KELLEY   PHOTOGRAPH BY JERRY GREENBERG

ALMOST WITHIN SIGHT of the oceanside palaces of Miami Beach, a pencil-thin chain of islands begins its 221-mile sweep to the Dry Tortugas.

Just offshore, paralleling the scimitar curve of these Florida Keys, lies an undersea rampart of exquisite beauty—a living coral reef, the only one of its kind in United States continental waters. Brilliant tropical fish dart about its multicolored coral gardens. Part of the magnificent reef, a segment off Key Largo roughly 21 nautical miles long, has been dedicated as America's first undersea park.

I know this reef intimately. For more than 30 years I have sailed its warm, clear waters and probed its shifting sands and bizarre formations in quest of sunken ships and their treasure of artifacts.

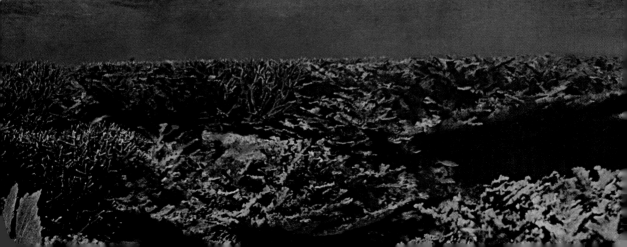

JOHN PENNEKAMP
CORAL REEF STATE PARK

BEARING THE NAME of a Miami conservationist, Florida's underwater park spreads a 21-mile rampart of reef beauty off stringy Key Largo. Snorkeler (below) glides above prongs of elkhorn and staghorn coral. Divers also can plunge to wreck sites or to the "Christ of the Abyss," a bronze copy of the undersea statue off the Italian Riviera revered by seamen.

Spanish galleons, English men-o'-war, pirate vessels, and privateers foundered on the reef's hidden fangs. In the 19th century alone, several hundred vessels met death here, and the salvagers of Key West gleaned close to ten million dollars.

In today's salt-water preserve, an increasing number of sightseers ride glass-bottomed boats above the lovely coral gardens. More active visitors fasten on mask and snorkel and gaze face-down at gaudy reef fish. The most adventurous strap on breathing units and descend to the beautiful coral world that underwater photographer Jerry Greenberg describes in the next chapter.

Heavy seas break directly on the outer coral barrier, where the seaward edge of the reef rises abruptly from the deep canyon of the Gulf Stream. Here, years ago, I found the scattered remains of H.M.S. *Winchester,* which sank off Carysfort Reef, five miles east of Key Largo.

A British ship of the line with 60 guns, the square-rigged *Winchester* fought in the West India Squadron against France, harrying ports of the French islands. Mission accomplished, she refreshed at Jamaica and in 1695 set sail for home. But scurvy—that age-old plague of the sea—struck.

The unhappy captain logged: "we had not above 7 men Well our Shipp increasing upon us by the water She made in the holds & we Left Distitute of all ability to pump it out our people being all dead and Sick."

Ten days later a vicious gale struck the ship. With her crew of 350 helpless, the *Winchester* broke her back on the reef. An accompanying vessel rescued eight men —the only survivors.

For 244 years *Winchester*'s guns, some weighing more than two tons, lay five fathoms deep, while shipworms made a sieve of her rotten hull. When we raised the cannon, the ship had disintegrated.

Some of the *Winchester*'s artifacts will be displayed in a museum to be built at park headquarters on Largo Sound. The headquarters already offers camping and picnicking grounds, grocery and snack shops, a nature trail through a mangrove swamp, and a marina housing rental boats and the sightseeing craft that continually cruise out to the reef.

Here soft-bodied coral polyps—tiny anemonelike creatures that build protective cups of lime—flourish in the warm Gulf Stream. Billions of their limestone skeletons form the foundations of the reef; vast colonies of living coral animals grow on the dead, fashioning a fantasyland of strange forms.

MIXED BATTALIONS *of porkfish and white grunts maneuver in close-order drill. Yellow stripes and black bars distinguish the porkfish* (Anisotremus virginicus) *from its relative, the grunt* (Haemulon plumieri). *The school will disband at night when members forage for food.*

GOLD WATCH *raised from H.M.S.* Winchester, *which sank off the park's Carysfort Reef in 1695, shows hours in Roman numerals and minutes in Arabic. Here a lump of ship's ballast, pressed against the watch on the bottom for 264 years, bears an imprint of the dial's face.*

The author discovered the Winchester's *grave in 1939 and salvaged cannon and fittings. Returning 20 years later he found the watch and a universal ring sundial, which will be exhibited in a park museum.*

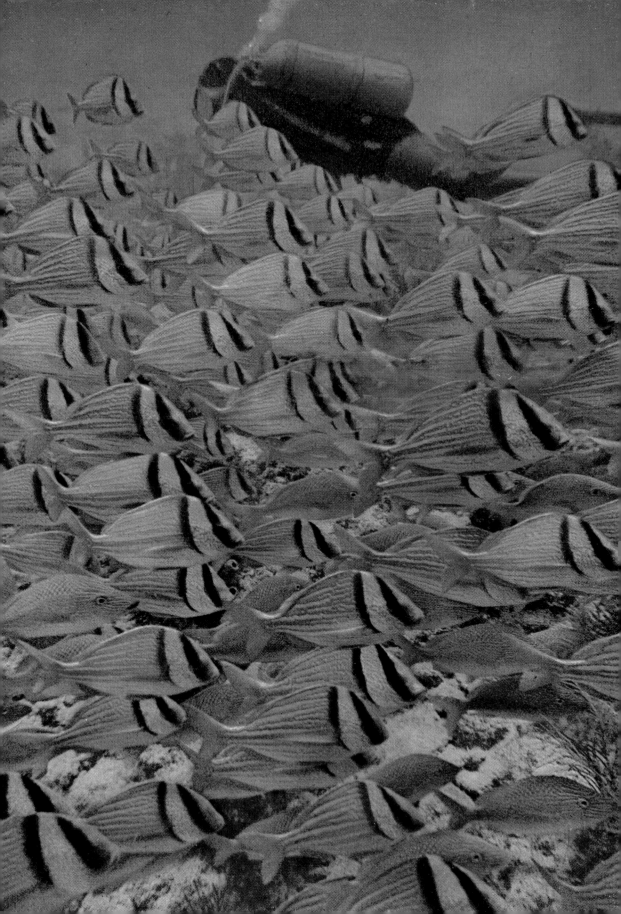

DAVID GREENFIELD (ABOVE), AND JERRY GREENBERG

"**WATCH OUT FOR FREE DIVERS,**" *the red-and-white banner tells boatmen sailing the waters around Molasses Reef. The swimmer's boat, stocked with spare air tanks, appears to float on air. The preserve welcomes divers and rod and reel anglers to its 78,000 acres, but prohibits spearfishing. From a marina at park headquarters on Largo Sound, visitors may ride glass-bottomed boats above the coral gardens. Sunlight filtering through the iridescent water glitters against coral of more than 40 varieties and tropical fish of two or three hundred species.*

SPOTTED MORAY *lurks in coral ambush.*

QUEEN ANGELFISH *glides past elkhorn coral.*

RAZOR-TOOTHED BARRACUDA *awaits prey.*

ORANGESPOT HAWKFISH *rests on pectoral fins.*

Tourists who buy coral at roadside curio shops see only the bleached white skeletons of the once-living colony. But a visitor to the reef may feast his eye on living colors—the green, brown, and gold of stony corals; the blue, purple, and yellow of coral fans and plumes that sway with the current; the pastel tints of towering sea feathers and graceful coral whips. The more than 40 different species form a submerged landscape of awesome beauty.

Florida conservationists, meeting in 1957, discussed a preserve to safeguard this underwater world. Dr. Gilbert L. Voss, of the University of Miami's Institute of Marine Sciences, warned that the reef might soon become a watery desert.

His statement raised many an eyebrow. What could destroy a reef?

"Man," Dr. Voss told the group.

Collectors were harvesting the coral. With its slow rate of growth—only half an inch a year among some varieties—this could lead to the reef's gradual destruction. Sponges and imposing queen conch shells, attractive mementos to tourists, could also be depleted. Spearfishermen took their toll.

Despoliation of the reef would have other consequences, Dr. Voss predicted. The coral served as a haven for small tropical fish and a nursery ground for game fish. Without small fish to feed on, the game fish would go elsewhere. In Florida, where one out of four visitors comes for salt-water angling, such a shift could be painful.

Dr. Voss's plea spurred conservationists into action. The Florida Board of Parks and Historic Memorials approved a 75-square-mile section—10 percent of the entire reef—as a permanent preserve. The National Audubon Society's staff in Miami encouraged Floridians to write to the state and federal governments. Approval of both was needed because the park's boundaries would straddle the three-mile line that divides Florida and federal waters.

Complications were overcome, and in 1960 President Eisenhower proclaimed the Key Largo Coral Reef Preserve. Gov. Leroy Collins, dedicating the preserve, gave it the name of John D. Pennekamp, a Miami editor who, in the press and in person, had crusaded for conservation.

Subsequent additions have enlarged the preserve until it encompasses 122 square miles. By agreement, Florida administers the entire area as a state park.

Today the 21-mile-long preserve is dotted with fishing boats and smaller craft tending free divers. Mingling with man, fish-hunting cormorants ride the waves, porpoises leapfrog whitecaps, flyingfish skim the sea, and loggerhead turtles pop up for air.

Park rules prohibit spearfishing, but sanction rod-and-reel fishing and lobstering, provided the ocean floor suffers no damage. Bobbing floats mark the traps of commercial fishermen seeking the spiny lobster.

Lighthouses and tide-exposed rocks alone break the surface of this unique underwater preserve. The three lighthouses studding the seaward side of the reef—Carysfort, Elbow, and Molasses—all perch on iron piles.

I shall never forget my first night on Carysfort, more than 40 years ago. I had gone out in my cabin cruiser with meat and vegetables for the keeper and two assistants manning the light.

At bedtime my companions and I settled on the lower deck of the light's dwelling,

LLOYD D. DAVIDSON (OPPOSITE) AND JERRY GREENBERG

HEAD IN AIR, *body in the water, a diver submerges near Carysfort Light. Water refracts sunlight to magnify his torso about 25 percent as the camera sees above and below the surface. Scrawled filefish (right) puckers as if asking for a kiss. Actually,* Alutera scripta *is making a grunting sound.*

REEF DWARFS: *The yellow or threespot damselfish* (Pomacentrus planifrons, *upper) seldom attains five inches; four is large for the harlequin bass* (Serranus tigrinus). *Threespots dwell among gaudy corals; the harlequin's blotched garb blends with bottom rubble.*

151

Magic World of a Coral Reef in Dayligh

BY DAY *a reef bustles like a boom town, but what takes place after sundown, when darkness drops its curtain? Aqua-Lungers Walter A. Starck II, Robert E. Schroeder, and William P. Davis, assisted by the National Geographic Society, made nighttime studies off the Florida Keys. Their cameras, flashing in the inky depths, recorded these glimpses of night life on a reef.*

BLUE TANG (Acanthurus coeruleus) *dresses drably as it feeds by day (above) but blossoms boldly at rest on a reef by night (right). Polka-dotted yellowtail damselfish cleans away parasites.*

SPOTTED GOATFISH (Pseudupeneus maculatus) *wears dark markings at noontime (below), turns to red blotches for after dark (right).*

but I could not sleep. As I lay restless, a groan echoed through the lower deck.

"Did you hear that?" I asked.

My friends snored blissfully. I had about convinced myself my imagination was playing tricks when the moan was repeated, as if from a soul in torment.

Jumping up, I circled the stairs to the tower, where a keeper stood watch at the lantern. "Have you ever heard any funny noises down below?" I panted.

"Oh, sure," he said, "but we don't pay attention to 'em any more. It's only Captain Johnson, and he just comes around to see if all's well. He died out here on the light, you know. Must have been a great sinner, he groans so. Sometimes he rattles his chains."

Thus reassured—I use the word somewhat loosely—I went below and slept, groans or no groans.

Next morning I solved the mystery of the moans, I believe. Under the hot sun, the tower's iron walls expand; in the cool of darkness, they contract, making sounds startlingly human. My theory may not be true, but I have clung to it.

When the *Winchester*'s keel struck Key Largo's coral barrier more than 250 years ago, the crew thought only of cruel rocks and surging seas. Crushing timbers fell about them, and the sea rushed in through gaping holes in the ship's bottom. Swirling waters brought death.

No one aboard the ill-fated vessel could have dreamed that the treacherous reef possessed a rare beauty man would one day deem worthy of preservation.

SPINY BALLOONFISH (Diodon holocanthus) *inflates with water and bristles when a diver intrudes. This nighttime feeder crushes prey in its powerful mouth.*

BEADY EYE, *downturned mouth, and hazy contour are all that mar the near-perfect camouflage of a resting spotted scorpionfish.* Scorpaena plumieri *has poisonous spines that cause extreme pain.*

PINSTRIPED *Spanish grunt* (Haemulon macrostomum) *schools in the sunshine (left). At night, colors subdued, it hunts alone for food. Daytime hues may help a fish identify others of its species.*

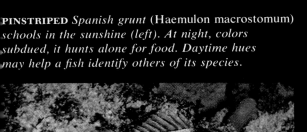

LIKE A BIRD IN FLIGHT, *a spotted eagle ray* (Aetobatus narinari) *gracefully plies the clear Caribbean. Venomous spines that can inflict excruciating pain sprout from its rat tail. The rays reach eight feet across and weigh up to 600 pounds.*

EERIE-EYED PUDDLE *on the Caribbean floor, the southern stingray* (Dasyatis americana) *grows a stiff tail spine that once made Indian spear tips and knife blades. Averaging three feet across, the rays abound south of Hatteras.*

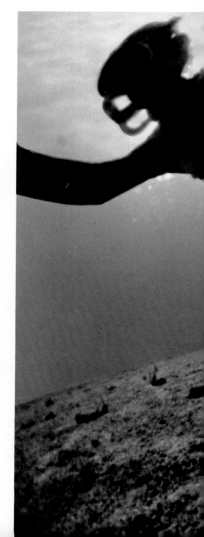

BRILLIANT HUES *paint the barred hamlet* (Hypoplectrus puella), *a six-inch member of the sea bass family, and the ornamental blue chromis* (Chromis cyanea), *a five-inch damselfish. Both inhabit reefs from Bermuda south.*

BEWARE — HIGH VOLTAGE: *Camera in hand, a diver keeps his distance from a lesser electric ray* (Narcine brasiliensis). *Though only 18 inches long, the ray can generate nearly 40 volts with battery-like muscles in its pectorals.*

CHAPTER NINE
By JERRY GREENBERG

Florida's Underwater Wonderland

LEMON SHARK, *10 feet of malevolence, seizes a snapper in razor teeth. Hitchhiking remoras loosen suction disks from its flanks and rush headlong for scraps. The author photographed the monster at a distance of only seven feet.*

B UT THE SHARKS . . . aren't you afraid of the sharks?" This is a familiar question. My answer is "No," with some reservations.

When working under water, I regard sharks as the man in the jungle does the tiger, or the midtown pedestrian does the reckless driver. I know the unpredictable fish are there; sometimes I see them. But I go out of my way to avoid them.

I have spent thousands of hours in the depths off the Florida Keys, and I have seen countless sharks—hammerhead, blacktip, lemon, nurse, bull, tiger. But not one of them has even threatened me, though some in curiosity have approached to within a few feet. Not long ago I spent two months roaming the waters of John Pennekamp Coral Reef State Park, and I encountered only three or four sharks. They did not molest me or any of my party.

Working off my 20-foot runabout, I dived four or five days a week in Florida's unique underwater preserve. Many days I stayed submerged six hours, ascending only to switch air tanks and reload the cameras.

Often we made underwater photos at dusk. Sometimes we dived under a full moon and could see 30 feet in any direction.

To photograph the reef's eerie beauty, I used four Rolleiflex cameras in Rolleimarin housings, four Leicas in special Seahawk housings, three electronic flashes in underwater casings, and assorted flash guns. To facilitate the changing of cameras, I suspended all gear on lines dropped over the 157

JERRY GREENBERG

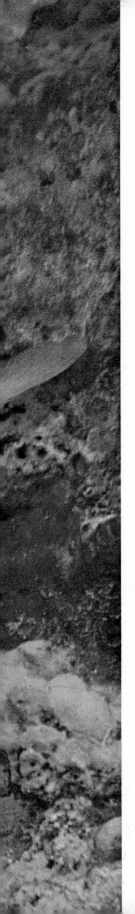

AUTHOR-PHOTOGRAPHER *Jerry Greenberg has spent more than 3,000 hours roaming the ocean floor off Florida's east coast. He himself designed the Seahawk housings for his cameras and flashes. Here, adjusting his electronic flash unit, Mr. Greenberg stands on the ladder of his 20-foot, twin-engine runabout.*

FINS BRISTLING, *an eight-inch squirrelfish darts for a crevice. When disturbed,* Holocentrus ascensionis *makes a chattering noise. Pale star coral appears at upper and lower left.*

boat's side. We worked mostly at 15 to 30 feet, where a tank of air can last an experienced diver about an hour and a half.

And what wonders we saw!

Let me show you this world beneath the waves that I find so intriguing and that claims so much of my life. Slip a mask over your face, clench the Aqua-Lung's rubber mouthpiece between your teeth, and drop down with me into the sea.

As you sink slowly, you experience an exhilarating sense of buoyancy. The air tank felt heavy above the surface; now you are scarcely aware of it on your back. Freed from the demands of gravity, you move like a bird, free to dive or soar with no other power but your arms and flippered feet.

Just below the surface, jellyfish pump past as you submerge. Living parachutes, they range in size from a dime to a dinner plate. At 20 feet you touch down on the reef. What had seemed a blurred tapestry of color assumes dimensions and patterns.

Deep, winding gullies carpeted with sand slice plateaus of coral seemingly so soft, so untouchable you fear they may fade away before your eyes. Such primitive beauty and solitude

DIVER AND DOG SNAPPER *play follow-the-leader among stands of elkhorn coral. The dog snapper* (Lutjanus jocu), *a popular sport fish, attains a weight of 50 pounds.*

WHITE GRUNTS *hold a meeting beneath a ledge; one club member seems to voice an opinion. Early families that settled on the Keys lived on "grits and grunts."*

make a man feel he is trespassing on forbidden ground.

The silence is awesome. Only the sound of breathing through the mouthpiece and exhaled air bubbling up from the regulator break the quiet. Later, when you have become more acclimated, you may hear the snapping of shrimp, the crunching of the parrotfish as he feeds, and the grunting noises that many fish make.

You sense an air of subdued expectancy. The reef waits in hushed judgment until you make clear your intentions, and it is certain that friends have come to call.

Graceful gorgonians, sometimes tall as a man, raise arched coral branches like uplifted arms. Pastel-hued sea fans spread their lace to the eddying currents.

Forests of staghorn coral, amazingly like antlers, crown the crest of the reef. Star coral, cactus coral, and leaf coral suggest decorations in a potentate's palace.

Three queen angelfish in blue and gold lose their sense of caution, emerge from hiding, and swim toward you. A silvery school of spadefish shimmers into view and lazily surrounds you, as though to be your underwater guide.

You accept the welcome and begin the tour of a coral metropolis where every square inch teems with life. A red squirrelfish, its dorsal fin spread like a fan, peers at you from its rock crevice. Black groupers rest in shadows of an elkhorn coral.

In the dark recesses of a coral cavern, a massive jewfish lurks to grab the next passing neighbor. Dwellers in this underwater housing development convert every hole, crack, and crevice into a home.

Now before your eyes parade all the beautiful and graceful tropical fish that you have seen hitherto only in an aquarium: sergeant majors in yellow with black bands; queen triggers, gray with two prominent blue stripes on the face; parrotfish arrayed in green, blue, purple, and even polka dots; blue tangs and other surgeonfish ranging from yellow to purple; spadefish in silver with black stripes; unicorn filefish—studies in olive brown with black-and-white markings; and others with all the hues of rainbow and sunset.

All look larger than anticipated, an illusion caused by the magnifying refraction of light by the water.

Flickering shadows darken the reef as a huge school of porkfish glides by, yellow tails glinting like ornaments of gold. Slowly the fish follow the turns of a coral canyon and disappear in the gloaming.

A pancake-thin stingray flaps batlike wings, waves a buggy-whip tail, and skims the sand. An evil-looking barracuda bares razor teeth and swims past. A vicious moray eel keeps vigil in a rock cavern. He is no menace to you unless you try to dislodge him from his lair.

Now a bright green-and-yellow fish attracts your attention. Swimming closer, you watch a parrotfish hover like a blimp above a brain coral. Its parrotlike beak and small sharp teeth nibble on the living coral.

You approach a sea whip, or gorgonian, and one of the many thin "branches" appears to fall off, slither away, and wriggle into a narrow opening. The branch is a trumpetfish. Its long body finds perfect camouflage among the gorgonians.

You wave your fins gently and glide. Beneath you a small pale-blue fish disappears into the sand. At the spot where it vanished, you spy a mound of coral fragments with a hole at the top. The yellowhead jawfish has excavated a burrow, then built up the entrance by picking up coral fragments in its mouth and piling one on another. The fish backs in tail first to escape pursuit.

Survival of the fittest is the rule of the underwater jungle; size and might determine the hierarchy. The shark devours the grouper, which feeds on the snapper, which preys on the sardine, which eats the plankton.

Suddenly a flicker of gray cuts through

DREAMLIKE SCENE *of shapes and colors curtains the ugly head of a moray eel at lower right. Tiny wrasse close by escapes in a blur of speed. A yellow-and-black rock beauty* (Holacanthus tricolor) *flits past the wavy wall of millepore, a stinging coral, and the shrublike gorgonian beyond.*

162

BOLD WHITE GRUNT *inspects a slice of sea urchin held above a huge brain coral. Minnow-size wrasses hover near for leftovers. The coral shows remarkable resemblance to convolutions on the surface of the human brain.*

YELLOWBELLY HAMLET *and filigree sea fan blend their beauty as in a Japanese print. This six-inch* Hypoplectrus aberrans *floats above a boulderlike colony of star coral and branching fingers of pink coral.*

JERRY GREENBERG

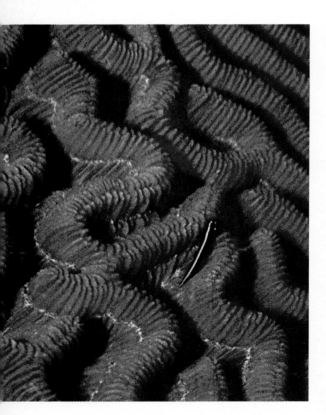

CORRUGATED BRAIN CORAL *spreads a rugged terrain beneath a darting neon goby (about three-fourths life-size). Tiny* Gobiosoma oceanops *plucks parasites from the mouths and bodies of predatory fish.*

the distant blue haze: A 12-foot tiger shark is rocketing in. You stand motionless, frightened and fascinated as the streamlined giant sweeps through the water, caudal fin swishing. On and on the monster comes until only 10 feet separate you. Then he turns away. But relief is short-lived as he shoots upward and traces two fast circles above your head. He leaves as abruptly as he arrived.

Breathing becomes more difficult; your compressed air is running low. You pull the air reserve rod on the breathing unit and earn a brief reprieve before you start a reluctant return to the surface.

As you rise toward the roof of the liquid world, you try to recall its bewildering variety of life. How jumbled the impressions are in your memory! Many more tours will be required before the mind's eye sorts out the reef's fleeting beauties.

For visitors to the Key Largo preserve, I offer a few simple but vital tips. First, and most important, the beginner who wants to use self-contained diving apparatus should take lessons from a qualified instructor. Before each dive he should make a thorough check of his equipment.

Never dive alone or stray far from the boat on a low tank of air. Always stay up-

current of your boat; in case of emergency, the current will carry you toward it. If you spend more than two hours in water cooler than 78°, wear a rubber suit. After you've been down for awhile, the water begins to feel chilly at 30 feet.

Coral is sharp; watch your step. Be careful, too, where you place your hand. Beware of treading on long-spined sea urchins or brushing against stinging coral.

I remind the amateur photographer that he needs no special magic. If he can take reasonably decent surface photographs, he should be able to get good underwater shots. Obey the basic rules of surface photography, and you will improve as you practice and experiment under the sea. If you can see your subject you can photograph it—provided your film gets the proper exposure.

Despite my thousands of dives on the reef, I envy the man who is going below for the first time. It is an incomparable thrill.

James Aldridge, an Australian writer and veteran diver, has expressed it well:

"You are in another world—absolutely—the moment you put your head under the water. This thought will occur again and again, and you will never become tired of saying this trite thing to yourself. *It's another world, it's another world.*"

GOLDSPOTTED EEL (Myrichthys oculatus) *slithers over the floor of the tropical Atlantic feeding primarily on crabs. The three-footer belongs to the snake eel family* (Ophichthidae), *most of whose more than 200 members burrow dens with their sharp tails.*

WARY GREEN RAZORFISH *seeks concealment in Florida seagrass. If further alarmed,* Hemipteronotus splendens *will use its narrow brow for a shovel and burrow into the sand.*

ROBERT E. SCHROEDER (LOWER RIGHT OPPOSITE) AND WALTER A. STARCK II

SEE-THROUGH FISH: *Schooling glassy sweepers* (Pempheris schomburgki) *display transparent muscle tissue along their sides. The popeyed three-inchers feed above reefs by night and rest in reef caves during daylight.*

SPECKLED GRAYSBY *shows remarkably little fear of divers who invade its reef home. Growing about a foot long, the graysby* (Petrometopon cruentatum) *belongs to the large family of sea basses, the Serranidae.*

BACKING INTO ITS GARAGE, *a pearlfish* (Carapus bermudensis) *parks inside a sea cucumber, an invertebrate bottom dweller. The eight-inch pearlfish hunts by night, then wriggles into the cucumber's partly hollow body for protection by day.*

BLUE HAMLET (Hypoplectrus gemma), *a five-inch sea bass unique to Florida waters, dons whitish blotches when it rests at night in coral. The sea basses range from tiny hamlets to giant jewfish and groupers weighing hundreds of pounds.*

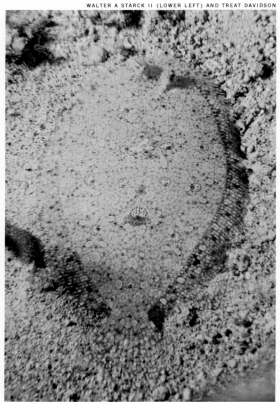

KINGS OF CAMOUFLAGE *are the peacock flounder* (Bothus lunatus, *left*) *and its smaller, drabber cousin the eyed flounder* (B. ocellatus, *right*). *In normal dress they wear the peacock's eyed pattern. But when nestling onto a sandy bottom they uncannily adapt their pigmentation to blend, as the eyed flounder does here. Thus concealed, they wait for prey to swim into range.*

PEPPERMINT BASS, *a secretive three-incher, hides in recesses of reefs off Florida and in waters to the south. Popular with aquarists,* Liopropoma rubre *is also called the swissguard basslet because its stripes resemble those that adorn the Vatican papal guard.*

RESPLENDENT BIGEYE (Priacanthus arenatus) *hides by day in nooks of the deeper reefs, swimming forth at night to snap up prey in bulldog jaws. The glassy eyes of this eight-incher can reflect a light beam upward. Abounding in the Caribbean, bigeyes straggle to Cape Cod.*

ARMED WITH NET AND ANESTHETIC, *a diver captures specimens on Florida's Alligator Reef. The flamefish and high-hats in her collecting jar revive from the drugging.*

FALSE EYES *and look-alike ends protect the foureye butterflyfish. As deluded predators lunge for the "eye" near the tail,* Chaetodon capistratus *escapes with a burst of speed. It and the spotfin butterflyfish (C. ocellatus, below) use their elongated snouts for poking into crevices.*

DORSAL HOISTED LIKE A SAIL, *a spotted drum* (Equetus punctatus) *forages on a Caribbean reef. Frequently called spotted high-hat or spotted jackknife, the secretive, often solitary 10-incher ranges from southern Florida through the West Indies.*

CHAPTER TEN

By CLARENCE P. IDYLL, Ph.D.

Chairman, Division of Fishery Sciences,
Institute of Marine Sciences, University of Miami

Grunion: Fish that Spawn on Land

FIRES FLICKERED along the dark shore, silhouetting dozens of people on a warm June night at Cabrillo Beach in San Pedro, California. Picknickers spread out upon the sand; children romped amid what seemed to be a beach party. Yet the exuberance was tempered with an air of expectation, for we were there to witness a remarkable spectacle: a run of grunion, the fish that comes ashore to spawn.

Despite the crowd around me, relatively few people ever see the grunion's astounding performance, for it occurs only in two areas of the world (map, page 174).

These small fish—adults are six to eight inches long—must time their landing just after peak tides have begun to ebb. Only in that brief period can eggs be laid in the sand where the tide will not disturb them until hatching time. During the spawning season, the highest tides on the Pacific coast occur at night, twice a month. Those on the Gulf of California, the other spawning ground, come in either day or night. The grunion have simply adapted to the local situation.

Where we were the tide had passed the full. Now was the time—unless the commotion of the crowd had sent the grunion to a more secluded spot. Lights, and the jarring of sand by running feet, can make the skittish fish head back to sea.

The smooth wet slope of sand threw up a blurred reflection of distant lights. Then, like a magician's cloth being snatched from a table, the water was whisked away by a retreating wave, leaving the sand littered with dark little knobs of writhing fish. Our wait was over; the grunion were running!

I crouched amid hordes of these blue-and-silver fish as they cavorted in their highly stylized mating dance. I watched a female drill herself backward into the sand with side-to-side jerkings of her body. Excited males curved their bodies alongside. With rhythmic motion the female spawned 1,000 to 3,000 pinkish eggs; simultaneously the males emitted milt that soaked the sand. Then the female wrenched herself free and with her mates was gone. The whole incredible performance lasted but 30 seconds.

170

FORSAKING THE SEA, *California grunion, like the seven-inch female above, ride ashore on high tides to lay their eggs in the sand. As the wave that brought her recedes, the female bores tailfirst into the sand. Quickly she deposits 1,000 to 3,000 eggs; simultaneously a male flops alongside, curves his body around her, and soaks the sand with fertilizing milt (right); as many as 10 males may join her in spawning. With the ritual ended, the female swings her body back and forth to pull free from the sand. Then she wriggles toward the water until a friendly wave arrives to taxi her back to the sea she had emerged from 30 seconds earlier (lower).*

Succeeding waves will gently heap sand on eggs of Leuresthes tenuis; *eventually the spawn could be buried as deep as 16 inches, protected from sun, storm, and the probing beaks of birds. In about 10 days, waves of another high spring tide will immerse the eggs, causing them to hatch.*

"GRUNION ARE RUNNING!" *Young and old scramble for the slithering spawners. Law permits*

ROBERT F. SISSON, NATIONAL GEOGRAPHIC STAFF

harvest of the tasty smeltlike fish only with the bare hands, and not at all in April or May.

"**LOOK I'M A MOTHER!**" *laughs a girl in a do-it-yourself demonstration of hatching. Annually some 70,000 schoolchildren visit Cabrillo Beach to study grunion. In spawning season, an instructor digs up eggs deposited 10 days earlier and distributes a few, along with a jar, to each student. They add water, shake the jars to simulate wave action, and start counting. By 60, eggs begin to pop as baby grunion explode from their cases.*

PACIFIC BEACHES *see* Leuresthes tenuis *slip ashore only after dark. A Gulf of California relative,* L. sardina, *spawns by day, too.*

★ Carson City
★ Sacramento
San Francisco
Monterey
Morro Bay
Point Conception
San Pedro
San Diego

NEVADA
Las Vegas
CALIFORNIA
Los Angeles

UTAH
Lake Powell
Colorado
COLO.
Lake Mead
ARIZONA
★ Phoenix
N. MEX.

Puerto Peñasco
U.S.
MEXICO

Pacific Ocean

BAJA CALIFORNIA
Gulf of California
Bahía de San Rafael
Guaymas
Mulegé
Bahía Concepción
California

Punta Abreojos

Range of the Grunion
Leuresthes tenuis
Occasional limits
Leuresthes sardina
Occasional limits

0   300
STATUTE MILES
ⓒ NATIONAL GEOGRAPHIC SOCIETY

Many thousands of grunion came and went that night on Cabrillo Beach. Happily, parenthood need not end their life cycle as it does that of Pacific salmon. Back in the water, grunion usually remain close to their breeding grounds until tides and some inner signal tell them it's time to go ashore again. A female may return to spawn up to eight times a season, from March to August.

Persons who get close to spawning females report that they make a peculiar sound. They describe it as a noise like the squeak of a mouse, but lower in pitch. The name "grunion" is believed to derive from the Spanish *gruñón*, which means "grunter."

Bedded in the warm, moist beach, eggs are ready to hatch in about 10 days. But the young will not emerge until high tides return. When water immerses the eggs and shakes them in the roiling sand, they hatch in a minute or two. Fry pop out and swim with a receding wave into the ocean.

The wanderings of the Pacific grunion are not fully known, but apparently they do not move far from shore or much below depths of 40 to 60 feet. They grow to five inches in their first year and are then ready to spawn.

The timing of the spawning and the development of the eggs in relation to the tides is remarkably precise. Grunion usually wait to spawn until the night after the highest tide and the next two or three nights. If they spawned with the very highest tide, the next peak might not reach the eggs. Scientists still puzzle over this ability to arrive at the beach at exactly the right time.

It is reasonable to suppose that the fish somehow may construct their own tide tables. Perhaps they do it by measuring gravitational forces that produce high tides, by detecting variations in water pressure as the tide rises, by noting cycles of light intensity or some other variable. It is likely that the grunion owes its punctuality to an "internal clock," which somehow sounds the "all-ashore" signal at precisely the right moment.

And as long as the grunion's clock continues to work, it will also summon spectators to warm California beaches to observe this unique phenomenon, the fish that comes ashore to spawn.

CHAPTER ELEVEN

By GILBERT L. VOSS, Ph.D

Research Professor, Institute of
Marine Sciences, University of Miami

Solving Life Secrets of the Sailfish

National Geographic Society—
University of Miami studies
reveal tiny forms that grow
into Gulf Stream giants

BILLS ALOFT, *hooked sailfish tailwalk
on the edge of the Gulf Stream. This
charter boat off Florida plays a
double-header, but slack line may
let one prize throw the hook.
Tissue-thin sails fold into grooves
along the back when sailfish
submerge. Dark blue dots become
lighter as the fish change mood.*

SAILFISH behind the port outrigger!"
The cry from the flying bridge galvanized the *Dream Girl*'s party into action. All eyes focused on the mullet bait skipping over the blue Gulf Stream.

A purple shadow shot up from the deep behind the dancing bait.

"He's coming up on it now!" I shouted to the sportsman, already seated in the cockpit's fighting chair. A magnificent blue sail broke the surface. Water swirled, and a slender bill slashed at the bait.

"Strike!" came the cry as the mullet disappeared. The line pulled free from the outrigger's clothespin with a startling snap. For a moment it ran slowly off the reel, then a sudden spurt showed that the fish had turned with the bait. The angler threw on his reel drag and struck hard to set the hook.

Even as the reel screamed and the rod bent under the strain, the giant sailfish broke water. Again and again he leaped, sail showering spray as he tailwalked on the surface. Brilliant blue back and silver sides and belly sparkled in the afternoon sun.

For a quarter of an hour they battled. With every roll of the boat and pull of the rod the sweat-drenched angler reeled in, fighting always to keep the line taut.

At last the big fish came alongside, tired— but still a dangerous package of sandpaper-surfaced bill and 45 pounds of bone and muscle. I seized the leader wire and clipped it with a pair of cutters. The big fish lay motionless, then with a savage shake of its head swam slowly into the depths.

As it disappeared, the captain broke out a triangular red flag. It flapped in eloquent testimony of a battle won and a gallant foe freed to fight again.

I have experienced this excitement many times as angler and as charter-boat mate and skipper. I myself have boated a sailfish 8 feet 8 inches long—close to maximum size encountered in the Atlantic.

But my greatest thrill came one quiet night aboard the research ship *Megalopa*. It was then that I caught three sailfish hardly an eighth of an inch long.

My search for these pygmies had begun months before, when the National Geographic Society and the University of Miami's Institute of Marine Sciences embarked on a study of sport and food fishes of the Florida Current, a major spawning ground for the western North Atlantic. We wanted to learn where and when these fishes spawn, when they reach maturity, what their numbers are, and how heavily they may be fished without upsetting the balance of life in the sea. Such information proves invaluable to conservationists, sportsmen, and commercial fishermen.

Strange as it may sound, our knowledge of the lives of ocean fishes is a scientific Swiss cheese, full of blank spaces. At best we can sketch the histories of one out of a hundred of all ocean species. The only clue we had about baby sailfish, for example, was a tentative description made by an ichthyologist years before.

Identifying the larva of a species of fish is not as easy as it would seem. While a baby pig or a puppy looks much like the adult hog or dog, a newly hatched fish bears little or no resemblance to the grown-ups. Fins are undeveloped, heads are huge, eyes gigantic. Further, many parent fish lay their eggs and swim unconcernedly away—except when they tarry to eat their own larvae.

To trace a fish's history, one must collect all stages from hatchling through adult. If, like fresh-water larvae, open-ocean young could be reared in an aquarium, their growth could be easily observed. But this is next to impossible, partly because of the difficulty of supplying their natural microscopic food. Specimens must be plucked from the ocean at each stage of growth. One history can represent months or years of patient larva-fishing and study.

Our job on the *Megalopa* was to comb the 60-odd miles of water between Florida and the Bahamas, searching for needles in the ocean haystack. Day after day, rolling in the ocean swell, we lowered silk plankton nets on steel cables to depths of 1,200 feet and more. Nights I would idle the engines and we would put a big net over the side, its 34-foot-long cone tapering to end in a glass collecting jar. Between hauls we gathered above a light rigged over the side, and

with long-handled dip nets scooped up darting copepods, fairy shrimp, tiny fish, and spurting squids.

Specimens went into preservatives for later study. Sometimes our labors with hand net or haul brought weird, entertaining creatures: lanternfish with headlights to attract prey, hatchetfish with gold and silver sides and rows of light organs, viperfish armed with saberlike teeth.

The night of our sailfish discovery we were near Cat Cays in the Bahama Islands, over the edge of the Gulf Stream's deepwater canyon. A calm had flattened the water. A phosphorescent streak astern marked the position of our trawl.

We cut the throttle and hauled in the net. Gently we lifted in the glass jar at its end. Under the cabin light we saw familiar forms dart about—arrowworms, comb jellies, siphonophores, medusae, and the transparent larvae of fish.

At the bottom, just as we were about to add preservatives, we spied three tiny creatures. They were fish we had never seen before—steel blue in places, transparent elsewhere, with toothed spines projecting from their heads. Far from sporting a bill, they had short, broad snouts. Far from cutting a figure as lean greyhounds of the sea, the potbellied little fellows could hardly swim.

B. ANTHONY STEWART, NATIONAL GEOGRAPHIC STAFF

SHIPBOARD SCIENTISTS *trawl for infant Gulf Stream fishes. Specimens slide down the silk funnel into jars for study ashore. Magnified five times, the ocean's Lilliputians take on identities (right). Directly under the round sargassum weed "float" is an eel larva, flanked by a polychaete worm on the left and a shrimplike euphausiid. Below, a wide-eyed flatfish swims away from a sail larva sporting long spines (extreme right).*

FISH STOMACHS *often prove a scientific treasure chest. From a dolphin like this 12-pounder, the author (left) cut an intact three-inch sailfish. One fish produced a set of false teeth!*

But—excitement soared—they closely fitted that tentative description of infant sails. We had opened the door a crack on the secret life of the sailfish.

Even now, after extensive trawling and study of a quarter-million larval fish, gaps remain in our knowledge of Florida sails. But this much we have learned:

Sailfish spawn from late spring to early fall in shallow water along the Florida sands. At this time the females, heavy with roe, are sluggish fighters.

After spawning, the eggs float northward in the Gulf Stream, scattered about in the plankton—the living, drifting chowder of the sea. The number of young sailfish would be fantastically large if all the larvae survived, for a single female may spawn as many as 4,675,000 eggs. But countless predators feed on eggs and young as they float helplessly in the sea.

The hatchlings themselves gorge on tiny shrimplike copepods, the "milk" of the sea. Soon the baby sailfish sample small mollusks called heteropods and gobble down fish. We found one greedy specimen, all of three-quarters of an inch including bill, that had squeezed into its stomach a viperfish nearly as long as itself.

As they grow able to fend for themselves, the sailfish work inshore. Juveniles five to eight inches long are found along the Carolina coast during summer. Cold weather and northerly winds head them south. Tagging of adults indicates a substantial spring migration through the Straits of Florida into the Gulf, and an opposite movement in autumn.

In only a year they have grown to five or six feet. Soon they are the fighting heavyweights sought by sport fishermen. Three or four years seems to be old age for them.

Until recently scientists recognized several sailfish species, including an Atlantic sail, *Istiophorous albicans,* and a Pacific, often labeled *I. orientalis.* Now all are believed to belong to a single species given the name *I. platypterus.*

The "sail" is an overgrown dorsal fin that collapses into a groove along the back except when the fish surfaces. It has encouraged some misunderstandings. This odd "sailing fish," wrote a fanciful 19th-century Englishman, "hoists a mainsail, and often sails in the manner of a native boat."

Cousin to the marlin and the swordfish, the sailfish shares with these giants the long spear or bill used for defense and for hunting food. I have seen a sailfish with the broken bill of another sticking out on either side—a mute reminder of a savage undersea duel.

How well the sailfish uses this weapon I discovered one calm winter day off Stuart, Florida, when we backed our boat into a school feeding on sardines.

The sailfish circled slowly, sails half raised, herding their prey tighter and tighter. First one and then another broke from the circle and swam through the milling prey, thrashing right and left with their bills. Then the predators would submerge and lazily gorge on the dead and stunned fishes as they drifted downward.

Hundreds of sea gulls clamored overhead. Diving pelicans tore raised sails to shreds in the frenzy of feeding. One sailfish, evidently angered at a gull swooping low after a sardine, lunged and knocked the bird flapping into the water.

Leaning over the side, I could touch the sails of the big fish as they milled about. An excited guide on another boat gaffed one. The resulting battle taught him new respect for his quarry. I had learned that respect long ago when a leaping sailfish slashed with its bill and left a scar across my chest.

Not until the early 1920's was the sailfish "discovered" as one of the world's showiest and hardest-fighting game fishes. At first it was taken on hand lines by anglers who went out with commercial fishermen for a day's sport catching kingfish and mackerel. Today in Florida sailfishing is a multi-million-dollar industry, with hundreds of cruisers plying the blue Gulf Stream in search of the wily fighters.

Sportsmen are justly proud of the sailfish they have fought and then freed, and of the mounted gamesters that hang in their recreation rooms back home.

But my prize trophies are still those pot-bellied youngsters that I caught one quiet night in a plankton jar.

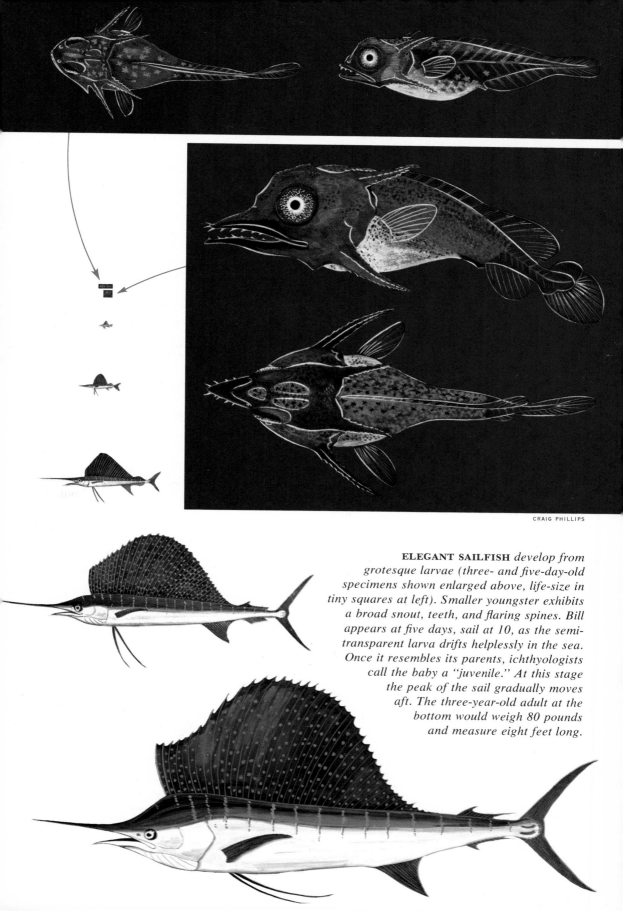

CRAIG PHILLIPS

ELEGANT SAILFISH *develop from grotesque larvae (three- and five-day-old specimens shown enlarged above, life-size in tiny squares at left). Smaller youngster exhibits a broad snout, teeth, and flaring spines. Bill appears at five days, sail at 10, as the semi-transparent larva drifts helplessly in the sea. Once it resembles its parents, ichthyologists call the baby a "juvenile." At this stage the peak of the sail gradually moves aft. The three-year-old adult at the bottom would weigh 80 pounds and measure eight feet long.*

CRUISERS RACE *from Palm Beach Inlet in the Silver Sailfish Derby—a feature of Florida's multimillion-dollar sailfish industry. On the fishing grounds, the boat's tall outriggers carry anglers' lines up and out so they trail astern. When a sailfish swats the mullet bait with its bill, the line drops from the outrigger's "clothespin"; this sudden slack makes the lure act like stunned prey, tempting the sail to grab it.*

STRIKE! *and the fight is on. A sailfish hurls itself into the air or tailwalks (right) in frantic struggles to throw the hook. Sporting anglers often free their conquered catches. Longest reported Atlantic sail stretched 10⅓ feet; the heaviest weighed 141 pounds.*

CHAPTER TWELVE

Gallery of Marine Fishes ▶

NONGAME SPECIES

IN THE CEASELESS struggle for survival during 300 million years on earth, marine fishes have gone through countless experimental changes. Some grew lungs, then abandoned them for gills. Some grew flippers and padded onto Devonian rock to launch the land animals. Today some throw electric shocks, illumine their bodies like ocean liners, give birth to a million young. Each species, adapting to life in its special way, enriches the gallery that follows.

North America's 3,200 kinds of salt-water fishes, a tenth of earth's total, form an almost isolated faunal system; few species overlap onto other shores. With ocean highways linking the continents, what keeps fishes from mingling? Temperature gradients, salinity variations, and oceanic distances erect formidable travel barriers.

What kind of home appeals to marine fishes? Most dwell over continental shelves such as the Grand Banks off Newfoundland, a prime world fishing hole. The greatest variety of fishes—and fish colors—occur in tropical waters. Northward, pigments fade and species grow fewer, but numbers increase; cold waters harbor herrings and other fishes of stupendous populations.

Mailed-cheek Fishes

BONY PLATES under the eye distinguish the mailed-cheek fishes, a major segment of the world's marine fish fauna. The order Scleroparei includes species both valuable and strange. Its huge-headed searobins walk solemnly across ocean floors. A sculpin holds forth as one of the world's most comical fishes, the stonefish as the most poisonous. Rockfishes and greenlings sport bizarre colors; the spotted scorpionfish so masters camouflage as to make itself almost invisible. An Atlantic rockfish, called redfish or ocean perch *(Sebastes marinus),* ranks among the most valuable of food fishes.

Typical mailed-cheek fishes live on the bottom, bear live young, grow spines on the head, and have winglike pectoral fins. All have spiny pelvic and anal fins, and spiny rays preceding the soft ones in the dorsals.

SEAROBINS
Family Triglidae

Favored with gay colors and large, appealing eyes, searobins excite only groans from surf fishermen. They snap up bait intended for game fishes, fight as hard as an old boot, and painfully stab hands with their pelvic spines.

Searobins are noisy fishes, with the northern searobin *(Prionotus carolinus)* one of the most vocal. Vibrating a network of muscles against a huge air bladder, the plaintive oddities croak like frogs, especially at spawning time.

Dragging themselves stealthily over the bottom, searobins use their separated pectoral fin rays as fingers, nimbly overturning stones and poking in the sand for crustaceans. Occasionally they glide upward after small fishes, then spread the large pectoral fins and settle gracefully back.

Fish of brackish water and moderate depths, searobins apparently winter deep. In the summer they lay buoyant yellowish eggs. They make palatable food, but their peculiar appearance deters eating.

Characteristics: large bony head; separated front rays of pectoral fins, divided dorsal, sharp pelvic spines. *Range:* tropical and temperate waters; all but one of 22 North American species dwell on the Atlantic coast. *Weight:* seldom more than a few pounds.

NORTHERN SEAROBIN

RED IRISH LORD SCULPIN (top) and GRUNT SCULPIN

SCULPINS
Family Cottidae

The grunt sculpin reigns as jester of King Neptune's court. A dumpy figure dabbed with gay clown colors, *Rhamphocottus richardsoni* bounces amusingly over the bottom in short jumps. Hurrying, it rises from the bottom like an escaping child's balloon.

Its eyes roll independently in looking about. Lifted from the water, it grunts disapproval. Attacked, it menacingly flares spiny cheek plates, then scoots away to make another stand. During courtship, bashful males flee females.

Sculpins share the searobins' large bony head and range of colors, but they lack separate pectoral rays. More than 100 species of the family range our coasts, a majority preferring the Pacific where they swarm as "tide-pool johnnies." Generally coarse and tasteless, many end their lives as bait in lobster pots. Eighteen fresh-water species, small specimens often called miller's thumbs, spawn under logs and rocks.

The gaudy red Irish lord *(Hemilepidotus hemilepidotus)* grows 20 inches long in coastal waters from northern California to Alaska. In March it lays tough pink eggs in conspicuous masses. It feeds on crabs, mussels, and worms.

Giant of all sculpins is the 30-inch, 25-pound cabezon *(Scorpaenichthys marmoratus,* page 207), a Pacific crab-eater with tasty bluish or greenish flesh and poisonous roe. An Atlantic sculpin, the sea raven *(Hemitripterus americanus),* inflates like a balloon if removed from water and floats helplessly when first returned.

Characteristics: eyes atop head; fanlike pectorals; head encased with bone except on top; often scaleless or partially scaled. *Range:* mainly Northern Hemisphere; temperate and arctic, salt and fresh water. *Length:* 3 to 30 inches.

LINGCOD (above) and KELP GREENLING

LINGCOD
Ophiodon elongatus

Brightly hued lingcod change colors with lightning speed. West Coast trawl fishermen, subduing three-footers with a rap of the gaff hook, may see dark brown sides flash light yellow, orange spots turn to brown.

Pacific lingcod share the family Hexagrammidae with kelp greenlings. The valuable food fish are misleadingly called "cultus"—Indian for worthless. Mailed cheeks and flaring pectoral fins mark them as close kin of the bony-headed sculpins.

Lingcod favor reefs and kelp beds that feel strong tidal movements. They often rest on the bottom on pectoral and pelvic fins. Their canine teeth snap up herring, flounders, cod, whiting, squids, and little lingcod.

The fish spawn in winter, nesting in sheltered rocky areas. Eggs number up to half a million, laid in adhesive pinkish-white masses. Males, less than half the size of females, fan oxygen-rich water over the nest and drive off intruders with vicious rushes.

The intense green flesh of tasty young lingcod often dismays the uninitiated, though the coloring vanishes with cooking. Livers are rich in vitamins A and D.

Characteristics: small scales; large toothy mouth; long, slightly notched dorsal fin. *Range:* Baja California to Bering Sea. *Weight:* males to 22 pounds, females 70. *Length:* males to 3 feet, females 5.

PAINTINGS BY HASHIME MURAYAMA

KELP GREENLING
Hexagrammos decagrammus

Kelp greenlings carry color-consciousness into every phase of their lives. Males wear various shades of blue; females tend to browns and reds. The flesh, quite delicious, bears a blue-green hue until cooked. And greenling eggs, spawned in fall, form a pale blue mass.

Living around rocks among kelp and other seaweeds, greenlings fall prey to salmon and steelhead trout. In turn they devour worms, small fishes, and crustaceans. One of their victims is the ghost shrimp *(Callianassa californiensis,* lower left), whose beating heart shows through its transparent shell, and whose burrowings in the bottom often bury young oysters alive.

Anglers still-fish for kelp greenlings, baiting with crustaceans and marine worms. Commercial fishermen take few, finding that boated fish quickly spoil. Often called sea or rock trout, they join lingcod in the mailed-cheek family Hexagrammidae.

Characteristics: small mouth and teeth; a stubby antennalike cirrus above each eye, usually another midway between the eye and front of dorsal fin; male and female differ in color. *Range:* Point Conception in California to Kodiak, Alaska. *Weight:* average 2 to 4 pounds. *Length:* to 21 inches.

187

ROCKFISHES
Genus *Sebastes*

The Pacific coast's 56 varieties of rockfishes, spiny nonvenomous cousins of scorpionfishes, form a large part of the Pacific fish fauna. Often lumped as "ocean perch," they add 40 million pounds a year to the U.S. commercial catch and stand high among California market fishes. Anglers hook myriads. On the Atlantic coast, valuable redfish rank as the only important rockfish.

All rockfishes are viviparous, females bearing half a million, perhaps even two million, tiny living young.

The 15-inch starry rockfish, a leading western beauty, abounds in deep water from San Diego to San Francisco. Vermilion rockfish, three-footers with red lips, range north to British Columbia. Stripes marking the two-foot tiger rockfish, found from California to Alaska, change rapidly from deep red to black. The abundant black rockfish, widely distributed along the coast, is often confused with the blue rockfish, or priestfish (page 205).

Characteristics: mailed spiny cheeks, fanlike pectorals. *Range:* temperate Pacific and Atlantic. *Length:* to 3 feet.

VERMILION ROCKFISH *(S. miniatus)*

TIGER ROCKFISH *(S. nigrocinctus)*

STARRY ROCKFISH *(S. constellatus,* left) and BLACK ROCKFISH *(S. melanops,* below)

RON CHURCH (OPPOSITE AND TOP), JOHN TASHJIAN (CENTER), AND CARLETON RAY

189

Flatfishes

RIPPLING through the water like flying carpets, flatfishes glide to the bottom, flip sand on their backs, and vanish except for protruding eyes. Water squirted from the underside gill jet-propels them off the bottom in pursuit of small fishes. Man chases the flatfishes with trawlers, seeking flavorsome halibut, flounders, soles, plaice, and sanddabs.

Born upright with normally placed eyes, young flatfishes (order Pleuronectiformes) quickly find their skull twisting, carrying one eye toward the other side. Simultaneously the fish tilt. Soon both eyes peer from the same side, and the fish swim with the eyeless side down. The mouth, distorted in the process, ever after wears a crooked, pained look.

ATLANTIC HALIBUT
Hippoglossus hippoglossus

Ocean giants, halibut live in a woman's world: Males grow only a tenth their spouses' size. A female halibut caught off Massachusetts measured nine feet long and half as wide; it weighed 625 pounds dressed.

Overfishing decimated the Atlantic halibut, a fate that menaced the similar Pacific species (*H. stenolepis*) until U. S. and Canadian experts acted. Today laws protect Pacific nursery areas, fostering a yearly catch of 40 million pounds.

Atlantic halibut lay perhaps two million eggs that drift in mid-water. Larvae reach nearly two inches before the left eye migrates. The fish live as long as 40 years.

Less wedded to the bottom than most flatfishes, halibut groups flap through the water gobbling small fishes, crustaceans, even sea birds.

Characteristics: swims left-side-down; body relatively elongated. *Range:* Arctic south to New Jersey. *Weight:* seldom 450 pounds but up to 700. *Length:* maximum about 9 feet.

190

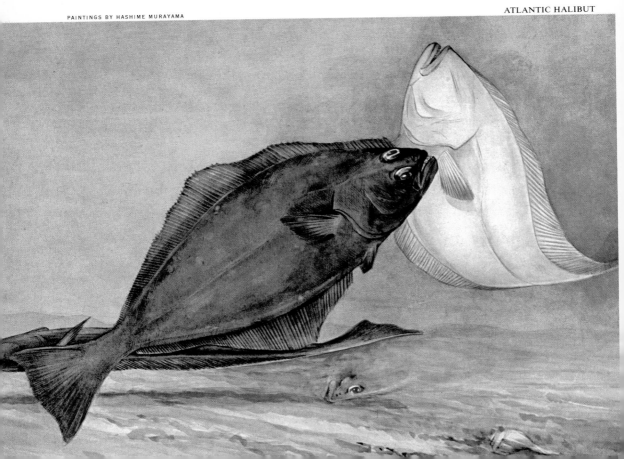

WINTER FLOUNDER
Pseudopleuronectes americanus

Hugging shores of bays and estuaries, winter flounders, or blackbacks, favor the chilly waters of New England, only occasionally venturing south of Chesapeake Bay. Welcomed everywhere by epicures, their white, firm, delicious flesh encourages a commercial fishery that lands some 20 to 25 million pounds each year.

Flounders deposit half a million eggs, sometimes a million, spurning food during winter breeding. Their eggs, like those of all right-eyed flounders, lack the conspicuous oil globule that characterizes spawn of left-eye species. Eggs sink to the bottom; in water 5° F. above freezing they hatch in about two weeks. Hatcheries once liberated tens of millions of fry but abandoned marine fish culture as ineffectual.

Adult winter flounders feed on sea worms, shrimps, and small shellfish and crabs. Anglers tempt the small-mouthed scrappers with bits of clam and bloodworm on tiny hooks.

Characteristics: topside gray to green; swims left-side-down. *Range:* Labrador to North Carolina. *Weight:* maximum about 5 pounds. *Length:* average 10 to 12 inches, maximum 20.

SUMMER FLOUNDER
Paralichthys dentatus

Summer flounders, zooming up from bottom, leap clear of the water in pursuit of small fishes. Bottom-fished on light tackle with minnow bait, these flatfish provide spicy sport. Goal of most fishermen is a "doormat," a flapping spread of flounder weighing 10 pounds or more.

During cold weather summer flounders, or flukes, descend several hundred feet on the continental shelf. There they spawn. Eggs apparently float until hatching occurs. In late spring flukes move inshore over sandy and muddy bottoms gobbling on small fishes, crustaceans, and shellfish. A flashlight trained in shallows may reveal eyes poking from the mud and a vague body outline, but no more, for flounders are gifted color changers (pages 31 and 168).

New England and Middle Atlantic trawlers each year haul up some 15 million pounds. Another species, the yellowtail (*Limanda ferruginea*), ranks as the East's most valuable flounder.

Characteristics: brown or gray back; swims right-side-down. *Range:* Maine to South Carolina. *Weight:* rod and reel record 21¼ pounds. *Length:* average 15 to 20 inches, 24 not rare. 191

WINTER FLOUNDER (top fish) and SUMMER FLOUNDER

STARRY FLOUNDER (bottom pair), DUNGENESS CRAB (top), and PACIFIC SANDDAB

STARRY FLOUNDER
Platichthys stellatus

Flatfish rules about eye migrations break down in the case of starry flounders. Off California, half have both eyes on the right side, half have them on the left. In Alaska two-thirds are left-eyed, in Japan three-quarters. Yet the starry is a right-eye flounder, for its eggs lack a globule of oil that characterizes the left-eyes.

Abrasive, widely spaced scales give starry flounders the names grindstone and emerywheel. Primarily residents of sandy ocean shallows, they enter brackish estuaries and run up rivers. They provide recreation for anglers and a portion of the commercial catch labeled "sole."

In late winter and early spring starry flounders ripen with pale, yellowish-orange eggs.

Characteristics: sprinkling of rough star-shaped scales; yellowish fins striped with black small mouth. *Range:* southern California to Alaska and Japan. *Weight:* maximum 20 pounds. *Length:* average 14 inches, maximum 36.

NAKED SOLE
Gymnachirus melas

"Naked" because it wears no scales, this colorful flatfish also lacks in other departments. It has no ribs. Its close-spaced eyes are tiny. Few teeth grow in the small mouth. And the species itself is scarce.

Naked soles and three other American species of the family Soleidae, too tiny to be important, contrast with Europe's large, heavily fished soles. America's most abundant species is the hogchoker *(Trinectes maculatus),* a six-inch eastern coastal and stream dweller whose rough skin supposedly choked scavenging hogs as they ate specimens discarded by netters on the beach.

"Filet of sole," originally the common sole of Europe, in United States restaurants usually refers to any filleted flatfish.

Characteristics: vertical bars; pancake body; small eyes and mouth; swims right-side-up. *Range:* Massachusetts to Florida and parts of Gulf of Mexico. *Length:* about 9 inches.

192

PACIFIC SANDDAB
Citharichthys sordidus

One of the left-eye flounders, Pacific sanddabs abound along the temperate west coast but seldom grow large: two-pounders rank as giants.

Pacific sanddabs mature sexually at about eight inches, usually in the third year, and spawn in summer. They live about 10 years. Speckled topsides give them the widely used nickname "mottled sanddab."

At home over both sand and mud, sanddabs share the ocean bottom with valuable dungeness, or market, crabs *(Cancer magister)*, which are trapped by the tens of millions of pounds. The eight-inch, three-pound crustaceans earn gourmet praise for their firm, fine-flavored flesh; leg meat rates as choicest. Canned, or shipped iced, they reach even eastern markets.

Pacific sanddabs have the only commercial importance among a handful of small Pacific and Atlantic flatfishes termed sanddabs. Restaurants often advertise them, West Coast Chinese split and dry them. Atlantic sanddabs, seldom six inches long, are called whiffs.

Characteristics: swim left-side-up; brownish back marked with black and yellow blotches. *Range:* Baja California to Bering Sea. *Weight:* to 2 pounds. *Length:* to 16 inches.

HASHIME MURAYAMA (ABOVE) AND ERNEST L. LIBBY

NAKED SOLE

Herrings and Smelts

WHEELING ABOUT THE SEAS in schools of millions, herrings and smelts exist in staggering numbers and have enormous value. Perhaps the world's most sought-after fish is the Atlantic herring; it has led nations to wealth and war. More than a million pounds of related menhaden (genus *Brevoortia*) fall prey each year to U. S. fishermen, making oil, animal food, and fertilizer. Sardines swell the list of valuable herrings.

Several species of herrings (family Clupeidae) and smelts (Osmeridae) migrate up streams to spawn; alewives and shad literally crowd each other onto banks. The two families share oily flesh, soft fin rays, pelvics placed rearward on the body, and an air bladder that connects with the throat. Smelts have a fleshy adipose fin behind the dorsal.

PAINTINGS BY HASHIME MURAYAMA

RAINBOW SMELT
Osmerus eperlanus

Captain John Smith, exploring New England in 1622, found smelt "in such abundance that the Salvages doe take them up in the rivers with baskets, like sives." Delicious smelt still ascend New England's rivers, but dams and pollution have cut back their numbers drastically.

Midget salmon in appearance, smelt migrate like salmon into fresh water to spawn, usually from February through June with males arriving first. They are incredibly prolific; a two-ounce fish is said to lay 50,000 sticky eggs that adhere to the bottom. By fall, 1½-inch fry have swum down to sea. Several western smelts spawn on sandy beaches like grunion.

Smelt school inshore, traveling with kin of similar length. In autumn they swarm in bays and harbors, feeding on crustaceans and small fishes. Some have become landlocked in Lake Champlain and other eastern waters; conservationists have introduced them in Midwest lakes.

Characteristics: olive back, silver streaks down the side; adipose fin, soft fin rays. *Range:* arctic seas south to Virginia Capes and British Columbia, northern lakes west to Minnesota. *Length:* maximum about 14 inches.

194

ATLANTIC HERRING
Clupea harengus

Atlantic herring have helped shape century after century of world history. Their decline in the Baltic Sea wrought financial havoc on the Hanseatic League. North Sea herring made Holland one of the richest nations of the 16th century. In 1652 disputes over herring rights flared into war between the Dutch and the English.

Maine dominates the U. S. herring industry, specializing in fingerlings packed as sardines. Her 60-million-pound annual catch ranks herring with haddock, ocean perch, yellowtail flounder, and northern kingfish as the East's top food fishes. Fresh, salted, or pickled, the delicate herring earns lip-smacking plaudits.

Although preyed upon by man, bird, porpoise, and fellow fishes, herring are probably the world's most numerous fish. Mariners report schools estimated at three billion fish covering six square miles of sea.

Herring spawn from spring to autumn, laying up to 40,000 heavy, sticky eggs.

Characteristics: elongated body; steel blue back, silvery sides. *Range:* Cape Hatteras to Labrador; occurs both sides of Atlantic. *Weight:* to 1½ pounds. *Length:* to 18 inches.

ALEWIFE
Alosa pseudoharengus

The fish that New England Indians buried in hills of corn, "aylwifs" were prized by early colonists as food and fertilizer.

Today in spring—where dams and pollution permit—spawning alewives or "branch herring" crowd coastal rivers and squeeze up creeks only a few feet wide. Eggs, averaging 100,000 per female, stick to brush and stones. Young do not swim seaward until fall. Alewives landlocked in the Great Lakes enjoyed a population explosion when lampreys slaughtered lake trout and whitefish, alewife enemies. Now they fatten the Lakes' newly introduced coho salmon.

Fishermen catch more than 50 million pounds a year. Alewives rank first in volume among Chesapeake Bay food fishes. Packers salt and cure them, often as "river herring," and wash a silvery coating called pearl essence from the scales for use in making costume jewelry.

Characteristics: gray-green back, silvery sides, dark spot behind gill; large eyes, projecting lower lip. *Range:* North Carolina to Nova Scotia; also Great Lakes and several New York lakes. *Weight:* average ½ pound. *Length:* average 11 inches, maximum 15.

ATLANTIC HERRING (bottom pair) and ALEWIFE

Needlefishes and Flying Fishes

DISTURB A NEEDLEFISH, saury, halfbeak, or flyingfish and it will skitter violently across the surface or leap high out of the water. Scientists ponder the fact that the beak of these jumpers is inversely proportional to the length of the pectoral fins: A long-snouted needlefish has tiny pectorals, a snub-nosed flyingfish enormous ones. Their fins, perched astern near the tail, give them the swept-back appearance of jet fighters. Tasty but little eaten, most lay eggs equipped with tendrils which stick on drifting seaweed.

PACIFIC SAURY

PACIFIC SAURY
Cololabis saira

Meaty and plentiful, Pacific sauries are important food of other fishes and abound in the fish markets of Japan. Enormous schools churn the open ocean, feeding on fish eggs and larvae. Observers report seeing similar Atlantic sauries (*Scomberesox saurus*) skidding ashore or leaping 20,000 at a time into the air to escape attacking tunas and mackerels.

Characteristics: elongated body; 5 or 6 finlets behind dorsal. *Range:* southern California to Alaska, also off Japan. *Length:* to 1 foot.

TIMUCU
Strongylura timucu

Like a playful puppy, the timucu leapfrogs over floating sticks, drifting feathers, even lazing turtles. Often it pauses to run its beak exploringly over the object, then charges and leaps. Anglers find this garlike member of the needlefish family (Belonidae) gives a dazzling battle.

Feeding needlefish creep alongside prey, then slash with their fearsome teeth. Greenish bones make humans shy from the superb flesh.

Characteristics: long toothy jaws; greenish back. *Range:* Maine-Texas. *Length:* to 2½ feet.

TIMUCU

OTIS IMBODEN, NATIONAL GEOGRAPHIC STAFF (LOWER), AND CALIFORNIA DEPT. OF FISH AND GAME

HOUNDFISH

HOUNDFISH
Tylosurus crocodilus

Shooting houndfish with bow and arrow takes consummate skill; an expert hits only one out of 10. Trolled spoon attracts this giant needlefish into range. Line attached to the arrow drags in the target. Like living javelins, leaping houndfish sometimes impale boaters with their beaks.

Characteristics: short powerful snout; elongated body, greenish in color; needlelike teeth. *Range:* Caribbean and Florida, young straggle to New Jersey. *Length:* average 2 feet, to 5.

HALFBEAK
Hyporhamphus unifasciatus

Romping halfbeaks put their long lower jaw under a floating object for leverage, flip and land tailfirst on the other side. Ancestors of flyingfishes, some halfbeaks can glide 40 feet, illustrating how leaping evolved into soaring flight. The surface fish eats crustaceans and algae.

Characteristics: red-tipped beaklike lower jaw, normal upper jaw; body greenish tinged with silver, white lateral bar. *Range:* Maine to Argentina. *Length:* to 1 foot.

HALFBEAK

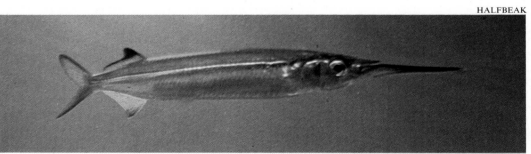

CALIFORNIA FLYINGFISH

CALIFORNIA FLYINGFISH
Cypselurus californicus

The cry "flyingfish!" from a liner's rail sends passengers scurrying to watch the "bluebirds of the sea" put on their show. Fish in taking off spread paired fins and scull violently with the tail, taxiing to attain flight speed. Then they lift off, glide a few seconds with pectorals rigidly outstretched, and splash back in the sea. A one-pounder in flight can deal a man a knockout blow. Do flyingfish really fly? Not if "flying" means flapping fins like birds flap wings (page 44).

Largest of North America's 14 flyingfish species, California flyingfish school in the open sea, searching for invertebrate foods. Fishermen attract the meaty delicacies with lights, often playing a beam on a boat's sail which serves both as lure and backstop. Open, illumined portholes at times bring them soaring inside.

Characteristics: bluish back; spreading pectoral and pelvic fins. *Range:* southern and Baja California. *Length:* average 12 inches, to 18.

ATLANTIC COD
Gadus morhua

The staple codfish drew Europeans like a magnet across the North Atlantic to settle New World shores. Cod-rich Grand Banks off Newfoundland and coastal shelves of Greenland still lure the world's fishing fleets.

Cod populate sand and rock bottoms 100 to 1,500 feet down, searching in hungry packs for mollusks, worms, herrings, crustaceans, mosses. Their stomachs also have yielded rocks, finger rings, corncobs, rubber dolls.

Prolific cod breed from autumn to spring, probably releasing spawn a little at a time while schooling. They grow immense: Records tell of a six-footer that weighed 211 pounds. Cod flesh is dry but excellently flavored. Young cod and haddock are split and served as "scrod."

Characteristics: 3 dorsal fins, 2 anals; barbel under chin. *Range:* Arctic seas south to Virginia. *Weight:* average 10 to 35 pounds, rod and reel record 74¼. *Length:* average 3 feet.

198

Cods and Hakes

FLAVORSOME, NUTRITIOUS, fantastically prolific, cods and hakes stand out as food fishes. Largely cold-water bottom dwellers, they venture to polar seas and abyssal depths. They support huge, valuable, centuries-old fisheries. Atlantic cod lead members of the family Gadidae in size and importance. All of North America's 24 species of cods and hakes are marine fishes except the burbot *(Lota lota)*, which occurs in deep lakes south to the latitude of Kansas. All Gadidae bear an array of soft-rayed fins, pelvics placed forward under the head, and an air bladder that lacks a connection with the throat. Some species have internal clusters of luminescent bacteria that set the fish aglow.

HADDOCK
Melanogrammus aeglefinus

Fishermen haul up nearly 150 million pounds a year to make the flavorsome haddock a leading East Coast food fish.

Huge, compact schools roam smooth areas of ocean bed feeding on crustaceans, mollusks, and small fishes. Unlike cod and pollock, haddock will not surface, even in pursuit of prey. Females deposit up to two million eggs.

Characteristics: dark blotch above pectoral fins; barbel under chin. *Range:* Greenland to Virginia; occurs both sides of Atlantic. *Weight:* average 3 pounds, to 37. *Length:* to 44 inches.

POLLOCK
Pollachius virens

Gluttonous pollock, most active of the cods and hakes, roam the sea from surface to bottom pursuing small fishes, especially young cod. Often sold as "Boston bluefish," they provide sport to anglers and an annual commercial take of nearly 10 million pounds. The winter spawners lay up to 400,000 buoyant eggs.

Characteristics: green back, white lateral line; small chin barbel; projecting lower jaw. *Range:* St. Lawrence to Virginia; occurs both sides of Atlantic. *Weight:* average 4 pounds, rod and reel record 42. *Length:* to 3½ feet.

Top to bottom: POLLOCK, ATLANTIC COD, HADDOCK

SQUIRREL HAKE
Urophycis chuss

An aerial-like filament sprouting from the back gives squirrel hake a Martian look. Their flesh, tasty but soft, often ends up as an ingredient of cat food. Summer-spawning squirrel, or red, hake feed on shrimps and other small crustaceans, foraging to depths of nearly 1,000 feet. Fishermen hauling up scallops often find hake fry hidden in the mollusks' shells.

Characteristics: two dorsal fins, the first topped with a filament; long filamentous pelvics; chin barbel; sides red, brownish, or greenish. *Range:* St. Lawrence to North Carolina. *Weight:* maximum 8 pounds. *Length:* to 30 inches.

CUSK
Brosme brosme

A fondness for rocky, uneven ocean floors protects tasty cusk from depopulation by bottom-scouring trawlers. Sluggish swimmers, cusk prowl the northeast coast gulping crustaceans and shellfish. They lay up to two million buoyant eggs, each with a yellow or pink oil globule. Young swim near the surface until two inches long, then descend to the depths for life.

Characteristics: back color varies—brown, gray, or yellow; long dorsal and anal fins; chin barbel. *Range:* Arctic south to New Jersey. *Weight:* to 27 pounds. *Length:* maximum 3½ feet.

SILVER HAKE
Merluccius bilinearis

Modern freezing methods have transformed the abundant but soft-fleshed silver hake into a valuable food fish. Strong, swift, and voracious, silver hake may run ashore in the frenzy of chasing prey. One three-footer's stomach yielded 75 three-inch herring. Found at 1,000-foot depths, they lay large buoyant eggs that show a conspicuous brown or yellow oil globule.

Characteristics: sides silvery tinted with brown; two dorsal fins. *Range:* continental shelf from South Carolina to the St. Lawrence. *Weight:* maximum 5 pounds. *Length:* to 2½ feet.

Top to bottom: SQUIRREL HAKE, CUSK, SILVER HAKE

HASHIME MURAYAMA (ABOVE) AND JERRY GREENBERG

Silversides and Mullets

IMMENSE, TIGHT SCHOOLS of silversides and mullets race and leap in coastal shallows around the world, providing forage for other fishes, bait for salt-water fishermen, and food for man. North America's six kinds of mullets present a gray, drab appearance compared to the dozen silversides species with gleaming body stripe. Torpedo-shaped mullets (family Mugilidae) and silversides (Atherinidae) share such features as divided dorsal fins, pelvics placed rearward on the abdomen, small, weakly toothed mouths, vestigial or missing lateral line, and tasty flesh copiously endowed with oil.

SILVERSIDES
Family Atherinidae

Making up in numbers what they lack in size, silversides dart about both coasts and the Gulf of Mexico in cloudlike schools, flashing the silvery lateral band that gives them their name. Scooped up for food, they offer so delicate a flavor that Spanish-speaking gourmets call them *pescados del rey,* "fish of the king."

Studies of Atlantic silversides *(Menidia menidia)* at New York's American Museum of Natural History indicate that fry start life shy and antisocial. Quarter-inch hatchlings flee from each other. Half-inchers may associate for a few seconds but avoid meeting head on. At three-quarters of an inch, 10 fry may group in a ragged formation. From then on they school steadily and with increasing discipline. Typical schoolers are the three-inch reef silversides *(Allanetta harringtonensis)* of warm Atlantic waters. Famed silversides are California's grunion *(Leuresthes tenuis)* which ride waves ashore to spawn.

Characteristics: usually a silvery streak along sides. *Range:* all temperate and tropical seas, normally inshore. *Length:* 2 inches to 2 feet.

REEF SILVERSIDES

STRIPED MULLET
Mugil cephalus

Energetic jumpers, striped mullets leap to escape nets and predators, and seemingly for the fun of it. The habit gives them the common name "jumper." They spawn in late fall and winter; juveniles, stubby and silvery, stay close inshore. Found worldwide in warm seas and often up fresh-water streams, they are one of the most widely distributed fishes. In Florida they are called "black mullet"; they rank as the Sunshine State's leading food fish.

Banqueting Romans, marveled Izaak Walton, "had music to usher in their Sturgeons, Lampreys, and Mullets, which they would purchase at rates rather to be wondered at than believed." Less prized in the United States but widely eaten, mullets are so oil-rich they can be fried in their own fat.

Striped mullets are bottom grubbers, dipping up mouthfuls of ooze and filtering out small plants and animals. Food enters an unusually long digestive tract: In a 13-inch fish the intestine may measure seven feet.

Characteristics: large scales; two dorsal fins; silvery belly, back gray to green; small, nearly toothless mouth. *Range:* all warm-temperate and tropical seas. *Weight:* to about 14 pounds. *Length:* to 30 inches.

SHEEPSHEAD
Archosargus probatocephalus

Sheeplike nose and teeth name this dignified, delicious porgy, one of the species of perchlike fishes. Once a favorite fish in eastern markets, overfishing has reduced it to a rarity north of the Virginia Capes and slashed the Gulf catch.

Bottom-feeding sheepshead browse on barnacles, shrimp, crabs, and shellfish, crowding about food but never schooling. In spring they spawn in sandy shallows. Quick to hatch, the buoyant eggs become wriggling fry in 40 hours. Young sheepshead only three-fourths of an inch long possess the high, distinguished brow of their parents. Nonmigratory members of the family Sparidae, sheepshead move in and out with tides and often ascend to fresh water.

Anglers who like to test their mettle against a shy and wary antagonist go after sheepshead around jetties, wharves, and wrecks. The fish exasperatingly steal bait of crab or shrimp. Hooked, they bore toward bottom, wrap line around pilings, cut leaders with sharp teeth, and lunge desperately when brought to boat.

Characteristics: 7 dark vertical bands; deep body; dorsal spines alternately stout and slender. *Range:* Bay of Fundy increasing in numbers southward to Mexico. *Weight:* average 5 pounds, to 30. *Length:* maximum 2½ feet.

STRIPED MULLET (top) and SHEEPSHEAD

Perches and Their Relatives

O F THE WORLD's 32,000 kinds of fishes, an estimated one-fourth are perches or perch-like. They range from the world's smallest fish, the quarter-inch Philippine goby *(Pandaka pygmaea),* to mammoth marlins and tunas that push the scales toward a ton. They include live-bearing surfperches and blennies, tumor-ridden spadefish, scrappy tautogs, elusive tilefish, garish garibaldies, filmy angelfishes, irritable opaleyes, and commercial bonanzas such as scup, sheepshead, and butterfish.

One unvarying characteristic ties the perch potpourri together: In each species spiny rays stiffen the front of the dorsal fin. Other traits apply to most: pointed teeth; scales usually saw-edged, or ctenoid; pelvic fins set forward; air bladder present but in adults unconnected to the throat.

TILEFISH

PAINTINGS BY HASHIME MURAYAMA

TILEFISH
Lopholatilus chamaeleonticeps

Fishermen trawling for cod off Nantucket in 1889 stared at the large, blue fish in their net, then threw the unfamiliar creatures back. More and more came up. The men ate some, found them delicious, and began salting them down. Back in port, excited scientists identified the catch as a new species, labeled it tilefish, and envisioned a vast new fishery.

But before fishermen could exploit the discovery, incoming vessels brought disastrous news: Immense rafts of dead tilefish were floating offshore. One schooner "ploughed for no less than 150 miles through waters dotted as far as the eye could reach with dying fish"—an estimated billion and a half. The species vanished. Analysts blamed gales that had blown icy Arctic water down into the tilefish's domain on the edge of the warm Gulf Stream.

For a decade tilefish were feared extinct. Then eight were taken, next year 53, soon 342. Finally re-established, they created a fishery that in 1916 marketed some 11½ million pounds. But popularity declined, and today they have little commercial significance.

Tilefish live from 270 to more than 1,000 feet deep on outer reaches of the continental shelf. Bottom feeders, they eat squids, shrimp, mollusks, and crabs. The summer spawners lay floating eggs.

Characteristics: unique fleshy tab before soft dorsal fin; two rows of teeth in both jaws. *Range:* Nova Scotia to Gulf of Mexico. *Weight:* maximum 50 pounds. *Length:* average 1½ feet.

203

STRIPED SEAPERCH
Embiotoca lateralis

Seldom a foot long, striped seaperch bear up to 44 live young, each fry at least an inch and a half long. The colorful inhabitants of western shores live beside spiny blue rockfish *(Sebastes mystinus),* often called priest-fish. Striped, or blue, seaperch feed on crustaceans, worms, and herring eggs. Fishermen find them fair fighters but dull food.

Characteristics: horizontal stripes; high rays in soft part of dorsal fin. *Range:* Alaska to Baja California. *Length:* average 8 inches.

GARIBALDI
Hypsypops rubicunda

Living alone or in small groups, garibaldies show little love for one another, but inquisitively follow under-water swimmers. The gaudy westerners and other damselfishes (family Pomacentridae) lay eggs in rocky clefts and guard them fiercely, even nipping humans.

Garibaldi fry are green, spotted with blue. Shrimplike prawns *(Pandalus platyceros),* found north to Alaska, are born males, change to females when 1½ years old.

Characteristics: bright golden. *Range:* southern California to tropics. *Length:* average 8 inches.

204

GARIBALDI and PANDALID PRAWN

SERGEANT MAJOR
Abudefduf saxatilis

Sergeant major fry swarm gaily about reefs and docks; nesting adults grow pugnacious and solitary. The omnivorous midgets trail divers curiously. Threatened, they bluff and bluster, then flee in a flash.

Characteristics: dark stripes on yellow sides. *Range:* both sides of tropical and temperate Atlantic; Indo-Pacific. *Length:* to 6 inches.

205

TAUTOG
Tautoga onitis

The toothy mouth and throat of the tautog can quickly grind the hardest shellfish to paste. Divers find them reclining on rocks or retreating reluctantly only a few feet ahead. Tautogs support a small commercial fishery and provide exciting sport for anglers, who call them blackfish or oysterfish. They often swim with the similar cunner *(Tautogolabrus adspersus);* both belong to the wrasse family.

Characteristics: chin whitish, sides blotchy olive. *Range:* Maine to Carolinas. *Weight:* rod and reel record 21³/₈ pounds. *Length:* to 3 feet.

BLACK PERCH
Embiotoca jacksoni

Anything but black, black perch usually wear brown bars tinged with blue or green; occasional specimens appear in smoky blue or sport orange lips. Probably most abundant of the surfperches, they are also the most primitive and may be the founders of their western family Embiotocidae. Netters catch small numbers; surf sportsmen hook multitudes in bays and around pilings. Nicknames include bay perch and porgy.

Characteristics: variable coloring; enlarged scales between pectoral and pelvic fins. *Range:* northern to Baja California. *Length:* to 14 inches.

PAINTINGS BY HASHIME MURAYAMA

STOPLIGHT PARROTFISH (male, above; female, lower left)

PARROTFISHES
Family Scaridae

Colorful algae-eating "cattle of the sea" graze over reefs with parrotlike beak, crunching rock-hard coral with a noise audible to divers. After feeding they may tilt up their heads to let wrasses clean their mouths. At night some of them sleep tucked in a mucous nightgown (page 45).

Male and female stoplight, or green, parrotfish *(Sparisoma viride)* wear dissimilar colors that once caused them to be listed as different species. The stoplight's pasty flesh serves as food in Puerto Rico. Male blue parrotfish *(Scarus coeruleus),* three-footers that stray to Chesapeake Bay, grow a comical humped snout.

Characteristics: powerful fused jaw teeth and pharyngeals; brilliant coloring. *Range:* worldwide in tropical waters, north to Maryland and southern California; Hawaii. *Weight and Length in American waters:* to 25 pounds, 1 to 3 feet.

BLUE PARROTFISH

ATLANTIC SPADEFISH
Chaetodipterus faber

Spadefish school gracefully among reefs and pilings, ravenously downing crustaceans, occasionally emitting sounds as they eat. Bony tumors on ribs and spines plague them, but their fine white flesh markets well in the West Indies and Bermuda.

Characteristics: dark stripes that dim with age; high anal and second dorsal fins. *Range:* Cape Cod to Rio de Janeiro. *Weight:* to 20 pounds. *Length:* to 3 feet, average 1.

BUTTERFLYFISHES
Family Chaetodontidae

Vivid in color and majestic of movement, butterflyfishes beautify tropical reefs around the world. The clan includes the angelfishes, who carry a brace of daggers—a sharp spine on each cheek. Five angelfish species frequent Atlantic shores: blue *(Holacanthus isabelita)*, rock beauty *(H. tricolor)*, gray *(Pomacanthus arcuatus)*, French *(P. paru)*, and queen *(H. ciliaris)*.

Characteristics: compressed body, bristlelike teeth. *Range:* all warm seas. *Length:* to 2 feet.

ATLANTIC SPADEFISH (left) and LOOKDOWN

PAINTINGS BY WALTER A. WEBER, NATIONAL GEOGRAPHIC STAFF (OPPOSITE, TOP) AND HASHIME MURAYAMA

Marine Oddities

PUFFERS
Family Tetraodontidae

An angler disgustedly pulling in a puffer finds rewards despite the lack of sport: Before his eyes the fish frantically gulps air or water until it balloons into a near-perfect sphere. Thrown back, it floats like a beach ball, noisily belching as it struggles to deflate.

The East Coast's abundant northern puffer (*Sphaeroides maculatus*) yields in Florida waters to a close cousin, *S. nephelus*. Teeth of both fuse into a formidable, snapping beak, and the liver can be poisonous. Certain Asian puffers become permeated with an incredibly virulent poison—150,000 times more toxic than that used by South American Indians on their arrowheads.

Characteristics: black spots on sides; ability to inflate with air or water. *Range:* all warm and temperate seas. *Length:* seldom to 12 inches.

TRUNKFISHES
Family Ostraciidae

Boxes made of bony, fused scales encase trunkfishes like turtles, exposing only eyes, lips, tail, and shaving-brush fins. Armored at the expense of mobility, the rigid freaks poke along by sculling with dorsal and anal fins and steering with the tail. In emergencies the tail paddles, too, producing a brief burst of speed. When chased they periodically glance back at their pursuer—a rare trait among fishes.

North America's five trunkfish species change colors frequently, survive up to two hours out of water, eat plants and small invertebrates. Edible, they are sometimes baked in their shells.

Hornlike spines name the cowfish (*Acanthostracian quadricornis*), an eight-inch trunkfish found north to Massachusetts. The 10-inch smooth trunkfish, or cuckold (*A. triqueter*), likes sandy patches between reefs. It strays to New England. Hatchlings of the common trunkfish (*A. trigonus*) often drift helplessly in the Gulf Stream from Florida spawning beds.

Characteristics: body-covering shell. *Range:* all warm seas. *Length:* to 16 inches.

LOOKDOWN
Selene vomer

Stern, high-browed lookdowns patrol with haughty air. Beautifully iridescent if viewed from the side, their wafer bodies, seen head on, virtually vanish.

Members of the jack and pompano family, lookdowns have delicious white flesh but lack numbers for commercial importance. They strike on light tackle with jolting force, showing a preference for deeply sunk bait. Schools frequent sandy shores of both coasts, seeking small fishes and invertebrates. In autumn legions of young appear off New York, riding the Gulf Stream.

Similar Atlantic moonfish (*Vomer setapinnis*) lack the lookdown's streamer fins.

Characteristics: compressed body; long face; filamentous dorsal and anal fins. *Range:* Cape Cod to Brazil, but chiefly tropical; both sides of the Atlantic. *Weight:* average ½ pound, maximum 2. *Length:* average 8 inches, to 1 foot.

SMOOTH TRUNKFISH (top), COWFISH, COMMON TRUNKFISH (lower pair)

HOWARD F. HORTON (TOP), RALSTON PRINCE (LOWER LEFT), AND WALTER A. STARCK II

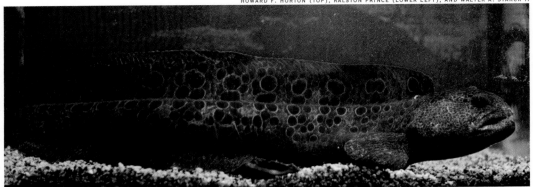

WOLF-EEL

JAWFISHES
Family Opistognathidae

Reluctant to wander from its self-dug burrow, the spotfin jawfish *(Opistognathus macrognathus)* peers out suspiciously or hovers erect over the den by fluttering its fins. If another jawfish nears, it darts out, threatening but never quite biting. Then it shoots home tailfirst.

Ten jawfish species dwell in the tropical Atlantic. The yellowhead *(O. aurifrons)* lines its underground chamber with bits of rock and coral. Some jawfishes have jawbones so long that they can scoop up prey larger than their head. At least two species cram their mouths full of eggs for incubation.

Characteristics: bulldog head; large mouth; long dorsal and anal fins. *Range:* world-wide. *Length:* to 1 foot.

WOLF-EEL
Anarrhichthys ocellatus

Ferocious in look and nature, wolf-eels own a mouthful of sharp fangs and crushing molars that shatter shellfish. The grim, defiant predators star as exhibits in West Coast aquariums. One stubbornly refused food for nine months.

Three Atlantic and two Pacific wolffish species (family Anarhichadidae) inhabit northern waters, solitarily preying on bottom dwellers. The Atlantic wolffish *(Anarhichas lupus)* has attacked waders. Wolffishes occasionally take clam neck bait, startling anglers. Eastern markets sell half a million pounds annually.

Characteristics: elongated tapering body with full-length dorsal and anal fins, no pelvics; some 350 vertebrae. *Range:* Alaska to southern California. *Length:* to 8 feet.

YELLOWHEAD JAWFISH (left) and SPOTFIN JAWFISH

OCEAN SUNFISH
Mola mola

Seemingly all head, ocean sunfish or "headfish" have pitifully small brains: That of a 450-pounder weighs only an ounce and a half. Munching largely on jellyfish, ocean sunfish grow to tremendous size. The record, a fish which ran afoul a steamer off Australia and sent it limping, measured 10 feet long, 2½ feet thick, and 13 feet high. It weighed 4,400 pounds.

Headfish bob blissfully about, basking in the sun. The scaleless, elephant-like skin—one and a half inches thick on a four-footer—envelops a useless, scalloped tail fin. Stiff dorsal and anal fins, beating back and forth, push the inflexible body; often the ponderous fish paddles lazily on its side. Parasites feed on it everywhere—skin, gills, muscles, intestines. A thick slime covers the sluggard.

Should harpooners approach, the ocean sunfish grinds pharyngeal teeth in disapproval, then sways heavily along the surface or bores determinedly for bottom. At one spawning headfish lay an incredible number of eggs—an estimated 300 million. Fry bristle with spines.

Characteristics: gray disklike body; high dorsal and anal fins. *Range:* tropical and temperate seas. *Weight:* average 175-500 pounds, to 4,400. *Length:* to 10 feet.

OCEAN SUNFISH (above) and OPAH

OPAH
Lampris regius

Gaudy, roly-poly opahs, or moonfish, wander solitarily about the seas, pectoral fins beating like wings. When occasionally caught off U. S. coasts, the unusual fish invariably draw crowds and local reporters.

Opahs clamp a toothless mouth on squids, crustaceans, and seaweeds, fattening flesh that is red, oily, and delicious. Long-line fishermen off Madeira catch a few; fishery biologists hope to discover a depth at which the potentially valuable food fish abound. The open North Atlantic yielded the specimen at right.

Characteristics: deep thin body; blue back, rosy belly, scarlet fins, silver spots. *Range:* all temperate seas. *Weight:* to 600 pounds. *Length:* average 2½ feet, to 6.

INSHORE LIZARDFISH (above) and RATFISH

RATFISH
Hydrolagus colliei

Like their distant relatives the sharks, ratfish have cartilaginous skeletons and fertilize internally. And like modern bony fishes, the in-between creatures wear gill covers.

Named for their rodentlike tail, ratfish exhibit mucous ducts on the head. A spine forward of the dorsal fin inflicts a mild sting, and an appendage sprouts from the head of many males. Its purpose is unknown. The liver contains oil valued as a lubricant for precision instruments. Ratfish usually live deep.

Characteristics: short nose; pointed tail; silver sides tinted gold, green, and blue; sawtoothed dorsal spine which is mildly toxic. *Range:* Alaska to Baja California. *Length:* to 3 feet.

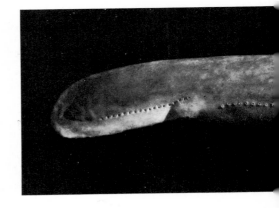

216

INSHORE LIZARDFISH
Synodus foetens

Propped on its pelvic fins and masterfully camouflaged, the lizardfish waits motionless in ambush for crustaceans and small fishes. Let prey wander in range and the lizardfish shoots up faster than the eye can follow. It seizes the victim with viciously toothed tongue and jaws and bolts it in a single gulp.

Inshore lizardfish seldom swim leisurely; they either crawl on their pelvic fins or spring catlike with tail thrashing. Confirmed predators, in aquariums they will starve themselves unless offered live food.

Nine kinds of lizardfishes (family Synodontidae) station themselves along North America's shores. The carrot-shaped fish are largely tropical except the inshore and California species (*S. lucioceps*). An alert lizardlike head supplies the reptilian name. The young of some are slender white larvae which, until they reach two inches, bear no resemblance to their parents.

Characteristics: mottled tapering body; adipose fin, large pectorals. *Range:* Cape Cod to Brazil. *Length:* average 8 inches, to 12.

ATLANTIC HAGFISH
Myxine glutinosa

Atlantic "hags," the sea's most primitive living fish, are notable for what they lack: eyes, bones, scales, hinged jaws, paired limbs. Fond of dead or disabled food, they writhe from mud burrows to follow the scent with their single sensitive nostril, then tear into the fish's vitals with dual rows of sharp teeth. Fishermen catching haddock and hake find the scavengers a destructive nuisance.

A hagfish often has reproductive organs of both sexes, with only one set functioning. Females lay up to 30 eggs, each in a horny case an inch long. Males eat the eggs, curbing the hagfish population. Handled roughly, hags or "slime eels" secrete thick films of mucus through pores along their length. Scientists find the hag's heart ideal for dissection and study because of its independence from the body's nervous system.

Characteristics: finlike fold around body; eyeless, scaleless; 8 barbels. *Range:* arctic waters to North Carolina. *Length:* to 31 inches.

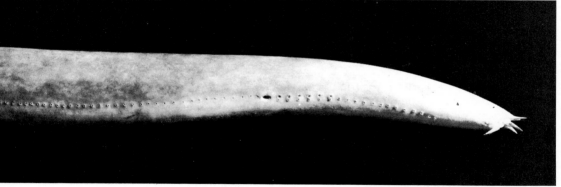

ATLANTIC HAGFISH (close-up of head above)

NORTHERN STARGAZER
Astroscopus guttatus

Jolting electric charges, measured up to 50 volts, shoot from the oversize head of the stargazer. Modified optic nerves generate the electricity. The five stargazer species (family Uranoscopidae) and the electric rays are North America's only native electrogenic fishes.

Stargazers lurk buried in sand, exposing only upturned eyes and an open mouth. Inside wriggles a wormlike lure. To obtain sand-free water for respiration, stargazers inhale through a tube connecting the nasal cavities to the gills, making them the only fishes whose nostrils are not dead-end smelling sacs.

Characteristics: electric organs; nostrils connected to throat. *Range:* New York to North Carolina. *Length:* average 8½ inches.

From top: NORTHERN STARGAZER, PLAINFIN MIDSHIPMAN, OYSTER TOADFISH

WILLIAM H. AMOS (TOP), JOHN TASHJIAN (CENTER), AND EMORY KRISTOF, NATIONAL GEOGRAPHIC STAFF

PLAINFIN MIDSHIPMAN
Porichthys notatus

Photophores along a midshipman's sides, gleaming like Navy midshipmen's buttons, can provide light for reading a newspaper 10 inches away. A tiny lens covers each luminous organ.

Spring-spawning midshipmen attach large amber eggs to rocks or shells by means of adhesive disks. Nest-guarding males, called "singing fish," hum alarm by vibrating air bladders.

Characteristics: 600 or more photophores; scaleless body. *Range:* Alaska to Mexico. *Length:* to 15 inches.

OYSTER TOADFISH
Opsanus tau

The dragon mouth of the oyster toadfish engulfs every lure that passes—to the disgust of anglers. Approached by swimmers, the fearless fish croak annoyance, even snap at fingers.

Oyster toadfish live and nest in tin cans and old shoes. North America's three toadfish species and three midshipmen form the family Batrachoididae.

Characteristics: huge head and mouth, fleshy tabs on lower lip; no scales; billowing dorsal and anal fins. *Range:* Maine to Florida. *Length:* average 10 inches.

ERNEST L. LIBBY (TOP) AND ROBERT C. HERMES

TRUMPETFISH (top) and GULF PIPEFISH

TRUMPETFISH
Aulostomus maculatus

Large eyes staring, trumpetfish pass through the water like drifting sticks, showing no means of propulsion. Close inspection reveals fluttering, nearly transparent dorsal and anal fins. Only when forced to make haste do trumpetfish swish their tails like other fishes. Their chief defense is concealment, ducking behind coral outcrops or freezing head-down amid matching branches of gorgonian.

Solitary but numerous, trumpetfish eat fishes, crustaceans, worms. They are the sole North American members of the family Aulostomidae.

Characteristics: elongated brown body occasionally yellow-tinged; small mouth at tip of tubed snout. *Range:* Atlantic coral reefs. *Length:* average 1½ to 2 feet, maximum 3.

GULF PIPEFISH
Syngnathus scovelli

Male pipefish, like seahorses, give birth to young they have incubated in a kangaroolike pouch. Elaborate courtship launches the male's maternal career. He and his mate pass and touch several times. They intertwine, and she spawns in his stomach pouch. Twisting, he jounces the eggs down to make room for more; then the ritual repeats until he carries up to 200 eggs.

Swimming feebly by vibrating dorsal and pectoral fins, pipefish suck up plankton. Alert collectors seize the sluggish aquarium pets by hand. Imitating the weeds they live among, pipefish evade tuna and other predators.

Characteristics: pipelike, bony-plated body; tubed snout. *Range:* eastern Florida through the Gulf, enters fresh water. *Length:* to 18 inches.

LAKE AND STREAM DWELLERS

*For boy with hook, fish fancier with aquarium pet, or
naturalist with microscope, fascination abounds in
fresh-water fishes—their struggles, their strange
courtships, their amazing migrations.*

CHAPTER THIRTEEN

By LEONARD P. SCHULTZ, Ph.D.

Former Curator, Division of Fishes,
Smithsonian Institution, Washington, D. C.

White-water Highways of the West

Salmon perform Herculean feats,

sturgeon set heavyweight records,

and even minnows grow bigger

in Pacific watershed streams

SOCKEYE SALMON, *their drab ocean*

W EST COAST STREAMS were as full of promise as they were of fishes in 1928 when I came as a young professor to teach at the University of Washington College of Fisheries. Almost any weekend would find me by a brook or lake near Seattle, armed with a dip net for catching specimens, a jar of formalin for preserving them—and a fly rod just in case.

Everything is supposed to be bigger out West, and fishes in those streams ran true to form. The largest fresh-water fish on the continent, white sturgeon, reach their

greatest size in the Columbia and Fraser Rivers. At the Smithsonian Institution in Washington, D. C., we have a cast of a 12-footer taken from the Fraser. The Columbia yielded a specimen six inches longer that weighed 1,285 pounds. Wanton netting of these giants early in the century decimated the population. Their eggs might have provided an important source of caviar.

To me, Pacific coast rivers rank among the world's most spectacular. The 2,000-mile Yukon rushes northwest across Alaskan wilderness to the Bering Sea. The Fra-

222

PAINTING BY WALTER A. WEBER, NATIONAL GEOGRAPHIC STAFF

colors changed to garish spawning hues, boil below Brooks Falls in Alaska's Katmai National Park.

ser in British Columbia coils like a snake out of the Rockies, cleaves the Coast Mountains, and empties into the ocean north of Washington. The powerful Columbia plunges down a staircase of dams in Washington and along the Oregon border.

Smaller rivers full of fish—the Umpqua, Coquille, Rogue, and a network of others —dent Oregon's sparkling coast. The beautiful Klamath, famous for salmon and trout, meanders out of Oregon to water northern California. Dominating the Golden State are the Sacramento and San Joaquin.

Standing on the banks of the Snake River, a tributary of the Columbia, I have watched hypnotized as salmon fought their way upstream to spawn. Some travel nearly 2,000 miles, refusing all food throughout their months-long journey.

It is almost impossible not to cheer them on as the fish battle heroically up rapids that seem impassable. They can leap vertically four times their length or more. Not all make it. Some, paralyzed by exhaustion, drift helplessly downstream to fall prey to birds, bears, or other predators.

223

SLAPPING TAIL *kicks up a cloud of sand as a sockeye digs an egg pit in her nest, or redd. She may work on her saucer-shaped redd for days, rarely helped by her mate. Male and female release eggs and milt simultaneously over the pit, then repeat the ritual upstream. Gravel from the newly dug pit washes down to cover the first. A female may spawn five times or more and lay 3,000 eggs before —tail frayed and life's mission completed—she dies.*

RIVALS FIGHT: *A sockeye on her redd nips at a female intruder. Salmon sometimes take more than one mate. Both sexes shun food during spawning; stomachs shrivel, males' jaws hook grotesquely.*

Not even the dauntless salmon could surmount an obstacle that man placed in the Fraser River in 1913. Engineers of the Canadian Pacific Railroad, preparing a rail bed along the bank, blasted the sheer walls of Hells Gate. When the dust cleared, a gigantic rockslide dammed the river.

Backed-up water spilled over the barrier, catapulting down with rocketlike force. One of the world's leading salmon highways became a river of death as hordes of fish hurled themselves futilely at the torrent.

It took years to restore the runs. The International Pacific Salmon Fisheries Commission built concrete fishways, restocked barren areas, and the catch has climbed.

The migration of salmon is one of the truly great marvels of the zoological world: The fish wander three or four years in the trackless ocean and then return to spawn in the exact stream of their birth.

This homing instinct was considered more legend than fact until ichthyologists noted that salmon from particular streams bore

MOMENT OF SPAWNING. *Sperm-laden milt floods an egg pit in this remarkable view from beneath a pair of spawning salmon. Eggs emerge from the female's red vent. Heads of both fish lie outside the photograph at right. Older, unfertilized eggs drift at left. Geographic photographer Robert F. Sisson worked with biologists at Lovers Cove Creek, Alaska, to devise this camera-windowed spawning tank (right).*

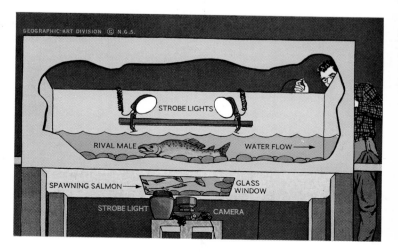

GEOGRAPHIC ART DIVISION © N.G.S.

STROBE LIGHTS

RIVAL MALE   WATER FLOW →

SPAWNING SALMON →   GLASS WINDOW

STROBE LIGHT   CAMERA

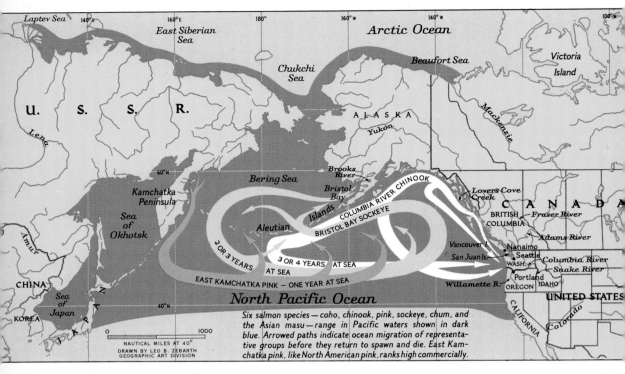

Six salmon species — coho, chinook, pink, sockeye, chum, and the Asian masu — range in Pacific waters shown in dark blue. Arrowed paths indicate ocean migration of representative groups before they return to spawn and die. East Kamchatka pink, like North American pink, ranks high commercially.

MYSTERY OF SALMON MIGRATION *puzzled man for centuries—until he learned the fish "smell" their way to the very stream where they were born. Dissolved organic material may produce the remembered scent. To illustrate this ability, Alaska fisheries men carried salmon back downstream from spawning grounds, then released them, tagged with balloons (below). Returning, fish chose the correct fork—yellow left, red right. Others with nostrils plugged often took the wrong turn. Now scientists study how salmon navigate at sea (opposite).*

TRACKING SOCKEYES *at sea, scientists utilize electronic gear and a minnow-size ultrasonic transmitter slipped into a salmon's stomach. Replaced in the water off Washington's San Juan Islands, the fish resumed its travels toward Canada's Fraser River. Hydrophone and receiver in the boat picked up the homeward-bound sockeye's telltale signal. In their study, the biologists found that fish chose a direct route instead of following shoreline indentations that could serve as a road map. Scientists theorize salmon may set their courses in the trackless ocean by taking bearings from the sun —tank experiments indicate that bluegills and other fishes have this ability. Electromagnetic clues in the sea may also be a navigation guide. Ocean currents generate small but measurable electrical voltages as salt water moves through earth's magnetic field. Certain eels can detect such weak signals, and salmon may be able to do the same.*

ROBERT F. SISSON, NATIONAL GEOGRAPHIC STAFF   227

certain racial characteristics; their scales, for example, carried markings unlike those of fish in the next stream. This could only occur if a clan of salmon reproduced time after time in the same place with few newcomers to dilute the trait.

To solve the mystery, scientists made distinctive fin markings on millions of fingerling salmon before they left their native streams. Then researchers went to sea, netted the same fish hundreds of miles from their home waters, and tagged them.

Months later, many of the fish bearing original markings and ocean tags returned to their childhood streams. Now few doubt the salmon's homing instinct.

How do they do it? Ichthyologists Warren J. Wisby and Arthur D. Hasler threw light on the mystery in 1954 while studying coho salmon in two branches of Washington's Issaquah Creek. They captured some migrating fish, marked them according to the branch in which they were found, plugged the nasal sacs of half, and released the whole batch below the fork of the stream. When the salmon ascended again, those without nasal plugs chose the same branch they had taken before. But ones with plugs became confused. Thus salmon, on part of their migration at least, follow their noses.

To detect, at a river's mouth, faint traces of a scent imprinted in headwaters years earlier requires a fantastic ability. The salmon has such a sense. It can perceive dilutions of one part in a billion. If a quart of water in which a bear's paw has been dipped

SWOOPING PLANE *bombs Bench Lake in Washington with a cottony cloud of fingerling trout. A placid surface mirrors 14,410-foot Mount Rainier, glacier-sheathed king of the Cascade Range. Five-gallon plastic bag above holds 3,500 young cutthroats raised by the U.S. Fish and Wildlife Service. The fry receive a squirt of oxygen to aid their breathing and ice to tranquilize them for the harmless 100-foot fall.*

for a minute is poured into a stream, it can cause salmon to stop climbing a fish ladder a hundred yards away.

For the ocean's vastness, other guides must come into play. Scientists theorize the salmon may take bearings from the sun, or chart a course by noting weak electrical voltages generated by ocean currents.

Nesting habits of salmon, like their migrations, call for incredible stamina. Years ago I had a chance to watch landlocked sockeyes nest in Swamp Creek near Seattle. The female located an appealing spot in a shallow riffle. Then she turned on her side and lashed her tail against the bottom. Sand and stones boiled up, to wash downstream with the current. Again and again she used her bruised body as a bulldozer.

Meanwhile her mate, brilliant red and jaws transformed into fearsome hook, defended the nest site. Occasionally he sank his teeth into a male intruder. Between tussles he courted, nuzzling with his snout.

Finally the nest was finished, a gravelly saucer some two feet wide and three inches deep. Within the nest the female dug a small egg pit. Over it she and the male settled side by side, quivered in a spawning ritual, and released eggs and milt simultaneously.

Then she moved upstream a bit and began scooping a second egg pit so she could spawn again. Loosened stones swept over the first pit, covering the eggs. Again and again the cycle was repeated until the fish, exhausted, drifted downstream to die—the fate of all Pacific salmon after spawning.

229

During spawning runs salmon shun food, living on stored fat. In the rivers their flesh grows coarse and tasteless, thus commercial fisheries operate in estuaries and offshore. Each year roughly a billion pounds of salmon are taken. Japan lands the most, followed by the United States, the U.S.S.R., and Canada. The biggest catch is of pinks, then chums, sockeyes, cohos, chinooks, and Asia's masu.

Runs are smaller now than in the past. But rules limiting catches, concern about dams and stream pollution, and such promising developments as artificial spawning channels could send numbers soaring.

Salmon share Pacific coast streams with a variety of trout, four species of which are native only to the West. Beautiful golden trout delight fishermen high in the Sierra Nevadas. Cutthroats and Dolly Vardens range from mountain streams to the open Pacific. The hardy rainbow has been transplanted to nearly every state in the Nation and to every continent.

Rainbow trout exhibit such a range of color and size that ichthyologists originally classified the variations as different species. Those that migrate like salmon into salt water acquire a steel blue color which earns

SCRAPPIEST OF TROUTS, *steelheads delight a boy and his dad on Oregon's Rogue River. Steelheads are rainbow trout that migrate to sea like salmon; they may top 10 pounds.*

them the name steelhead. Some rainbows grow so huge they have been distinguished as a species called Kamloops or Kootenay trout, after Canadian lakes of those names.

Idaho's rugged Pend Oreille Lake, which drains toward the Columbia, yields rainbows that dwarf even Canadian specimens. Thirty-pounders are common. What causes such giants? They probably gorge on landlocked salmon, a favorite food of trout.

Fauna of the Pacific drainage systems have much in common, yet each great watershed harbors species not found elsewhere. Of 46 fishes native to the Columbia, only 15 dwell in the Sacramento and San Joaquin Rivers. This system in turn has 25 species unknown in the Columbia, among them the Sacramento perch, sole bass relative native to the West Coast.

Even small areas claim distinct fish fauna. The Lake Lahontan region of Nevada, a vast inland sea eons ago, contains the unique Gila sucker and the Lahontan redsides, a minnow. The Washington mudminnow, which I discovered to be a separate species, lives exclusively in the Pacific-bound Chehalis River. This lone western member of the mudminnow family faces extinction if farming continues to encroach on its swampy spawning grounds.

The West, like the rest of North America, did not know the prolific carp until man introduced it as a potential food. It has become less a food than a menace. Running its vacuum-cleaner mouth over lake and stream beds, the predator voraciously sucks in eggs and fry of food and game fishes. In the Colorado, carp took over so thoroughly that conservationists poisoned hundreds of miles of waters in an attempt to eradicate the pest and build a new fish population.

The mighty Colorado is the home of a fish that has always struck me as being pure western. Called the squawfish, it is one of the minnows, those midgets of the fish world whose very name means "the least." But the squawfish, like the towering Rockies and massive white sturgeon, is a true touch of the West. For, regardless of its diminutive relatives, it insists on growing until it reaches an unminnowlike length of three feet!

RAY ATKESON (ABOVE) AND PAUL A. ZAHL, NATIONAL GEOGRAPHIC STAFF

PORTLAND GOES FISHING *in February and March when eulachon* (Thaleichthys pacificus) *swarm from the ocean to spawn in nearby Sandy River. Fishermen wielding nets, buckets, and even window screens and bird cages scoop up the legal 25 pounds a day. About every third year the tasty fish mysteriously fail to appear. The 12-inch-long eulachon is one of the larger members of the smelt family. Its oily flesh once prompted Pacific coast Indians to dry the fish and burn it as a candle.*

SILVERY HANDFUL *of surf smelt* (Hypomesus pretiosus) *makes a tasty, firm-fleshed dish— broiled, fried or baked. Fishermen scoop up net loads as the smelt ride foaming wave crests to spawn on the sand of Pacific beaches.*

FINNED PEDESTRIAN *ventures from a roadside ditch to jaywalk near Boca Raton. The Asian species invaded southern Florida in the mid-1960's when specimens imported by a tropical fish dealer literally walked out of captivity. Their progeny now crowd native fishes from many Florida waterways. Amazing* Clarias batrachus *"walks" by sculling with its tail as it elbows along on spiny pectorals (above). A lunglike organ enables the normally nocturnal wanderer to breathe.*

CHAPTER FOURTEEN

By CLARENCE P. IDYLL, Ph. D.

Chairman, Division of Fishery Sciences,
Institute of Marine Sciences, University of Miami

Florida Meets a Walking Catfish

FLORIDA'S PLEASANT CLIMATE attracts a few eccentrics, as well as hordes of ordinary mortals. One of the recent oddball newcomers is a fish that is charged with some most unfishlike behavior: It breathes air, it strolls on land, it fights dogs. The first two of these allegations—though not the third—are true, and a more serious one can be leveled: The "walking catfish" poses a real threat to the fresh-water ecology of Florida—and perhaps of neighboring states as well.

On May 25, 1968, a night watchman at a construction site near Boca Raton, investigating the barking of his dog, was startled to encounter a strange-looking fish traveling across bare ground. The story ballooned into a widely printed tale of an excited housewife who reported, "My dog is fighting with a big catfish in the backyard." But since then a great deal more attention has been given to the walking catfish in terms of its rapid spread through the state and the threat it poses to local species.

The walking catfish, *Clarias batrachus*, first arrived in Florida when tropical fish dealers imported young specimens for sale. Some apparently escaped in the mid-1960's; now they are thriving in an increasingly wide area of southeastern Florida.

I get the same questions from nearly everyone to whom I show a walking catfish: "Are they only that big?" and "Where are their legs?"

ESCAPEE FROM A DEATH TRAP, *a catfish climbs out of a poisoned pond (right); a fellow fugitive heads cross-country for purer water (above). After a three-month campaign of poisoning waterways with rotenone (lower right), Florida biologists had to admit, "Clarias is here to stay." The mobile fish demonstrates a keen avoidance of contaminated water.*

Their fabled ability to tramp over the countryside and fight dogs has apparently created the image of an enormous, menacing creature. In truth, *Clarias batrachus* grows to only about 22 inches in eastern India and Southeast Asia, whence it comes. The largest on record in Florida was 18 inches long.

Most of the walking catfish originally imported were albinos—pale pink with darker pink head. They have long, somewhat eel-like bodies and large flattened heads bearing eight long barbels. These are important sense organs; the fish reacts instantly when the barbels are touched.

Many of the individuals found in the wild in Florida are still albinos, but a substantial number of offspring have reverted to the normal colors, from pale slate-gray to mottled browns and blacks.

At first I was doubtful that the fish actually walked, in the sense of using limbs to propel themselves. But after virtually nose-to-nose observation, I am convinced they do. While much of their forward progress is made with a snakelike slither and vigorous thrashing of the tail, the walking is aided by use of stout spines in the pectoral fins.

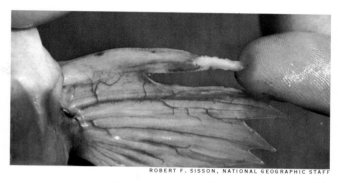

NATURAL PEG LEG, *a stiff spine on each pectoral fin, digs into the ground to help balance and propel the fish on land. If the spine scratches human skin, a mucous secretion enters the wound and may trigger a painful reaction.*

DOUBLE-DUTY APPARATUS *equips* Clarias *for its amphibious life. Elaborate organs behind the gills function much like lungs and enable the fish to breathe air for hours. Land jaunts may carry it a quarter mile or more. Even in water the catfish often surfaces to gulp air. Averaging about 10 inches, the fish have been seen marching "by the hundreds" across roads.*

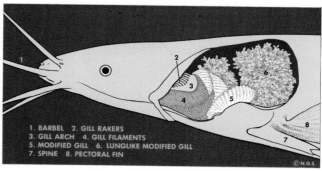

1. BARBEL   2. GILL RAKERS
3. GILL ARCH   4. GILL FILAMENTS
5. MODIFIED GILL   6. LUNGLIKE MODIFIED GILL
7. SPINE   8. PECTORAL FIN

© N.G.S.

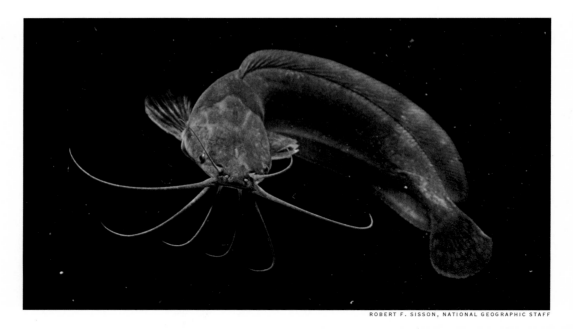

ROBERT F. SISSON, NATIONAL GEOGRAPHIC STAFF

TRUE COLOR SHOWING, *a naturally pigmented catfish wheels around as if to intimidate a challenger. Most* Clarias *specimens imported were albinos, but many descendants —including this one—have reverted to gray, brown, or black. Whiskerlike barbels, fitted with taste buds, brush along the bottom in search of food.* Clarias *devours almost anything edible —including food that native fish and birds need for survival.*

MAULING A BULLHEAD *unlucky enough to share its tank, a 13-inch albino catfish displays its ferocity. Like a cat playing with a mouse, it tormented its victim for four hours before killing it. Most fish give* Clarias *a wide berth; even a voracious piranha retreated to a corner when confined with a catfish. Though edible—the species is popular in parts of Asia—fast-breeding* Clarias *is already displacing more desirable food and game fish in Florida. Its continued spread may threaten the fresh-water ecology of the Southeast.*

To walk on land, the catfish must be able to breathe air. Indeed, even in the water *Clarias* comes to the surface to gulp air at intervals. To allow for this, the rear of each gill has been modified into a sort of lung.

Being a fish, *Clarias* prefers to remain moist. This is probably why it walks mostly at night and during periods of rain.

Sometimes the newcomers move across land in large numbers. At least one such migration was reported in autumn, 1968, when a bartender saw "hundreds" of them north of Fort Lauderdale, slithering across a road at 2 a.m. He caught three of them and reported the incident to biologists of the Florida Game and Fresh Water Fish Commission, who found five or six more on the road the next day, crushed by passing cars.

Two of these biologists, Vernon Ogilvie and Robert Goodrick, have conducted research on *Clarias* for the state; both are deeply concerned about its threat to native aquatic life.

Mr. Ogilvie has drawn the wrath of some dealers and aquarists by declaring the catfish a "disaster," and "extremely frightening" to him as an ecologist.

I talked to him at his laboratory in West Palm Beach. "In some bodies of water close to the original area of infestation," he said, "*Clarias* is now the dominant fish. There is no doubt that it has shouldered out the native fishes."

I got the same story from Dr. Walter R. Courtenay, Jr., ichthyologist at Florida Atlantic University in Boca Raton.

"In almost any place where a concentration of walking catfish is found," he told me, "little else remains except a few small fish called sleepers. The catfish have displaced valuable game fishes like largemouth bass, as well as panfishes such as bluegills and warmouths. In one pond no bigger than my living room, I caught 65 of these new catfish in two hauls of a seine, and it seemed there were hundreds more."

The walking catfish is exhibiting a classic response to introduction into a new environment. Without the biological checks and balances that control animal—and even plant—populations in their native lands,

exotic species often multiply exuberantly, sometimes completely displacing indigenous forms. Moreover, they often bring new diseases and parasites. With *Clarias*, Florida is again the loser, as it was with the water hyacinth, introduced in 1884 and now throttling waterways throughout the state.

Worse, I believe, is yet to come. It appears certain that *Clarias* will spread farther. Its equipment and its behavior virtually guarantee this. The south Florida water area is an enormously intricate complex of shallow lakes and ponds joined by drainage canals and natural channels. Populations of native fishes and other aquatic animals are greatly depleted during drought when many ponds and marshes go completely dry and water levels in the canals are greatly reduced.

But *Clarias* has the advantage of being able to breathe air when waters are low, and even to lie buried in the mud in extreme conditions. Or, better still, it can trek off across country to other ponds or canals, leaving its native competitors to perish, though its primary motivation for walking on land seems to be to seek food.

Clarias apparently reproduces very rapidly. It spawns at least nine months of the year, and is definitely breeding successfully in Florida. It also is viciously aggressive. Even the famous "man-eating" piranha avoids an adult *Clarias* when put in the same tank. Photographer Bob Sisson watched an "unbelievably ferocious" attack by a 13-inch walking catfish on a 7¾-inch yellow bullhead, one of the native catfishes, which it eventually killed.

Both Vernon Ogilvie and Walter Courtenay believe the catfish will spread at least to central Florida. Mr. Ogilvie thinks Georgia, Alabama, and even Tennessee may not be exempt. Colder climate will presumably stop it from moving farther north than that.

But walking catfish are in Florida to stay. In November, 1968, the Game and Fresh Water Fish Commission reluctantly concluded that they were already too widespread and gave up ideas of trying to eradicate them. Besides, as Vernon Ogilvie said sadly, "How do you kill a fish that simply walks away when you poison its pond?"

NO ONE would have expected such popularity from a nondescript pygmy fish an Anglican minister caught a century ago on the Caribbean island of Trinidad. The parson, interested in the natural sciences, sent several specimens to the British Museum, where they were named in his honor. Since then the fish's scientific name has changed, but the world still knows it through its association with the Rev. Robert John Lechmere Guppy.

The parson would not recognize the guppies that swim in home aquariums today. Through generations of selective breeding —the mating of specimens with pronounced color, fin, or other characteristics—guppy fanciers have created some of the world's most outlandishly clad fish. Tail fins stretch nearly as long as their bodies, forming myriad shapes often described in the fish's name: lyre-tail, pin-tail, top-sword, bottom-sword. Gaudy males contrast vividly with females, which tend to be dull, sluggish, and twice the size of their mates.

Interest in guppies has brought together aquarists from around the world. Their glamorous pets compete in international beauty contests fostered by guppy societies in half a dozen European countries, Australia, Canada, and the U.S.A. Magazines such as *Tropical Fish Hobbyist* and *Aquarium,* as well as numerous aquarium society bulletins, keep fish fanciers informed about new varieties and tank techniques.

Fishes show little interest in people— except at feeding time—so why are more than 20 million Americans interested in keeping fishes? One reason is that they offer something for everyone. Children can tell their biology class about the frolicsome courtship and devoted baby-sitting of jewelfish. Mother finds enchantment in the beauty of glowing tetras and of wafer-thin angelfish wearing lacy petticoats. Dad, grumpy after riding the subway home, soothes his jarred psyche by watching the antics of a school of guppies.

There are few reasons for not liking fish. They don't scratch the children, chase cars, or leave hairs on the sofa. They cost little: A quarter buys a respectable goldfish, 75

Aquarium Fishes: Enchanting Entertainers

America's most numerous

pets lure fortune hunters

to far corners of the world

B. ANTHONY STEWART, NATIONAL GEOGRAPHIC STAFF (ABOVE) AND T.F.H. PUBLICATIONS

KISSING GOURAMIS *do just that, and don't care who sees. They kiss other fishes, tank walls, even stones; nobody knows why. Guppies and a zebra danio cruise above them, a swordtail and platy below. Longfinned platies (right) school with their close kin, a scarlet sword, who wears the saberlike caudal fin of a male. Aglow like a coal, a Siamese fighting fish trails long fins reflecting years of selective breeding (opposite).*

cents a pair of guppies, a few dollars a tank and food. And when you go on vacation, you can forget about feeding them for a week or even two. No wonder this mushrooming hobby now ranks in popularity only behind stamp collecting and amateur photography.

Many exotic fishes once obtained by safariing up remote rivers are now raised domestically, with Tampa, Florida, the center of operations. Twenty million aquarium fishes a year—gleaming tetras, gay barbs, gaudy guppies, ghostly mollies, glamorous platies and swordtails—grow and breed in 2,000 sprawling ponds of Gulf Fish Farms, one of the world's largest hatcheries. Indoors swim more varieties, including 100,000 Siamese fighting fish, each kept in solitary confinement in its own glass jar. Everglades Aquatic Nurseries, which introduced the prized Madagascar lace plant, raises more than 100 different exotic aquarium plants.

Not all aquarium species breed in commercial ponds; collectors must still seine rivers to stock pet shops. The major source is South America, home of more species than any other continent.

SAVAGE PIRANHA, *armed with razor teeth and oversize jaws, infest South American waters alongside tetras, discus, and other aquarium favorites. The "man eaters of the Amazon" can skeletonize a cow in minutes. Federal and several state laws regulate importation.*

PAUL A. ZAHL, NATIONAL GEOGRAPHIC STAFF, AND ROY PINNEY (OPPOSITE)

King fisherman of the Amazon is Fred Cochu, president of Paramount Aquarium, who has fished almost every river system in tropical South America. His planes fly regularly to such collecting centers as Georgetown in Guyana, Iquitos in Peru, and Leticia in Colombia to gather specimens collected by native fishermen. Placed in plastic bags containing 10 per cent water and 90 per cent pure oxygen—and often a tranquilizer to ensure good behavior—the fish are quickly flown to Miami for sale to wholesalers.

It wasn't always this easy. In earlier days Cochu traveled by slow freighter to the Amazon. There he and native fishermen would board a river boat and chug upstream at four knots in "an eternity of boredom, heat, flies, and bad food." After setting up headquarters—often in tumble-down shacks abandoned by rubber prospectors—the party would strike out with seines and tin cans in search of popular fishes and new species. They found them, along with discomfort, danger, and sometimes death.

Cochu's ingenuity was taxed to the utmost in his quest for knifefishes. "Ghostfish," Indians called them, believing that they harbored the souls of dead relatives and neighbors. Cochu had to seine furtively behind the men's backs. He still wonders, "What if they knew I was exporting the souls of Uncle Pancho and Auntie Juana?"

It's like a prospector hitting pay dirt when a collector's net reveals a new or overlooked tropical. Paramount has introduced half a dozen tetras, numerous catfishes and dwarf cichlids. One of Cochu's agents discovered the neon tetra, an inch-long fish that shook the aquarium world and brought $200 to $250 apiece until supply caught up with demand. Another Paramount collector, pursuing rumors of a dazzling mystery fish later identified as the cardinal tetra, vanished in the jungle without a trace.

The elusive cardinal tetra finally surrendered to the nets of Dr. Herbert R. Axelrod, who has built a business empire by seeking prized tropicals in jungle wilds. Appropriately, cardinals bear the scientific name *Cheirodon axelrodi* for their discoverer.

Guyana rivers, threading jungles as un-

240

NATURE'S POLARIS SUBMARINE, *an archerfish fires a salvo to bag a beetle dinner. It can lob projectiles 15 feet and sometimes downs insects on the wing. Eighteenth-century scientists ridiculed reports of this Oriental oddity; today's researchers explain its unique weapon: Pressing its tongue against a groove in the roof of the mouth, the archer forms a tube like the bore of a gun. Then, forcefully compressing its gill covers, it squirts out a stream of water that breaks into drops and spray. The fish will bombard a worm held aloft in tweezers, a cockroach running across a glass tank cover, or the aquarist's eye when an eyelid flickers temptingly. It keeps shooting at a target until tired, then hunts underwater food like other fishes. Toxotes jaculatrix delights aquarium keepers but is difficult to ship from its native Indian and Southeast Asian waters.*

241

tamed as those of the Amazon, harbor angelfish, pencilfishes, head-and-tail lights.

African waters, second to South America's in number of fresh-water species, swarm with gay lyretails, Congo cichlids, and such oddities as upside-down catfishes and elephant-nose mormyrids.

South Asian waters from India to Indonesia produce gouramis, danios, rasboras, and barbs. Siamese fighting fish, raised by thousands of home aquarists, originated in Thailand's waterways. For years Thais have pitted pugnacious males in combat before a circle of wagering onlookers. Today Thai fish fights, like American cock fights, have been outlawed.

American aquarists increasingly find "exotics" in their own streams and lakes. River nets cast from New Jersey to northern Florida may bring in black-banded sunfish,

surpassed in beauty by few other fishes. Mollies abound from North Carolina to Texas, mosquito fish thrive in the Gulf states. Killifishes and sticklebacks inhabit almost every state. Gleaming shiners, elusive darters, red-bellied dace, and tadpole madtom catfish add to the variety.

Although the choice of tropicals constantly widens, a favorite pet is still the goldfish, first cultivated by the Chinese more than a thousand years ago. Today Americans buy some 60 million a year.

Selective breeding has worked wonders on these originally drab relatives of the carp. Colors range from blazing reds and golds to mottled calicoes that combine every shade of the rainbow. Changes in the fish's shape have introduced flowing fins, extra fins, missing fins, bulging eyes, raspberry-like heads, and nearly spherical bodies.

Pointers on Setting Up an Aquarium

TANK SIZE *depends on your pocketbook and the number of fish desired. Normally one gallon of water accommodates one inch of fish. An aerator used intermittently will double this capacity, used constantly will triple it. Tanks holding five gallons or less can be all glass. Larger ones require strengthening frames of non-rusting metal, attached to the glass with aquarium cement. Bottom should be glass or good quality slate. Choose a tank that has a large water surface area so the water can absorb a maximum of oxygen for fishes to respire. A glass cover will slow evaporation and keep fish from jumping out.*

WATER *from a tap, rain barrel, brook, or other fresh-water source will do provided it is conditioned by standing at least a day in an open container. This allows chlorine to dissipate, oxygen to dissolve, organic matter to settle, and fish parasites to die for lack of hosts. Rainwater and melted snow require mineral traces, so add one tablespoon of salt and five teaspoons of Epsom salts per five gallons of liquid. Test water for acidity and alkalinity (pH: hydrogen ion concentration); aquarium shops have inexpensive testers.*

SAND *anchors plants and provides a natural setting. Ask an aquarium dealer about the correct size of grain. If too fine, it packs and prevents plants from rooting; oversized grains hide food particles that will later decompose. Before placing sand in the tank, rinse it until the cleansing water appears clear.*

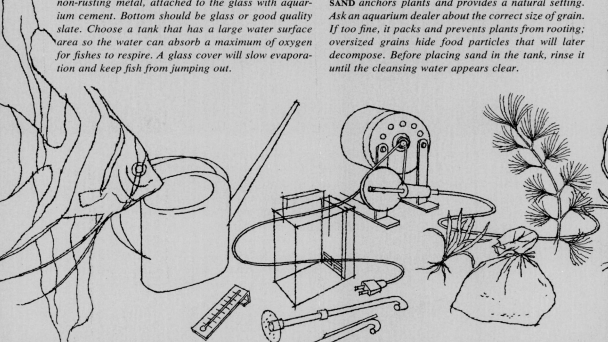

Breeding fancy goldfish takes Oriental patience. Troubles begin during courtship when agitated fish may tear aquarium plants to shreds. Once a female lays her thousand eggs the parents eat them if not removed.

After the eggs hatch the fancier begins a campaign of ruthlessly culling imperfect specimens. He force-feeds, trying to develop the paunchy fish that hobbyists esteem. At the end of six months, first-rate specimens number at most a dozen of the original thousand. Little wonder that most people settle for plainer, less expensive goldfish.

Oddly, the whiskered, oft-unwanted carp stirs one of the latest sensations among fish fanciers. Bred in Japan to wear the boldest of hues, brilliant carp, known as *koi*, sell by the tens of millions. U. S. dealers, who once paid as much as $5,000 for koi, now raise them in Florida ponds.

One of the delights of aquarium keeping is to watch fish lead their private lives. Swordtails are noted for their rigid "peck order." The top fish, usually a large male, utterly dominates the others, nipping them and taking his choice of mates without fear of reprisal. Number two fish bullies all but number one, and so on, in a fish hierarchy that finds one forlorn sword at the bottom.

A fish newly added to the tank nearly always starts at the bottom of the peck order. This characteristic is utilized by collectors of Siamese fighting fish, who normally cannot keep two males together. Fanciers cannily give a small fighting fish the advantage of prior occupancy, then add a larger one later. Prior residence balances superior size, and the two warily coexist.

Nesting fishes delight tank watchers. The male Siamese fighting fish builds a floating

243

PLANTS *are not essential but they help supply oxygen, absorb poisonous carbon dioxide, decorate the aquarium, and make fishes feel more at home. For small tanks use pygmy plants. Avoid vegetation that has brown leaves or rank smelling roots because decomposing organic matter robs oxygen from the water. Plants in darkness absorb oxygen instead of releasing it; thus a heavily planted tank requires longer periods of light. Many aquarists find the beauty of aquatic plants nearly as rewarding as their fish. Plastic plants, strikingly realistic and requiring no care, are fast increasing in popularity.*

LIGHTING AND TEMPERATURE: *Northern exposure gives ideal natural lighting. Electric bulbs (2½ watts per gallon) can substitute for daylight if turned on about 12 hours a day. Healthy plants indicate proper light; growth of algae usually means too much. Temperature for tropical fishes should range between 72° and 80° F.; for goldfish 55° to 70°. Water kept slightly on the cooler side enables fish to resist disease better. If water temperature should drop substantially, restore it quickly; a gradual rise only drags out the* fish's discomfort. *Simple heaters with thermostats are not expensive.*

FISH FOODS *on pet-shop shelves are steadily improving. Freeze-dried foods now replace old standbys such as live worms and baby brine shrimp, as well as dried food. Remember: Overfeeding ranks as the number one fish killer because rotting leftovers pollute water.*

AQUARIST'S GOAL *is a balanced tank that seldom needs cleaning. This results when fishes get plenty of oxygen; when all food is eaten, leaving none to decompose; when plants receive sufficient light and nutrition from fish wastes; and when pond snails or other scavengers eat debris and algae. Once in balance, the aquarium becomes a self-contained world in which the aquarist has little to do except feed his fishes and enjoy them.*

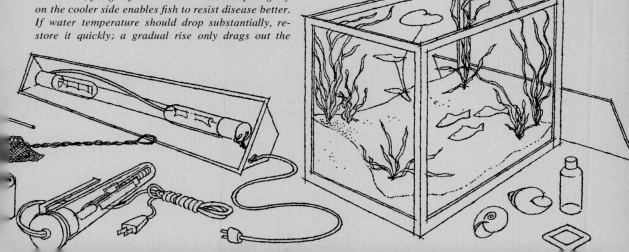

DISCUS FISH *from the Amazon behave uniquely among fishes: They "nurse" their young much as mammals do.*

Prospective parents nip aquatic growth to scrub the tile slab where they will spawn (left). Then the female lays a stream of sticky, beige-colored eggs while the male hovers to fertilize them (opposite). Fry hatch four days later and attach to the parents' sides (lower left). For about eight days they cling, nursing on whitish "milk" which adults secrete in skin cells.

Hard to breed, Symphysodon aequifasciata often eat their eggs or fry. Captives hide at first, and if excited may bang against the glass and kill themselves. But they soon recognize their owner and sail to greet him. Below, mama appears to teeter on outstretched fins as her babies hitch a ride. 245

GENE WOLFSHEIMER

nest by blowing air bubbles, coated with mucus, that stick together on the surface. His spouse fastens her eggs to the underside. Then the male, driving her off, busily catches falling eggs and straying fry in his mouth and spits them back in the nest.

Studies of aquarium fishes yield valuable data. Numerous discoveries of spawning and other behavior have been made by aquarists. Dr. Myron S. Gordon of the New York Zoological Society raised the prolific platy to study inheritance aspects of cancer. The U. S. Air Force, gathering information on how men would act cooped in space craft, observed fishes confined in tanks.

Salt-water tropicals, colorful and fascinating, were long out of reach of most fish fanciers because scientists could not reproduce sea water, a complex fluid containing 61 elements. Early salt-water aquarists had to haul ocean water inland or build tanks on the coast and pump in the sea.

Today manufactured concentrates mixed with tap water simulate sea water to the satisfaction of such ocean pets as butterflyfish, clownfish, and droll seahorses. Now marine tropicals can enjoy sea comforts even in the aquarium of a desert rancher.

FLAMES FROM WATER: *Netters harvest glowing goldfish at a hatchery in the Missouri Ozarks. The fish will be stripped of eggs and milt for artificial breeding. Fry are born silver-gray, later changing color. Some turn again as adults; the specimen below has paled from gold to white.*

GEORGE F. MOBLEY, NATIONAL GEOGRAPHIC STAFF

246

BEAUTIFUL OR GROTESQUE, *today's goldfish reflect centuries of selective breeding. Plump humpbacks grow filmy fins (below). Lionheads wear a hood that hampers respiration, calling for oxygen-rich water (above, right). Black popeye and mottled calico share the tank.*

CHAPTER SIXTEEN

Gallery of Fresh-water Fishes ▶

FEW ARE THE RIVERS, lakes, swamps—even caves and desert waterholes—of North America that do not harbor at least one of her 800 fresh-water fish species. Each has its favorite haunt. Trout like cool tumbling water rich in oxygen. Catfish grow fattest and laziest in warm sluggish rivers. Pike and pickerel dwell in weedy shallows, whitefish in lakes 600 feet down.

Fresh-water fishes need to be tougher than their ocean brethren. Changing seasons alter water temperatures (Alaskan blackfish stay alive even encased in ice). Droughts shrink ponds (mudminnows burrow in ooze until moisture returns). Rains alter concentrations of chemicals. And one force takes a pitiless toll: man's pollution.

Scientists debate whether fishes originated in salt water or fresh. It may have been simultaneous; fresh-water fish like the sturgeon rival in age the sea's most ancient types. Life cycles suggest a two-way exchange: Some species, anadromous, mature at sea and return to fresh water to spawn. Others, catadromous, live in streams and lakes and descend to sea to lay eggs.

Fresh-water fishes weigh as little as a hundredth of an ounce or more than a thousand pounds. They browse on plants, eat their own kind, even seize squirrels and water birds. And they live within walking distance of almost every American.

247

Ancient Fishes

NATURE HAS CREATED many a new fish model in the past few hundred million years, but the bowfin, gar, sturgeon, and paddlefish have never modernized; they preserve features common to earth's first fishes. A partly cartilaginous skeleton harks to the archaic sharks and lampreys. A spiraling baffle inside a straight intestine is another sharklike trait. The backbone turns upward at the tail, a configuration out of style for eons. An air bladder, like a human lung, connects with the throat and aids—or once aided—respiration. The sturgeon lacks the evolutionary improvement of paired jaws; it sucks up food through a tubelike mouth. Leftover relics today, ancient fishes share characteristics of the venturesome species which first slithered out of water, breathed into a lunglike air bladder, and launched the evolution of higher land vertebrates.

JOHN TASHJIAN (BELOW), TREAT DAVIDSON (OPPOSITE, TOP), AND ROBERT C. HERMES

BOWFIN

BOWFIN
Amia calva

Veterans of millions of years in lakes and streams, adaptable bowfins can survive even a full day out of water by using the air bladder as a lung. Fossils show them to be sole heirs of a family that once claimed many species. Called dogfish in the Great Lakes and grindle in the South, bowfins have few friends because of unsavory flesh and depredations on game fishes.

A dark spot edged in orange or yellow marks the tail of male bowfins. Females lack the edging and sometimes the spot itself. In spring the male digs a nest in weedy shallows, guards the eggs, and chaperones the young. Fry have adhesive snouts for anchorage to plants.

Characteristics: dorsal fin nearly the length of olive back; often a dark tail spot. *Range:* Great Lakes, Mississippi Valley, seaboard from Florida to Susquehanna River. *Weight:* to 10 pounds. *Length:* to 3 feet.

LONGNOSE GAR
Lepisosteus osseus

Gliding alongside and slashing sideways with razor-toothed jaws, gars destroy fishes wholesale. Heavy scales give them such armor that they roam lake shores and rivers virtually without enemies. Most of the United States' five gar species (family Lepisosteidae) like sluggish water, occasionally surfacing to gulp air. Longnoses will live in a current.

Characteristics: elongated beak. *Range:* Great Lakes to Gulf, most of East Coast. *Weight:* rod and reel record 50¼ pounds. *Length:* to 6 feet.

SPOTTED GAR
Lepisosteus oculatus

Spotted gars swarm in Florida's Everglades National Park; during low water they crowd mudholes, occasionally slithering overland to plop into the next hole. Seminoles shuck them from their tough skins for food. Alligators feast on them. Like other gars they wear bony, diamond-shaped, nonoverlapping plates. Eating gar eggs poisons man.

Characteristics: dark spots on gray-green back and head. *Range:* Great Lakes to Gulf. *Weight:* seldom exceeds 6 pounds. *Length:* to 4 feet.

ATLANTIC STURGEON

ATLANTIC STURGEON
Acipenser oxyrhynchus

Massachusetts settlers, catching and pickling Atlantic sturgeon, hauled in giants "18 foote long." Fishermen of the late 1800's netted millions of pounds, selling flesh and roe for food, the air bladders for making isinglass. Today a six-footer, once common, is a rarity.

Atlantic sturgeon browse over mud of the continental shelf, feeling with their four barbels for worms and mollusks. In late spring they work up rivers past tidewater, where "cows" strew as many as 2½ million adhesive eggs that hatch in a week. Parents descend at once to sea, fry in about a year.

Characteristics: back olive to brown; 5 body-length rows of plates. *Range:* St. Lawrence to Gulf of Mexico. *Weight:* average 60 pounds, to 600. *Length:* average 5 feet, to 10.

PAINTINGS BY HASHIME MURAYAMA

WHITE STURGEON
Acipenser transmontanus

Largest of North America's fresh-water fishes, the white sturgeon could hardly be more harmless. Four sensitive barbels, dragged over the bottom, help weak eyes detect food. A toothless, tubelike mouth shoots down to suck in snails, clams, and insect larvae liberally mixed with mud. Occasionally the sturgeon rears to gobble a eulachon, a type of smelt. Then it moseys on, sucking up more food and mud.

White sturgeon may mature as long as 20 years in the ocean or in brackish water before migrating up larger western rivers to spawn each spring. They shed hundreds of thousands of eggs over gravel beds, then ignore both spawn and fry. Dams probably have restricted spawning runs, accelerating a drop in the sturgeon population that began in the late 1800's when fishermen one year took six million pounds from the Columbia River.

Characteristics: whitish body; scaleless except 5 body-length rows of plates. *Range:* Monterey Bay to Alaska. *Weight:* rod and reel record 360 pounds, to 1,285. *Length:* to 12½ feet.

250

LAKE STURGEON
Acipenser fulvescens

> On the white sand of the bottom
> Lay the monster Mishe-Nahma,
> Lay the sturgeon, King of Fishes.

Awesome to red men of Longfellow's *Song of Hiawatha,* mighty lake sturgeon impressed white men too: Maps of the Great Lakes region list more than a dozen Sturgeon Rivers, Sturgeon Lakes, Sturgeon Bays, Sturgeon Falls. Lake of the Woods, one of the greatest sturgeon ponds in the world, yielded 1.6 million pounds in 1893.

Lake sturgeon comb shallows for snails, crawfish, and fishes. They often migrate up rivers to spawn, females shedding eggs as they forage.

Characteristics: brownish; 5 body-length rows of plates. *Range:* upper Mississippi south to Alabama, Great Lakes, to Hudson Bay. *Weight:* exceeds 300 pounds. *Length:* to 7 feet.

EULACHON (small fish) and WHITE STURGEON

PADDLEFISH

PADDLEFISH
Polyodon spathula

Little wonder that the Spanish explorer De Soto marveled when he saw the Mississippi paddlefish. Its broad beak stretches a third of its length. Its jaws open in a way that seems impossible, the lower half of the head dropping like an elevator. Its plump, rounded body has few scales, most of them embedded. And as it swims around with its great toothless mouth agape, it scoops in only tiny crustaceans and river plankton.

Why the paddlelike beak? Probably it serves as a planing mechanism, holding the fish's head up when water resistance against the open mouth tends to force the fish downward as it swims.

Paddlefish spawn in turbulent patches of river, and their eggs make acceptable caviar. Contact with water gives the eggs an adhesive quality, causing them to stick to gravel in the spawning beds. In a week larvae wriggle violently to free themselves from the egg capsule, then drift exhausted with the current. Hatchlings show a bump that on 1½-inch fry has become a beak.

Characteristics: spoonlike snout; embedded scales. *Range:* Great Lakes, Mississippi Valley. *Weight:* exceeds 200 pounds. *Length:* to 6 feet.

BROWN TROUT
Salmo trutta

Wariest of trouts, often disdaining every fly in the box, browns tax the fisherman's skill to the utmost. But the patient angler inevitably tries again, for brown trout often reach a formidable five pounds and put up a rewarding fight.

Fish culturists nearly a century ago introduced brown trout from Europe, importing a German variety and a Scottish strain called Loch Leven. These have since interbred. Fishermen have accused browns of crowding out brook trout. Now they generally agree that the brookie's enemies were deforestation and pollution, and were it not for the hardy immigrants some areas would have no trout at all.

Brown trout bite best in twilight and at night, when the nocturnal feeders seek insects, crawfish, worms, snails, and small fishes. They spawn in fall and winter, laying as many as 6,000 eggs.

Characteristics: brown and red spots surrounded by light rings; relatively large scales. *Range:* introduced coast to coast from Canada to northern part of Gulf states. *Weight:* 1 pound in small streams, 5 in rivers and lakes; rod and reel record 39½. *Length:* to more than 2 feet.

252

Salmons, Trouts, and Graylings

FAMOUS AMONG SPORTSMEN as fine fighters and among gourmets for fine flavor, the salmons, trouts, and graylings belong to a family noted for great migrations. Atlantic and Pacific salmon journey thousands of miles in the ocean, then struggle vast distances up rivers to spawn. To the continuing perplexity of science, a homing instinct guides them back almost unerringly to the stream of their birth. The five species of Pacific salmons die immediately after spawning; no fish ever sees its parents or children, and during the weeks that eggs incubate a family has no living members. The Atlantic species survives spawning unless exhausted by the run. Breeding males develop grotesquely hooked jaws; thus the Pacific salmon's generic name *Oncorhynchus*—"hook nose."

Trouts are not immune to the migratory urge. Rainbows, Dolly Vardens, cutthroats, browns, brook trout, and Arctic chars *(Salvelinus alpinus)* often live at sea, then return to fresh water to spawn. Even graylings and some of the landlocked trouts obey the migratory instinct, moving up streams to make their nests. Only the deep-dwelling lake trout and New England's Sunapee *(S. aureolus)* stay at home.

Salmons, trouts, and graylings share the family Salmonidae with the whitefishes (page 265). All bear soft-rayed fins, pelvic fins located midway along the body length, and a fleshy adipose fin perched behind the dorsal. Most are nesters, scooping shallow depressions in sandy or gravelly bottoms. Young are born with bulbous abdomens containing the egg yolk, on which they live during the first days. The eggs ship easily, and several species have been transplanted from their native Northern Hemisphere all over the world.

BROWN TROUT

WALTER A. WEBER

CUTTHROAT TROUT
Salmo clarki

Red slashmarks under the lower jaws name the cutthroat, known in the West as "native trout." Easily taken with flies and a variety of lures, it offers the angler a sturdy fight and a delectable table treat.

Thriving in cool mountain waters, cutthroats divide into several subspecies, generally varying according to locality. The Yellowstone cutthroat, hardy native of Yellowstone National Park, can live in streams two miles above sea level. A coastal variety, marked with more spots, often migrates into the Pacific, returning to fresh water to spawn.

Characteristics: red streak on both sides of lower jaw; teeth on roof of mouth. *Range:* northern California to southern Alaska mainly west of Rockies. *Weight:* rod and reel record 41 pounds; average ¾ pound in streams, 4 to 6 pounds in rivers and lakes. *Length:* to 39 inches.

BROOK TROUT
Salvelinus fontinalis

Favorite of trout fishermen, brook trout hit hard, fight gamely, taste great. No angler worries that technically they are not trout but chars, lacking teeth at the rear roof of the mouth.

Brook trout are wilderness fish, creatures of cool streams and spring-fed lakes. They retreat from pollution and require colder water than other trouts. Fishermen find them lying close to the bottom in eddies, pools, and undercuts along rocks, banks, and logs. Feeding on larvae, insects, crustaceans, and small fishes, they strike flies, spinners, and artificial bugs.

Characteristics: white forward edges of lower fins, red spots; minute scales. *Range:* native from northern Georgia to Labrador and in the Midwest; introduced California to Alaska. *Weight:* rod and reel record 14½ pounds; average ½ pound in small waters. *Length:* average 8 to 10 inches, to 31½.

GOLDEN TROUT
Salmo aguabonita

Anglers seek them in June after snow melts, climbing afoot or riding horseback to remote crystal lakes and frigid streams in the high Sierras. There, flashing like nuggets in the blue mountain waters, golden trout hunt insects along rocky shores, in pools below rapids, under overhanging banks. They willingly rise to the fisherman's fly, and, though seldom more than a pound in weight or a foot in length, put up an exciting scrap on light tackle.

Isolated protectively by nature, goldens introduced in waters harboring rainbow trout interbreed and soon lose their identity.

Characteristics: olive back, golden sides marked with brick red and 9 or 10 blotches called parr marks. *Range:* native only to Golden Trout Creek in California Sierras; introduced nearby. *Weight:* rod and reel record 11 pounds, average ½ to 1. *Length:* to 28 inches.

RAINBOW TROUT
Salmo gairdneri

Furious runs and spectacular leaps rank the rainbow as the fightingest of trouts. Add its love of exciting white-water rivers, its weight of several pounds, and its wide distribution, and the rainbow probably offers more sport to more anglers than any other trout.

Pacific-slope rainbows often migrate to sea, where they easily surpass five and 10 pounds and acquire a gray tinge that earns them the name steelhead. In southern states they thrive at the foot of dams, which release cool bottom water that aerates as it discharges. Rainbows tolerate warm water if it flows sufficiently to capture oxygen.

The spring spawners eat insects, flies, worms, minnows, crustaceans, and salmon eggs. Though they rise to dry flies, big ones wait deep for sunken lures. Rainbows often lie near rapids or where current gouges overhanging banks.

Characteristics: red band down sides, olive back; zig-zag rows of teeth on roof of mouth. *Range:* native to Pacific slope, transplanted throughout the Nation except in the southern parts of Gulf states. *Weight:* rod and reel record 37 pounds. *Length:* to 40½ inches.

Top to bottom: CUTTHROAT, BROOK, GOLDEN, RAINBOW

DOLLY VARDEN TROUT

DOLLY VARDEN TROUT
Salvelinus malma

Named for a colorful heroine of Charles Dickens' *Barnaby Rudge,* Dolly Vardens are villains among trouts. Gluttonous feeders, they maraud salmon spawning grounds and gorge on young salmon and trout—their own included. Alaska, where abundant Dolly Vardens often swim in schools, once offered a 2½-cent bounty to protect her giant salmon industry.

Like brook trout, lake trout, and Sunapees, Dolly Vardens lack teeth on the rear roof of the mouth and thus count as chars instead of pure trout. Chars also differ from the *Salmo* trouts by having light spots on a dark background while their relatives wear the reverse.

Hooked Dolly Vardens neither leap like rainbow trout nor tug like browns. But they grow large, take a variety of flies and spinners, and offer delicious flesh, often pink in color. Native to Pacific drainage, some go to sea as steelhead Dolly Vardens and attain 10 pounds or more. They return to spawn in fall and winter with those that stay in fresh water.

Characteristics: red and orange spots; forked tail. *Range:* west of Rocky Mountains from northern California to Alaska. *Weight:* commonly 5 to 10 pounds, rod and reel record 32. *Length:* maximum 40½ inches.

LAKE TROUT
Salvelinus namaycush

Each year for decades Great Lakes commercial fishermen netted and hooked more than 12 million pounds of lake trout. Hundred-pound giants were reported. Then the sea lamprey filtered in and by the 1950's climaxed its nightmarish depredations. The trout catch plummeted to less than a half million pounds. Now it is slowly climbing, thanks to all-out chemical warfare against the parasitic lamprey.

Creatures of the cold depths, lake trout avoid water warmer than 65° F. and prefer temperatures 20 degrees cooler. When the summer sun heats the surface they descend to rocky and sandy bottoms often 400 feet down. Not all deep northern lakes support them: Some harbor masses of decaying leaves and tree trunks which consume oxygen, leaving an inadequate supply at the bottom for the fish.

Lake trout rise in autumn and approach shore to spawn. Females shed as many as 18,000 eggs in rocky shallows. In a number of New England lakes, pesticides are blamed for causing sterilization of lakers.

Summer anglers seeking the deep-dwelling trout generally troll slowly just off bottom with large wobbling spoons and plugs. Linen and nylon lines tend to float the lure; thus fishermen often arm themselves with salt-water gear that will handle wire line or a nylon line braided over a lead core. One disadvantage: The weight of the line takes much of the fight out of the fish.

Fished at the surface in fall and spring, lake trout strike at flies, plugs, and spinners and put up a brisk fight. They can also be fished through the ice in winter.

Lake trout eat almost anything that comes along, reaching maximum size when surrounded with an abundance of smelt, eels, herring, and alewives. The stomach of one 20-pound laker yielded 13 lake herring. Introduced in California's Lake Tahoe, the voracious predators have wiped out the native Lahontan cutthroat trout. The meat of lake trout is rich and flaky, varying in color from off-white to deep pink.

Indians, French Canadians, and a variety of other fishermen have given lake trout a host of names: namaycush, togue, longue, forktail trout, mackinaw trout, salmon trout, Great Lakes trout, and laker. The generic name *Salvelinus* indicates the lake trout is a char, but some authorities regard it as true trout.

Characteristics: gray body peppered with pale spots and often tinged with pink; deeply forked tail. *Range:* New England across the northern states to California, north to Arctic Circle. *Weight:* average 4 or 5 pounds, rod and reel record 63. *Length:* to 51 inches.

PAINTINGS BY HASHIME MURAYAMA

ATLANTIC SALMON
Salmo salar

"Greatest game fish in the world" is risky praise in a sport famous for strong opinions, but many anglers bestow the title on the Atlantic salmon. In every department—speed, strength, size, endurance, flavor, trickiness—*Salmo salar* or "salmo the leaper" stands superb.

Native to both Europe and North America, the popular actor of sea and stream has won acclaim for two thousand years. Pliny declared that "the river salmon surpasseth all the fishes of the sea." Izaak Walton stated flatly: "The Salmon is accounted the King of fresh-water fish."

Lakes of Canada and the northeastern United States harbor a landlocked type—salmon unable or unwilling to go to sea. Anglers esteem both, and scientists lump them as one species. Landlocked salmon, often called Sebago in Maine and ouananiche in Canada, sport dorsal colors ranging from black to olive. They run smaller than sea-going salmon, but have larger eyes, scales, and fins.

Sea-run Atlantic salmon acquire new names at each stage of growth. Fry two or three months old develop bars or parr marks on the flanks and are called "parrs." They remain in fresh water a year or two, or for as long as seven. Then they assume a silvery color, the name "smolt," and descend to sea. Some, as "grilse," return in a year to fresh water to spawn. Those that remain longer at sea are true "salmon."

After up to five years in the ocean, salmon approach sexual maturity and enter rivers on breeding runs, usually in spring and summer, less commonly in fall. Trim figures grow lank, colors dull, fins grow fleshy, skins become slimy and blotched. The jaws of males, which show the greatest change, curve until they touch only at the tips. The fish eat little if at all as they work upstream. Eggs, laid in autumn in shallow gravel nests, hatch early the following spring.

Spent fish, called "kelts," are thin and exhausted; most apparently return to sea and die. But unlike Pacific kin, about 10 percent of the females and fewer males survive to make a second run. A handful return as many as four times.

Atlantic salmon choked the rivers of colonial New England and ran in the Hudson. After the Revolution, industry threw dams across many of these waterways. Waves of ripe homecoming fish leaped vainly at the barriers and died; in a few years the blocked rivers lost their entire salmon populations. Today, conservationists are restoring runs in Maine rivers, but commercial fisheries flourish only off Canada and Europe.

Anglers dream of pilgrimages to salmon Meccas. Among North American streams that attract fishermen are the Restigouche and Miramichi of New Brunswick, the Margaree and Medway of Nova Scotia, the Jupiter of Anticosti Island, and the Gander of Newfoundland. Scotland's Tay, Spey, Dee, and Tweed draw sportsmen from afar; so do England's Wye and Derwent, and Norway's Lærdal, Alta, and Årøy. Sweden, Spain, and Iceland also lure devotees.

Pursuit of the Atlantic salmon can be expensive. Sportsmen often pay $1,000, sometimes $5,000, for one week's fishing rights along a two-mile "beat" of prime European salmon river. And such an area may contain only a handful of pools where fishermen seek salmon that are resting during their upstream migration.

Salmon usually take wet flies, and occasionally streamers and other lures, but on many rivers only flies are legal. Landlocked salmon also take spoons and spinner-and-fly combinations. They hit with particular ferocity in spring when they pursue spawning smelt into inlets and streams.

Characteristics: Sea-run salmon have blue-gray backs and silvery sides; landlocked show dorsal colors ranging from black to olive. Both wear irregular black spots, often x-shaped. Both become blotchy and deformed at spawning time. *Range:* both sides Atlantic; originally Labrador south to Hudson River, now south to Maine, straying to New Jersey. *Weight:* Scottish fish reported at 103 pounds; sea-going rod and reel record 79 pounds, average 15; landlocked rod and reel record 22½ pounds, average 3 to 5. *Length:* average less than 30 inches.

LANDLOCKED SALMON

ATLANTIC SALMON (ocean phase, lower, and spawning stage)

WALTER A. WEBER

SOCKEYE SALMON
Oncorhynchus nerka

Sporting a lobster-red body and greenish head during spawning, sockeyes set a lofty standard of domestic behavior. The female laboriously scoops one gravelly nest after another; the hook-jawed male ferociously drives off interlopers.

Alone among salmon, sockeyes prefer streams above lakes for spawning. Fry use the lakes as a nursery for a year or longer, slowly growing a few inches long. Then they migrate to sea, thriving there for two or three years on a diet of plankton spiced with an occasional tiny fish. At spawning time unerring instinct guides them back. They fight upriver on arduous journeys in incredible numbers; perhaps 30 million sockeyes crowd into two areas alone, the Fraser River system in British Columbia and Alaska's Bristol Bay watershed.

When canned salmon shows a deep red coloring it probably comes from the flavorous sockeye. Small as salmon go—five pounds is average—sockeyes bring premium prices and support a multimillion-dollar fishery. To anglers, however, sea-going sockeyes mean little, for they seldom strike at bait or lure.

Though all sockeyes have access to the sea, some, called kokanees, refuse to make the trip. The fresh-water sockeyes course lakes in large compact schools, nest and die like their sea-going kin. Widespread plantings have introduced these one-pound game fish widely in the West and even in a few New England lakes.

Sockeye nicknames include redfish, red salmon, blueback, nerka, and Fraser River salmon.

Characteristics: back blue-gray or greenish with fine black spots, red in spawning. *Range:* San Francisco Bay to Alaska, widely introduced. *Weight:* to 15 pounds. *Length:* to 30 inches.

SOCKEYE SALMON (spawning stage)

WALTER A. WEBER, NATIONAL GEOGRAPHIC STAFF

PINK SALMON (ocean phase, top, and spawning stage)

PINK SALMON
Oncorhynchus gorbuscha

Ask an Alaska fisherman what salmon he catches in greatest numbers and he will answer "humpbacks" or "humpies." These are pink salmon, nicknamed for a grotesque hump of cartilage that forms behind the head of breeding males. Their pink flesh commands a lesser price than the rich, red hue of sockeyes, but their abundance—greatest of all Alaska salmon—makes the catches equal in commercial value.

Pink salmon do not have the wanderlust of other species, spawning in late summer only slightly upstream from tidewater. Young remain in their gravel nests until the next March or April,

then as inch-long fry venture directly to sea. After a year and a half they reach sexual maturity and return to spawn and die.

Principal fishing grounds begin at Puget Sound and improve northward. Fishermen set seines and traps offshore—pink salmon lose their best flavor with spawning changes in fresh water.

Pink salmon feed on crustaceans, squids, and fishes. They occasionally take flies, spoons, and plugs and will break water when hooked. They average three to seven pounds and are the smallest of the Pacific coast salmon.

Characteristics: black spots on tail; males' backs humped in spawning season; tiny scales. *Range:* southern California to Alaska. *Weight:* to 11 pounds. *Length:* to 30 inches.

261

CHUM SALMON
Oncorhynchus keta

Migrating in autumn, when their abundant numbers choke streams in the Pacific Northwest, chum salmon are the last Pacific salmon to run in the rivers. Most travel only a short distance above tidewater before spawning, though some fight 1,500 miles up the mighty Yukon River to Canada's Teslin Lake.

Chum salmon spawn on gravel in swift water. Nature has so coordinated the act that the milt instantly fertilizes the eggs, lest the current sweep it downstream without effect.

Like pink salmon fry, young chums go to sea shortly after hatching. They lose themselves in the ocean for about four years, then reach sexual maturity and a weight of eight to 18 pounds. Fishermen often call them dog salmon, perhaps because breeding males grow large canine teeth, perhaps because the chum's relatively pale pink, low-quality flesh once went principally into dog food. Other nicknames include keta, calico salmon, hayho, and lekai salmon.

Chum salmon feed mainly on crustaceans and other small invertebrates.

Characteristics: dusky back, blackish fins; sides brick red on breeding males. *Range:* northern California to Alaska. *Weight:* average 13 pounds, reported to 33. *Length:* to 3 feet.

ARCTIC GRAYLING
Thymallus arcticus

With even experienced fishermen, the gold-flecked, purple-tinged grayling commands a long, appreciative look before it goes into the creel. The beauty of a European variety prompted Saint Ambrose to call it "flower of fishes."

This relative of trouts and salmons finds the United States the southern edge of its range; even a little deforestation can alter its habitat critically. The closely related Michigan grayling vanished in the 1930's. Traveling in schools which greedy anglers can depopulate, pushed aside by trout introduced in its waters, so eager to bite it will meet an artificial fly in midair, the grayling once teetered on the brink of extinction in U. S. waters. Hatcheries aid its recovery.

In spring graylings lay 2,000 to 4,000 eggs in gravelly shallows. Eggs hatch in two weeks, and almost at once the young begin their hunting career. Equipped with small mouths, graylings feed almost entirely on larvae of such insects as midges and caddis flies. Their flesh gives off the aroma of thyme, thus the generic name *Thymallus*.

Characteristics: high dorsal fin; spotted flanks tinted a gorgeous purple; large scales. *Range:* upper Missouri River, north to Alaska, introduced in West and Midwest. *Weight:* average less than a pound, to 5. *Length:* average 1 foot.

CHUM SALMON (spawning stage)

PAINTINGS BY WALTER A. WEBER, NATIONAL GEOGRAPHIC STAFF

ARCTIC GRAYLING

COHO SALMON
Oncorhynchus kisutch

COHO SALMON (spawning stage, top, and ocean phase)

Coho or silver salmon are a favorite of fishermen, striking readily and hard, running and leaping when hooked. Nearly half a million 8- to 10-pounders a year have been landed along the Washington coast alone. Cohos transplanted to the Great Lakes may bring a similar bonanza. Commercial fishermen, aware of coho willingness to strike, take half the annual harvest trolling with spoons and herring bait.

Packers quick-freeze large quantities of coho; eggs make salmon caviar.

Coho funnel into seemingly every stream along their range during late summer and autumn. Some spawn just above tidewater, others push on to far-off headwaters. Breeding males show the hooked nose and reddish hue common to all species. Fry do not swim seaward for one or two years, returning to spawn between the third and fifth years.

Characteristics: slightly spotted blue back, reddish during spawning; caudal peduncle slenderer than chinook's. *Range:* Monterey Bay to Alaska, widely introduced. *Weight:* average 6 to 12 pounds, rod and reel record 31. *Length:* 2 to 3 feet.

CHINOOK SALMON
Oncorhynchus tshawytscha

Largest of salmons, the chinook or king surpasses 100 pounds and ranks as one of the world's more valuable food fishes. Its pink flesh delights the epicure, and its repeated freight-train lunges thrill the angler.

Chinook served as a bulwark in the diet of Pacific Northwest Indians and as the basis of their economy. The great fish probably kept Lewis and Clark from starving on their westward trek more than 150 years ago. Lewis, eating his first in present-day Idaho, savored it "with a very good relish." Better than its taste, the Pacific slope fish convinced him he had crossed the Continental Divide. Reaching the Columbia River after a spawning run, Clark observed that the "number of dead Salmon on the Shores & floating in the river is incredible."

The Fraser, Klamath, and Sacramento rivers also see huge chinook runs, and each supports a vast fishery in its estuary and off shore. Transplanted to New Zealand, chinook have built an important fishing industry there.

Most chinook enter fresh water in spring to spawn, though a number migrate in summer and a few straggle upriver all year. As mature males approach fresh water the gray back and silvery belly become blackish, blotched with dull red. The tail becomes cherry red, and the jaws distort and often grow teeth half an inch long. In both

sexes a growth of spongy skin covers the scales, particularly on the back. By spawning time, males become suffused with red.

Chinook shed 3,000 to 11,000 eggs about a quarter inch in diameter. Water must not be warmer than 54° F.; if it is, the fish delay spawning until it cools.

Young chinook linger in fresh water one to two years, growing slowly on a diet of small crustaceans. Descending to salt water as fingerlings, they gorge on herring, anchovies, and other aquatic animals, growing phenomenally. In three or four years they spawn and die.

Sport fishermen commonly take chinook by trolling with spoons, spinners, and herring. Growing numbers cast for the magnificent fighters, using wobbling spinners, underwater plugs, and even flies. The annual sporting catch in California, Oregon, and Washington is a third as great as the commercial take. Anglers find an inland chinook bonanza in the great Salmon River spawning grounds of Idaho. The rod-and-reel record chinook weighed 92 pounds and stretched nearly five feet.

Small chinook closely resemble coho salmon. Ichthyologists tell them apart by counting caeca: Chinook have 140 to 185, coho 45 to 80.

Characteristics: gray back, dorsal and caudal fins and back profusely speckled with black; stout caudal peduncle. *Range:* California's Ventura River to Alaska. *Weight:* average about 22 pounds, exceeds 100. *Length:* to 5 feet.

CHINOOK SALMON (ocean phase, top, and spawning stage)

Whitefishes

LARGE SCALES, WEAK JAWS, and a monotonous silver color separate whitefishes from the closely related salmons, trouts, and graylings. Another difference: Whitefishes show little urge to migrate or build nests, usually venturing only to shallow water to shed their eggs. Native to the colder half of the Northern Hemisphere, most dwell in lakes, a few in streams. In isolated waters whitefishes tend to develop independent racial characteristics.

Except for scrappy mountain whitefish, these members of the family Salmonidae provide little sport for anglers. Most feed deep on plankton and other small organisms and have tender mouths from which hooks easily tear. Several varieties are famous for flavor, especially when smoked. An exception is the largest whitefish, the dull 40-pound inconnu of Canada and Alaska, which often becomes food for Eskimo dogs.

LAKE WHITEFISH
Coregonus clupeaformis

Small head, thin-lipped mouth, and somber colors make lake whitefish look dull and undistinguished. But to lovers of sea food, the fat, rich delicacy has few peers among the freshwater fishes.

Lake whitefish go deep; fishermen often sink nets 300 feet. In spring the fish move toward shallows to spawn. A four-pound female deposits some 35,000 eggs—about a quart—on gravel and sand bottom. During nearly five months of incubation the eggs suffer attacks by yellow perch, crawfish, wildfowl, and a salamander called the mud puppy. Hatchlings move shoreward to foot-deep water until an inch long, when they make for the depths.

The Great Lakes catch of whitefish ran to ten million pounds a year—Lakes Huron and Michigan producing the lion's share—until parasitic lampreys and perhaps overfishing took their toll. Now fishermen use gill and trap nets in deep water, pound nets in shallows, to land a few million pounds annually.

Numerous whitefish nicknames include Great Lakes whitefish, whiting, shad, and Otsego bass.

Characteristics: slightly gray back, silver sides; scaleless head. *Range:* large lakes from New England to Minnesota and British Columbia and north. *Weight:* average 3 to 4 pounds, reported to 26. *Length:* 12 to 20 inches.

PAINTINGS BY WALTER A. WEBER, NATIONAL GEOGRAPHIC STAFF (OPPOSITE) AND HASHIME MURAYAMA

LAKE WHITEFISH

PAINTINGS BY WALTER A. WEBER, NATIONAL GEOGRAPHIC STAFF, AND HASHIME MURAYAMA (OPPOSITE)

CISCO (top) and MOONEYE

CISCO or LAKE HERRING
Coregonus artedii

The staggering 44 million pounds of ciscoes netted from Lake Erie in 1890 represents perhaps the greatest haul of fish from a fresh-water body in North America. Now sea lampreys and fishing pressure have slashed the entire Great Lakes yield to a fraction of that figure.

Adipose fin and small mouth identify ciscoes as whitefishes (Salmonidae), though they resemble herrings in shape and in fine flavor when smoked. Thirty-nine races have evolved in isolated lakes across the continent.

Ciscoes, or lake herring, leave deep water in November to spawn in gravel and sand shallows. They migrate shoreward again in spring, hunting food. Inhabiting moderate depths, they often live above the kiyi *(C. kiyi)*, another whitefish occurring deeper than 600 feet. Several other *Coregonus* species, known widely as chubs, yield a yearly catch of 10 million pounds.

In rare instances whitefish and canned tuna have been implicated in carrying deadly botulism bacteria. Defective canning and handling apparently permit growth of the microorganism.

Characteristics: blue-black back, silver sides; adipose fin. *Range:* Great Lakes, upper Mississippi, Hudson Bay, and Hudson River watersheds. *Weight:* to 8 pounds. *Length:* to 20 inches.

MOONEYE
Hiodon tergisus

The mooneye stares out on the world with a doleful look that belies a mouthful of vicious teeth. Oddly, the "toothed herring" grows its longest fangs on its tongue.

Mooneyes thrive in cool clear lakes and rivers; pollution and turbidity have reduced their range. They eat minnows, insects, and small crustaceans, and serve in turn as forage for other fishes. Humans find them tasteless and, like other herrings, infested with small bones.

To fly fishermen, wiry mooneyes mean action, striking hard and fighting all the way. Wary and quick, they often mouth a fly and spit it out before the angler can react. As the large, light-gathering eye indicates, the mooneye feeds in dim light, and fishermen make their best catches at early dawn and dusk.

The mooneye shares its range and the family Hiodontidae with the nearly identical goldeye *(H. alosoides)*.

Characteristics: pale olive-buff back, bright silvery sides; large scales except on naked head. *Range:* from Saskatchewan and southern Hudson Bay south to western Maryland, northern Alabama, and Oklahoma; most numerous in the Great Lakes region. *Weight:* average 1 pound, exceeds 2. *Length:* average 12 inches, to 17.

Fresh-water Herrings

PREDOMINANTLY a salt-water family (Clupeidae), the herrings include fresh-water species esteemed by fish eaters, fishermen, and other fishes. Tasty shad, alewives and blueback herring *(Alosa aestivalis)*, entering fresh water to spawn, are netted by the ton and draw anglers to riverbanks in droves. Landlocked gizzard shad teem in lakes and rivers east of Kansas, converting their planktonic diet into flesh. In turn they feed countless predaceous species, thus forming a vital link in nature's food chain.

Unspectacular in appearance, herrings exhibit silver-gray sides, unscaled head, small mouth, deeply forked tail fin, and a narrow dorsal that pops erect like a cowlick. Cycloid, or smooth-edge, scales converge at the belly to form a knifelike keel. Soft fin rays and a somewhat cartilaginous skull relate herrings to the ancient fishes.

AMERICAN SHAD
Alosa sapidissima

Easterners admiring hordes of migrating shad called them by the name of their particular river —Potomac shad, Susquehanna shad, Delaware shad. Enthusiasts carried them west in the late 1800's, and the prolific fish quickly spread. Like other anadromous fishes, they have suffered grimly from dams, pollution, and overfishing, but several million pounds a year still find their way to market and into anglers' creels.

American shad live most of their lives at sea, moving in huge schools as they feed on plankton. Spawning runs bring them into southern rivers in winter, northern progressively later. Buck shad usually arrive first in journeys that can exceed 300 miles upriver. Females deposit 30,000 or more eggs and return with the males to sea; fry follow six months later.

America's largest herring hold an exalted place among food lovers; to fillet them is an art (page 356). Easterners esteem shad roe; Westerners ship much of theirs east.

Characteristics: prominent dark spot behind gills, usually followed by several lighter spots; forked tail; adults toothless. *Range:* St. Johns River in Florida to St. Lawrence, southern California to Alaska. *Weight:* to 14 pounds. *Length:* to 30 inches.

AMERICAN SHAD

HICKORY SHAD
Alosa mediocris

Pouting lower lip and black spots on the shoulder identify the "hickory jack," undistinguished East Coast cousin of the American shad. Too bony for easy eating, hickory shad provide excellent roe. The rest of the fish often ends up in fertilizer or as bait.

Each spring hickory jacks flock into rivers of Georgia and the Carolinas and into tributaries of Chesapeake Bay. But unlike American shad, they may not spawn during these little-understood migrations into fresh water; some evidence indicates they lay their eggs in salt water.

Migrating hickory shad refuse live bait, but they strike bucktails and spoons, putting up a lively fight. At sea they live on small fishes, squids, fish eggs, and crustaceans.

Characteristics: protruding lower lip; 5 or 6 pronounced black spots behind head, gray-green back, silver sides. *Range:* Bay of Fundy to Florida. *Weight:* maximum 3 pounds, average 1. *Length:* to 2 feet, average 14 to 18 inches.

HICKORY SHAD (top) and CARP

PHOTOGRAPHS BY CHARLES A. PURKETT, JR.; PAINTINGS BY WALTER A. WEBER, NATIONAL GEOGRAPHIC STAFF

HORNYHEAD CHUB (*Nocomis biguttatus*)

SOUTHERN REDBELLY DACE (*Phoxinus erythrogaster*)

STONEROL

COMMON SHINER (*Notropis cornutus*)

BLUNTNOSE MINNOW (*Pimephales notatus*)

RED SHI

Minnows

MOST FISHERMEN lump together all bait-size fish as minnows, but to ichthyologists the 200 species of America's largest fish family (Cyprinidae) must meet certain qualifications: cycloid or smooth-edge scales, no adipose fin, toothless mouth, grinding teeth in the throat, a body-length network of hairlike ribs. Minnows show a surprising size range. Some mature at two inches, the average at four, but the mahseer of India grows to nine feet.

Minnows such as the creek chub (*Semotilus atromaculatus*) and golden shiner (*Notemigonus crysoleucas*) delight young anglers and often tempt the fly fisherman. Nature gives minnows a leading role as food for larger fishes. They make a natural live bait; minnow farming has become big business. Colorful redside daces (*Clinostomus elongatus*) double as bait and aquarium pets.

Almost every stream, lake, and swamp contains some minnow species; the upper Mississippi basin harbors the most. America's waters have become home to imported species, among them the bewhiskered carp and a smaller, clean-shaven brother, the goldfish.

Minnows have an air bladder which may serve as a resonating hearing aid because it is linked to the inner ear by a series of bones. The fish spawn in spring and summer, when many grow wartlike tubercles on their heads or upper bodies. The male bluntnose minnow savagely fends off fishes that would eat its eggs.

CARP
Cyprinus carpio

A native of Asia, the prolific carp has been introduced in temperate areas around the world to provide low-cost protein. Ponds can produce more than five pounds of carp to one of largemouth bass.

American fishermen hold carp in low regard. The sluggish fish roots up plants, muddies water beyond tolerance of game fishes, and smothers their spawn with silt.

Carp survive pollution that kills most fishes. They winter deep in holes, emerging to forage on plants, worms, insects, and crustaceans. In spring a 20-pound female may deposit two million eggs. The wary feeders ignore artificial lures, preferring worms, shrimp, and doughballs.

Characteristics: yellow to olive in muddy water, silvery in clear; one barbel hanging from each corner of a small suckerlike mouth. *Range:* southern Canada and coast-to-coast in the United States. *Weight:* average 5 to 10 pounds, rod and reel record 55¼. *Length:* to 42 inches.

mpostoma anomalum)

(Notropis lutrensis)

GOLDEN SHINER (top), CREEK CHUB (center), and REDSIDE DACE

SACRAMENTO SQUAWFISH
Ptychocheilus grandis

Massive minnows, Sacramento squawfish tip the scales at more than 10 pounds and measure three feet long. The Colorado squawfish, a nearly identical minnow, has been reported at five feet and 80 pounds.

Squawfish attack smaller fishes with pikelike ferocity, hence the nickname Sacramento pike. They trap victims in a toothless mouth and crush them with powerful pharyngeal grinders. Predations on sockeye salmon and eggs provoked Canadian authorities to curb the squawfish population. Bane of anglers because of their destruction of young game fishes, squawfish never-

theless provide some sport. They rise greedily to the fly, strike plugs and minnows, and fight vigorously for a few minutes.

Squawfish move into lake shores and up streams in spring to deposit eggs. The Colorado species *(P. lucius)* once was so abundant Arizona farmers pitchforked them from the river for fertilizer. They face possible extinction because dams block spawning runs. The Pacific slope harbors two other squawfish: the northern *(P. oregonensis)*, centered in the Columbia River basin, and the Umpqua *(P. umpquae)* of Oregon's coastal rivers.

Characteristics: elongated body; dusky back, silvery belly. *Range:* Russian, Sacramento Rivers, Monterey Bay streams. *Length:* to 3 feet.

HASHIME MURAYAMA   SACRAMENTO SQUAWFISH (top group) and SACRAMENTO SUCKER

Suckers

FLESHY LIPS PURSED about an underslung mouth, suckers vacuum-clean lake and stream beds seeking larvae, worms, fish eggs, and vegetation. Numerous features of North America's 61 species of suckers (family Catostomidae) ally them with the minnows: elongated body, soft rays, cycloid or smooth-edge scales, bony body, toothless mouth. Suckers grow a single comblike row of 10 or more pharyngeal teeth, while American minnows have a smaller number in one or two short rows.

Spring spawners, most suckers migrate up streams; there they lay up to 100,000 eggs which receive no parental care. Though suckers are primarily forage fishes, commercial landings of buffalofish in the Mississippi basin exceed 15 million pounds a year.

Suckers abound in every mainland state, most species occurring east of the Rockies. Redhorse suckers clog eastern shad seines. Carpsuckers have a limited commercial value on the Great Lakes. White suckers frequently adorn the stringers of young Izaak Waltons.

RIVER CARPSUCKER (*Carpiodes carpio*)

RIVER REDHORSE (*Moxostoma carinatum*)

NORTHERN HOG SUCKER (*Hypentelium nigricans*)

CHARLES A. PURKETT, JR.

LAKE CHUBSUCKER (*Erimyzon sucetta*)

WHITE SUCKER (*Catostomus commersoni*)

SACRAMENTO SUCKER
Catostomus occidentalis

Dwelling inconspicuously on bottoms of California rivers and lakes, Sacramento suckers migrate up tributaries in spring spawning rituals. Males gather over gravel riffles, usually after dark. When a female nears, one or two males eagerly attend her. They cluster, vibrate, and shed milt and eggs. A week later fry swarm.

Sacramento suckers seldom take bait, mouthing it first if they do and then putting up a feeble fight. Two-foot, four-pounders rank as giants.

Characteristics: thick-lipped mouth; elongated body. *Range:* centered California's Sacramento and San Joaquin rivers. *Weight:* average 1½ pounds. *Length:* average 15 inches.

SMALLMOUTH BUFFALO (*Ictiobus bubalus*)

271

Catfishes

HUCKLEBERRY FINN, using a skinned rabbit for bait, caught a 200-pound blue catfish, "as big a fish as was ever catched in the Mississippi, I reckon." No one else has taken one much more than half that size, but statistics mean little in the blissful world of catfishermen. Their whiskered quarry never troubles them to tend the line, obligingly swallows any bait that is offered, and flops on the bank with broad mouth smiling.

The blue cats (*Ictalurus furcatus*) that Huck loved share heavyweight honors with the flathead (*Pylodictis olivaris*), alias mudcat, goujon, and yellow cat. Identified by a sloping brow and rounded tail fin, the flathead reaches 100 pounds. Channel or spotted catfish (*I. punctatus*), often confused with blues when their spots fade with age, exceed 50 pounds. A lightweight of the family Ictaluridae is the 3½-inch brindled madtom (*Noturus miurus*). Unlike most cats, it and the 12-inch stonecat (*N. flavus*) show a marked preference for swift, crystal rivers and brooks. Both grow a venomous spine at the base of each pectoral that inflicts a wasplike sting.

The Great Lakes and Mississippi Valley form a vast catfishery. Because cats usually like murky water and gobble anything digestible, they lie suspect to many palates. But Americans buy nearly 20 million pounds a year, ranking catfish first in value among freshwater food fishes. Three widely distributed bullheads—yellow (*I. natalis*), black (*I. melas*), and brown or horned pout (*I. nebulosus*)—are cherished friends of boys with cane poles.

Catfishes feed largely at night, prowling river and lake beds with feelers spread, suddenly diving in the mud for crustacean, snail, or insect larva. They nest in spring and summer under logs and rocks. Males guard the eggs the few days of incubation. The bullheads, protective as mother hens, convoy young in milling swarms.

Characteristics: scaleless; eight barbels; broad head. *Range:* native east of Rockies, introduced in West and Hawaii. *Weight:* some species a few ounces, others more than 100 pounds. *Length:* some 3 inches, others more than 5 feet.

BLACK BULLHEAD (bottom pair) and FLATHEAD CATFISH

Top to bottom: CHANNEL CATFISH, BROWN BULLHEAD, YELLOW BULLHEAD, BLUE CATFISH

STONECAT

BRINDLED MADTOM

Pikes

DUCKBILL JAWS studded with wicked teeth snare fishes, frogs, snakes—even aquatic birds and mammals—as the pikes (family Esocidae) devour up to a fifth of their weight a day. Solitary hunters who wait motionless for prey, they are the muskellunge, northern pike, and pickerel. They lurk in cool lakes and quiet rivers throughout the Northern Hemisphere. Notorious cannibals, they can swallow kin their own size (page 41). Fishermen esteem their brute power but condemn their destructive appetites. Canadians catch millions of pounds commercially, agreeing with Izaak Walton that pike properly cooked tastes "choisely good."

Pikes grow opposing dorsal and anal fins that flare from a shaftlike body like feathers from an arrow. These soft-rayed fins link them with the ancient fishes. Color differences between species tend to blur, but scale distribution on cheek and gill cover tells them apart. Pikes spawn in spring in shallows and give no care to eggs or young.

MUSKELLUNGE
Esox masquinongy

Barracuda of fresh water, the mighty muskellunge tips the scales officially at 70 pounds and unofficially at 100 to vie with lake trout as heavyweights of popular fresh-water game fishes. When a hook sets in the bony mouth and tackle withstands the powerful lunges, it is a good bet the angler will have his trophy mounted—proud of its size, strength, and relative rarity.

Native to the Great Lakes-St. Lawrence River region and transplanted widely, muskellunge abound nowhere. Probably their depredations of suckers, perch, and almost everything else that swims limit the number nature can maintain. Their gluttony serves conservationists, who plant them to curb undesirable fish populations.

In early spring muskies lay as many as 100,000 eggs which, neglected thereafter, stick to weeds and bottom. Fry hatch in about two weeks and quickly turn killers. Consuming hundreds of forage fish, they grow to six inches in 60 days. Adults become lone-wolf hunters, lurking motionless, surging forward to engulf prey.

Characteristics: sides may be spotted, barred, a mixture of spots and bars, or "clear"; cheek and gill cover scaled only on upper half. *Range:* St. Lawrence and Great Lakes areas, Ohio and upper Mississippi drainages west to Minnesota, Canada. *Weight:* average about 15 pounds, rod and reel record 70. *Length:* to 64 inches.

PAINTINGS BY WALTER A. WEBER, NATIONAL GEOGRAPHIC STAFF

MUSKELLUNGE (pursuing yellow perch)

WALTER A. WEBER

NORTHERN PIKE
Esox lucius

A venturesome red squirrel, paddling across a Minnesota lake, warily eyes what looks to be a submerged stick of wood. Almost imperceptibly the stick moves, drifting under the squirrel's wake. Suddenly the wood churns into life and surges upward. Its front end splits into massive jaws; razor teeth clamp the terrified squirrel. Dropping under widening ripples, a northern pike gulps part of a day's nourishment.

Pike have long stirred man's imagination. In medieval literature they gobbled swans, attacked men and mules. One supposedly lived 267 years. A mounted specimen on display measured 19 feet—until exposed as many pike artfully hitched together. One fancy persists: Since in summer pike teeth often fall out and mouths turn an irritated red, many anglers believe the fish do not eat. Actually they eat so heavily those lush months that their teeth are constantly breaking and regenerating.

Exceeding 45 pounds and four feet, pike resemble their relative the muskellunge in ravenous appetite, lone wolf habits, and spawning traits. When pike and muskies live side by side their spawn often cross-fertilize and produce the boldly striped tiger muskellunge.

Almost any lure cast into weedy, relatively shallow water will catch northern pike, although spoons and jointed plugs enjoy an edge in popularity. The fish may tantalizingly follow a lure to the boat, then sheer off. Ice fishermen on northern lakes and rivers often attract pike with lures or live bait, then spear them.

Angling for pike can be exasperating. The fish's razor teeth may sever all except wire leaders. Its vicious first lunge may snap a flyrod before the fisherman can react.

Boated with net or gaff, pike call for caution in removing the hook. Formidable teeth can shred the hand, and a toss of the head whips the gang hooks of a lure into anything in range. Anglers often resort to a subduing rap between the eyes before handling their catch.

Characteristics: gray-green splashed with pale bean-shaped spots; cheek fully scaled, lower half of gill cover unscaled. *Range:* Alaska to Labrador, southward to New England and Ohio Valley; introduced south to Maryland and in Pacific Northwest; occurs also in Europe and Asia. *Weight:* average 3 pounds, rod and reel record 46. *Length:* to 52 inches.

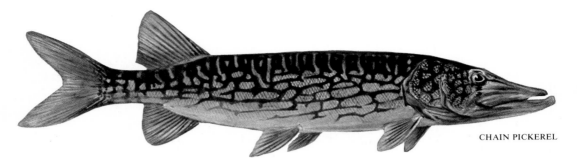

CHAIN PICKEREL
Esox niger

Never one to pass up an easy meal, the chain pickerel has cheered many a fisherman who would otherwise have gone home with an empty creel. Reaching nearly 10 pounds, "chainsides" is the largest of the pickerels and is often mistaken for a small northern pike.

Chain pickerel hunt with pike ferocity, pouncing on frogs, crawfish, mice, birds, and fishes up to half their size. Quick to take a lure, they respond best to bright wobbling spoons. The scrappers like clean, quiet streams and weedy lake edges where anglers usually seek bass.

Characteristics: dark chainlike markings on sides; cheek and gill cover completely scaled. *Range:* seaboard from St. Lawrence to Florida, states of Deep South, introduced elsewhere. *Weight:* average 2 to 3 pounds, rod and reel record 9½. *Length:* to 30 inches.

GRASS PICKEREL
Esox americanus vermiculatus

Pygmies among pikes, grass pickerel seldom grow a foot long. Yet like their bully brethren of the *Esox* clan, they hunt alone and destroy quantities of fishes. Conservationists, thinking they were transplanting other pikes, have inadvertently extended their depredations.

Grass, or "mud," pickerel like weedy, mud-bottom edges of lakes and quiet streams. These spring spawners rarely if ever frequent mountain waters. They and a fifth pike species, the eastern redfin pickerel *(E. americanus americanus),* do not grow big enough to interest anglers.

Seizing prey, pickerels usually maneuver it in their mouths until they can swallow it headfirst.

Characteristics: wavy bars on sides; cheek and gill cover scaled. *Range:* southern Wisconsin, Michigan, and Ontario to the Gulf Coast, introduced elsewhere. *Length:* to 12 inches.

Perches

PERCHES, DARTERS, and related basses and sunfishes rank among the most modern of fishes, dating back a mere 100 million years to an era when dinosaurs were vanishing from a hostile world and mammals were gaining a foothold. The air bladder has become useless as a respiratory device and in many darters has disappeared. Bones have hardened, contrasting with the cartilage-filled skeleton of ancient fishes. Fins have grown spiny rays. Pelvics have moved forward almost under the pectorals. The dorsal has divided, with a spiny portion forward of a soft-rayed one. Scales are saw-edge, or ctenoid.

Almost everyone who has wetted a line east of the Continental Divide has caught a member of the family Percidae—a yellow perch, a walleye, or a sauger. The perches lack strength as fighters (their elongated figures do not give the pulling power of deep-bodied bass), but they compensate in their abundance and renowned good flavor. All greedily devour insects and smaller fishes.

PAINTINGS BY WALTER A. WEBER, NATIONAL GEOGRAPHIC STAFF, AND HASHIME MURAYAMA (OPPOSITE, TOP)

YELLOW PERCH (lower pair) and LARGEMOUTH BASS (young specimen)

YELLOW PERCH
Perca flavescens

Thoreau found yellow perch "a true fish, such as the angler loves to put into his basket." Put on the dinner table, perch inspire even greater love, for they have the reputation of a delicacy one never tires of. Restaurants specializing in perch rim the Great Lakes, where each year U. S. and Canadian fishermen haul in 30 million pounds to make them the Lakes' leading fish.

Spawning at night in spring, perch lay eggs in a gelatinous rope, which entwines in shallow water weeds and may stretch seven feet long. Absorbing water, the rope becomes several times the parent's weight. Fry hatch in a week.

Perch ravenously gobble crawfish, insects, small fishes, and fish eggs; in the Great Lakes they make heavy raids on whitefish spawn. Innocently introduced in ponds and lakes, the predators often wipe out other species. Anglers take them on anything from grasshoppers to wet flies, often call their catch ring, raccoon, or striped perch, also convict.

Characteristics: 6 to 9 (usually 7) dark bars down the sides, orange-tinted fins. *Range:* native from Hudson Bay drainage south to Florida and west to Kansas; introduced in West. *Weight:* average less than a pound, rod and reel record 4¼. *Length:* seldom 1 foot.

277

WALLEYE
Stizostedion vitreum

Largest of perches, the powerful walleye easily overtakes minnows, bass, and yellow perch, locking them in canine teeth. More at home in lakes than rivers, it demands clear water and a sand or gravel bottom.

Nearly 60 colloquial names given to walleyes include yellow pikeperch, walleyed pike, yellow pike, glasseye, white-eye, marble-eye, dore, dory, even Susquehanna salmon. The related blue pike *(S. glaucum)* is nearly identical.

Walleyes feed nocturnally. Still-fishermen go deep, dangling bait inches from bottom and remembering that walleyes toy with food before mouthing it. Trolling works best at slow speed with deep active plugs and spoons.

Prized by anglers and caught commercially at a rate of some three million pounds a year, the prolific walleyes hold their own. They spawn in April, without nesting, in shallow water over beds of gravel and rock.

Characteristics: sides blotched, dark blotch at rear of first dorsal fin. *Range:* New York across Great Lakes and throughout Mississippi Valley; Canada; introduced widely, especially in Tennessee Valley. *Weight:* average 3 pounds, rod and reel record 25. *Length:* to 41 inches.

SAUGER
Stizostedion canadense

Many a game warden, suspecting an angler of taking home an undersize walleye, has conceded that the little fish might be a legal-size sauger. But close inspection reveals differences. Saugers lack the walleye's dark blotch at the rear of the first dorsal fin; dissection shows that saugers have five to eight caeca, walleyes only three.

Like the walleye, the sauger's pikelike teeth and body have led to misnomers: sand pike, gray pike, rattlesnake pike, pikeperch, pickerel, pickering. Saugers tolerate silty water, where they hungrily pursue smaller fishes and crawfish. They spawn prolifically in spring in lake shallows and tributary streams, depositing small eggs that settle to the bottom.

Anglers often catch saugers in the same water as walleyes and in much the same manner, trolling deep or still-fishing near bottom. Commercial fishermen land less than a quarter-million pounds annually, with Lake of the Woods the leading producer. In 1885, Ohio ports on Lake Erie reported an amazing 5¼-million pounds.

Characteristics: resembles walleye but smaller; often a translucent look. *Range:* same as walleye. *Weight:* average less than a pound, rod and reel record 8¼. *Length:* average 15 inches.

WALLEYE (lower pair) and SAUGER

HASHIME MURAYAMA (ABOVE), WILLIAM AMOS (OPPOSITE, TOP), AND CHARLES A. PURKETT, JR.

JOHNNY DARTER (*Etheostoma nigrum*)

DARTERS

Brilliant and fin-tassled, the tiny fish sits still as a rock, its head cocked alertly. The shadow of a river bird crosses the surface. Pectoral fins flare, and the fish scoots away like a bullet. Safe behind a stone, it stops on a dime and settles warily once more on its fins. This shooting star of lake and stream is a darter, one of 98 dwarf perches found east of the Rockies.

Timid predators which feed largely on larval insects and crustaceans, darters hide among stones and weeds; a few bury all but eyes and snout in the sand. They dart or sit, seldom merely cruising like other fishes.

Johnny and fantail darters, widespread on both sides of the Appalachians, spawn upside-down, laying eggs on the undersides of stones. Striped rainbow darters range across the Midwest. Stippled and Arkansas saddled darters glint in the waters of the Ozarks. Breeding males of numerous darter species take on vivid colors and devotedly guard their nests.

RAINBOW DARTER (*Etheostoma caeruleum*)

FANTAIL DARTER (*Etheostoma flabellare*)

ARKANSAS SADDLED DARTER (*Etheostoma euzonum*)

STIPPLED DARTER (*Etheostoma punctulatum*)

279

Temperate Basses

Fish of varied habitats, the temperate bass family includes members who dwell in fresh water, others who live in the sea, some who swim freely between both. The range of several species, particularly the illustrious "striper" (page 122), steadily expands as conservationists acknowledge their value for sport and food by introducing them into new waters. Temperate basses (Perichthyidae) are close kin of the sea basses (page 118); ichthyologists distinguish the two by a difference in gill structure, by the more deeply divided dorsal of the temperate basses—and by the fondness of most temperates for fresh water.

WHITE PERCH
Morone americana

Cheerfully inhabiting either fresh water or salt, white perch seem to prefer a middle ground, occurring in greatest numbers in brackish inlets and estuaries along the Atlantic coast. They often migrate into fresh-water streams to spawn. Some years have seen millions of these temperate basses strewn on the shores and river mouths of Chesapeake Bay, their deaths thought to be caused by a little-understood bacillus.

Eastern fishermen regard the white perch as one of the top fly-rod gamesters of its weight class. Smacking with trout ferocity at wet fly or light lure, the perch rushes madly until exhausted. It responds to bait-casting, trolling, and still-fishing and bites almost irresistibly on minnows, small eels, worms, grasshoppers, and shrimp. White perch swim in schools; thus a fish on the line may mean more below. Pan or deep fried, they are delicious.

Chesapeake Bay and coastal fishermen catch more than two million pounds a year using pound nets and baglike fyke nets. White perch spawn in spring, some in brackish water, some in streams. The eggs, neglected by the parents, hatch in about two days.

Characteristics: olivaceous back, silvery sides; often darker when landlocked; small web connecting the dorsal fins. *Range:* tidal region and coastal rivers from Nova Scotia to South Carolina; eastern ponds and lakes, especially in New England. *Weight:* rod and reel record 4¾ pounds, average less than a pound. *Length:* record 20 inches, average 8 or 9.

WHITE PERCH

WHITE BASS
Morone chrysops

Little known outside the Midwest, white bass gain a reputation as a fish to introduce where anglers deplete other species. Their climbing popularity reflects a high quality as game and food fish and an amazing prolificacy: Laying as many as a million eggs, they quickly colonize new waters and hold their own against anglers.

White bass live in deep water over sand and gravel bottoms. Occurring in greatest numbers in larger lakes and rivers, they often school on the surface. In spring they move into shallows or up tributary streams to spawn, on the way striking avidly at minnows and minnowlike lures.

Stocked artificial lakes in Missouri, Arkansas, and Texas offer prime white bass fishing. Anglers seek patches of churning surface and the "chop chop" of closing fish mouths, which mean bass are rising to slaughter schooling gizzard shad (*Dorosoma cepedianum*). Almost any lure cast into such a melee catches fish.

Characteristics: dark, body-length stripes on a silver or yellowish background; teeth on base of tongue. *Range:* St. Lawrence, Great Lakes drainage except Lake Superior; Mississippi River system; southern waters from Alabama to Texas. *Weight:* average 1 to 2 pounds, rod and reel record 5¼. *Length:* average 1 foot.

PAINTINGS BY WALTER A. WEBER, NATIONAL GEOGRAPHIC STAFF, AND HASHIME MURAYAMA (OPPOSITE)

WHITE BASS (top) and YELLOW BASS

YELLOW BASS
Morone mississippiensis

Yellow bass, or "barfish," are southerners, familiar only on the Lower Mississippi. If more widely distributed, doubtless they would acquire greater fame, for they are scrappy contenders that many claim outfight the black basses.

Like white bass, yellows prefer deep lakes and rivers. At spawning time they search out slow-moving streams. Deadly hunters, they churn water to foam as they slash through a school of gizzard shad. Other small fishes, in-sects, worms, and shrimp round out their menu.

Anglers take yellow bass much as they do white bass: casting, trolling, and still-fishing with wet flies, minnows, and minnowlike baits. The gamesters often bite best when fished deep. Gour-mets rank them tastiest of the temperate basses.

Characteristics: usually 7 dark longitudinal lines, several interrupted above the anal fin; brassy yellow sides, often a greenish back; mem-brane connecting the dorsal fin sections. *Range:* Gulf states to Indiana and southern Minnesota. *Weight:* average 1 to 2 pounds, reported at 5. *Length:* average 1 foot.

281

Sunfishes

Largemouth bass, smallmouth, bluegill, crappie—this lineup of fishing favorites belongs to the family Centrarchidae, 30 sunfishes native exclusively to North America. But—goodwill ambassadors—they thrive ever more widely around the world as nations import them for sport and food.

Generally gregarious, sunfishes do not let living together inhibit their penchant for eating each other. Farm ponds capitalize on this by stocking bluegills as food for bass. Juvenile sunfishes of different species are almost identical, and the varieties of adult black basses are notoriously confusing to anglers. Sunfishes wear saw-edge scales, forward-placed pelvic fins, and a single, though often deeply notched, dorsal. All except Sacramento perch are nesters, males usually doing the digging and guarding the eggs.

PAINTINGS BY WALTER A. WEBER, NATIONAL GEOGRAPHIC STAFF, AND HASHIME MURAYAMA (BELOW)

ROCK BASS

ROCK BASS
Ambloplites rupestris

Black bass fishermen will swear they hook two "rockies" for every largemouth or smallmouth, and they scarcely exaggerate. Attracted to almost any lure, rock bass put up a feeble fight, then usually go free as the angler seeks something bigger, gamier, and tastier.

Dubbed a boys' fish in sporting circles, rock bass make ideal family men. A nesting male, fanning with his fins on a gravel bottom, scoops a soup-bowl-size depression. He drives in a female, and the two lie side by side, she extruding a few eggs at a time, he instantly fertilizing. She soon departs, but he conscientiously stays to defend the nest.

Hatchling rock bass seek shallows, darting among weeds and stones when danger threatens. They eat waterfleas and other small insects, graduating to crawfish and small fishes. Often called bream, their bulging, bloodshot eyes also earn the names redeye and goggle-eye.

Characteristics: olive back, yellowish sides, dark spot on gill cover, often dots on scales that form longitudinal lines. *Range:* lakes and streams throughout the Mississippi Valley, Great Lakes, St. Lawrence system, eastern and southern United States; introduced into Pacific coast states. *Length:* average less than 10 inches.

LARGEMOUTH BASS
Micropterus salmoides

Big, prolific, hard-fighting, and good-tasting, the largemouth black bass holds a claim as America's most popular game fish. It lurks in lakes and sluggish streams in every state except Alaska, and also has been transplanted widely abroad, winning admirers on every continent.

Predatory largemouths greedily eat almost everything: insects, frogs, crawfish, snakes, mice, fishes (including little largemouths), young birds, baby muskrats. Bass society is patriarchal, males digging the nest, guarding eggs, chaperoning a cloud of young. Fry school, but adults tend to hunt in pikelike solitude. Southern largemouths, often called "trout," grow enormous; reports place them at 25 pounds.

Characteristics: olive to black on back, usually darker in murky water; irregular dark stripe from gill to tail. *Range:* native in Midwest and South, introduced coast to coast and to Hawaii. *Weight:* average 2 pounds, rod and reel record 22¼. *Length:* record 32½ inches.

SMALLMOUTH BASS
Micropterus dolomieui

In the time-honored argument about which bass has more zip, most anglers side with the spirited smallmouth. This predator of clear flowing streams and cool lakes strikes ferociously and fights with a strength that invariably excites admiration.

Highstrung and sensitive, smallmouths can detect a man's footfalls on a bank. If water temperature drops much below 60° F., a breeding male will abruptly abandon a half-dug nest.

Smallmouths look like half-size largemouths —but with differences. Their mouth ends beneath the eye; the largemouth's extends well behind. Smallmouths usually have 11 scale rows above the lateral line, largemouths 8 or less. Smallmouths lack a deeply notched dorsal fin.

Characteristics: olive back, no blotchy horizontal stripe. *Range:* Minnesota to Quebec south to northern Alabama and Arkansas; widely transplanted. *Weight:* average 1 pound, rod and reel record 12. *Length:* record 27 inches.

SMALLMOUTH BASS (top) and LARGEMOUTH

WHITE AND BLACK CRAPPIE
Pomoxis annularis   *P. nigromaculatus*

The look-alike crappie cousins live side by side throughout the eastern half of the United States, to the endless confusion of fishermen. Crappie experts point out that the more streamlined white crappie often shows perchlike rings, contrasting with dark blotches that mark the deep-bodied black crappie. White crappies predominate to the south, black to the north, both swarming in vast numbers wherever found.

Wide distribution has bred a rash of nicknames. On the Great Lakes white crappies are strawberry bass, ring crappies, pale crappies. Louisianans call them sacalait. Between these areas occur a score of other names such as lamplighter and millpond flyer. Black crappies, widely known as calico bass, also bear the names papermouth, tinmouth, grass bass, bitterhead, and some 20 additional aliases. To many fishermen, any crappie is simply a "croppie."

Crappies adapt to both clear and muddy water and show a fondness for underwater weeds, brush, and stumps. In this underbrush they spawn from May to July. Females deposit as many as 100,000 eggs in three to six feet of water. The male fans the spawn with his pectoral fins, supplying oxygen-bearing water and washing off silt. As a nest guardian the normally amiable crappie gives invaders a savage bite.

Introduced widely in the West and in impoundments everywhere, prolific crappies usually thrive. During the day they frequent deep holes; toward evening they feed near the surface in schools. Oddly, fishermen seldom catch crappies smaller than keeping size. Still-fishing with cane pole and minnow bait takes most, though crappies strike at artificial flies, spinners, and active plugs. The fish's mouth, which unfolds like a bellows to suck in insects and small fishes, tears free of the hook unless handled gently. Throughout their range crappies rank as superb food fish.

Characteristics: flaring fins; indented forehead; compressed body. *Range:* native in United States and southern Canada from Kansas east, widely introduced. *Weight:* average less than a pound; rod and reel record for white crappie 5 pounds 3 ounces, for black crappie 5 pounds. *Length:* average 9 inches, to 21.

SACRAMENTO PERCH

SACRAMENTO PERCH
Archoplites interruptus

Sole member of the sunfish family native to the Pacific slopes, Sacramento perch are older than the Rockies themselves; they probably represent the ancient fauna which extended across the continent before earth's convulsions raised the mountain barrier.

Unlike other sunfishes, Sacramento perch do not dig nests, but spawn around underwater objects. They lay their eggs in a long gelatinous string which drapes over submerged roots and brush. Because spawning Sacramento perch are less pugnacious than their eastern relatives, they suffer depredations from egg-eating carp and catfishes that man has introduced. An ability to live in alkaline waters leads to wide transplanting.

Sacramento perch reportedly grow two feet long, but fishermen prize 12-inchers. They take lures and natural baits readily and rank high as game and food fish. Natural foods include worms, insects, crustaceans, and small fishes.

Characteristics: variety of colors ranging from almost black to silvery, often streaked with dark vertical bars that usually number seven, dark spot at rear of pointed gill cover. *Range:* native to central California, introduced elsewhere in West and Midwest. *Length:* average 10 inches; to 24.

WHITE CRAPPIE (top) and BLACK CRAPPIE

REDBREAST SUNFISH (pair, top left), PUMPKINSEED (top right), SPOTTED (left center), BLUEGILL (right center), and WARMOUTH

PAN-SIZE SUNFISHES

A wriggling worm, chunk of sandwich meat, or dry fly—all suit the amiable sunfishes, animated iridescent disks that delight fishermen of all ages. Flashing in streams and lakes east of the Rockies, the prolific panfish generally look alike, nest in spring, interbreed, wear earlike lobes on gill covers, and share some 75 colloquial names, most commonly bream or sunperch.

Prince of panfish is the scrappy 10-inch blue-gill *(Lepomis macrochirus),* widely planted in stream and pond. In three years, 127 introduced in an Illinois lake multiplied to 67,700. The pumpkinseed *(L. gibbosus)* behaves similarly.

Long black ear lobes mark the redbreast *(L. auritus)* of Atlantic and Gulf states. The six-inch spotted sunfish *(L. punctatus)* swims in Mississippi Valley and Gulf states beside the dusky warmouth *(L. gulosus).* Warmouths, often called mudfish, goggle-eye, and black sunfish, lack the fine flavor of other sunfish.

Other Common Families

CALIFORNIA KILLIFISH

BLACKSTRIPE TOPMINNOW

KILLIFISHES
Family Cyprinodontidae

When a school of "minnows" flashes in pond or stream, likely as not the dwarfs are "killies." Seldom reaching four inches, killifishes nearly blanket the Nation. The U. S. has 36 species.

Mouths located conveniently atop the head, killifishes cruise near the surface snapping up tiny floating crustaceans. California killifish (*Fundulus parvipinnis*) and several others adapt to aquariums. The blackstripe topminnow (*F. notatus*) occurs across the Midwest. Several western killies are found only in a few desert waterholes. Killifishes serve as bait and forage.

Characteristics: protruding lower jaw; large scales. *Range:* nationwide and along both coasts. *Length:* 1 to 7 inches.

STICKLEBACKS
Family Gasterosteidae

North America's six stickleback species serve man by eating mosquito larvae. Four-spine (*Apeltes quadracus*) and brook sticklebacks (*Culaea inconstans*) build nests suspended among water weeds. Weaving plant stems into a roofed-over structure, they cement it with a sticky secretion, then drive in females to spawn.

Bristling with spines and fang teeth, the three-spine stickleback (*Gasterosteus aculeatus*) shreds attackers' fins and even fatally rips fish twice its 3½-inch length. The adaptable fish swims freely from salt water to fresh.

Characteristics: sharp separated dorsal spines; scaleless inland, plated in salt water. *Range:* Northern Hemisphere. *Length:* to 4 inches.

HASHIME MURAYAMA (BELOW), JAY C. QUAST (TOP), AND CHARLES A. PURKETT, JR.

THREE-SPINE STICKLEBACK

FRESHWATER DRUM

FRESHWATER DRUM
Aplodinotus grunniens

Unique among fishes, the freshwater drum helps raise its own food. Cruising the bottom to feed on pearl mussels, it sucks up mussel larvae and passes them back to the gills. There the clamlike organisms clamp to the drum's membranes and hang on. Maturing, they slough off to live independently—planting new mussel beds wherever they abandon ship.

Startled anglers often hear a purring noise rise out of a lake. It is a "thunder pumper" strumming its internal guitar. About 24 times a second the fish vibrates stringlike muscles against its air bladder, which, like a guitar's body, serves as a resonance chamber. The drum's ivorylike ear bones, bearing an L-shaped mark, have been talismans known as "lucky stones" to generations of young Americans.

Bottom-dwellers in large, silty rivers and lakes, freshwater drums are landlocked relatives of weakfish, croakers, and spot (family Sciaenidae). Great Lakes and Mississippi River fishermen, who net more than 10 million pounds a year, call them white perch, sheepshead, and croaker. To Louisiana anglers they are gaspergou.

Characteristics: olivaceous sides; long indented dorsal fin. *Range:* St. Lawrence and Great Lakes drainages except Lake Superior; Mississippi Valley; Mexico. *Weight:* average 1½ to 3 pounds, reported at 60.

ALASKA BLACKFISH

HASHIME MURAYAMA (OPPOSITE, TOP), JOHN TASHJIAN (OPPOSITE, LOWER), C. E. MOHR (BELOW, TOP), AND WILLARD E. DILLEY

SPRING CAVEFISH (top) and SOUTHERN CAVEFISH

ALASKA BLACKFISH
Dallia pectoralis

Alaska gold prospectors told how blackfish could freeze stiff in winter, thaw in spring, and live happily ever after. A dog reportedly swallowed a frozen blackfish that came to life in its stomach. Vomited up, the fish swam blithely in a bucket.

Tests show that if water freezes *around* a blackfish, but the fish remains unfrozen, it can survive briefly. But if internal cells freeze, they rupture, killing even blackfish.

Swarming in Alaska's rivers and bogs, blackfish feed Eskimos and their dogs. They share features and family (Umbridae) with temperate America's three mudminnow species.

Characteristics: pikelike fins; popeyes. *Range:* Alaska, Siberia. *Length:* to 8 inches.

CAVEFISHES
Family Amblyopsidae

Blind as the legendary bat, the southern cavefish *(Typhlichthys subterraneus)* thrives in eternal darkness of limestone caverns. Its entire body bristles with supersensitive nerve endings keyed to detect moving worms and crustaceans. The surface-dwelling spring cavefish *(Chologaster agassizi)* has eyes. But if the orbs are removed, it can still detect food.

All five North American cavefish species are thought to incubate eggs in the female's gill chamber. As the young cavefish mature, the vent migrates forward under the throat.

Characteristics: colorless in caves; pelvic fins missing or tiny. *Range:* limestone caverns of the South and Midwest, southern swamps and streams. *Length:* to 3½ inches.

289

PIRATE PERCH
Aphredoderus sayanus

Pirate perch, like trout-perch, stand at a stage of evolution between trout and perch. But pirate perch, devoid of adipose fins and having forward placed pelvics, come a step closer to the true perches. They survive as the earth's only living representatives of the family Aphredoderidae.

Fond of debris-cluttered ponds and lowland streams, pirate perch prey on larvae, insects, and small fishes. During spring spawning, parents grow iridescent; both are said to defend the nest. As with cavefishes, the vent of maturing pirate perch migrates forward under the throat. Specimens in the Mississippi Valley differ from East Coast representatives by having a poorly marked horizontal stripe.

Characteristics: two dark bars at base of tail fin, no adipose fin. *Range:* seaboard from New York to Texas, Mississippi Valley north to Michigan. *Length:* maximum 5 inches.

TROUT-PERCH
Percopsis omiscomaycus

The trout-perch is as ambiguous as its name— an intermediate creature torn between major levels of evolution. Like relatively ancient trouts, trout-perch retain unhardened skull bones, a rayless adipose fin, and a rudimentary connection between air bladder and esophagus. Like the more modern perch, they have spiny fins and saw-edge, or ctenoid, scales.

Trout-perch, or sandrollers, prefer shallow edges of larger lakes and streams but venture as deep as 200 feet. Easily hooked, they have provided many a thrill to young anglers fishing off Chicago piers. The spring spawners eat small crustaceans and aquatic insects, and are important forage fishes.

Characteristics: often a translucent look; two longitudinal rows of spots. *Range:* central Canada and Hudson Bay south to Kansas and Potomac River. *Length:* maximum 8 inches.

AMERICAN EEL
Anguilla rostrata

Streaming down rivers each year to spawn at sea, eels baffled man for centuries. Where in the vast Atlantic did they breed? A patient Dane combed the ocean for 17 years to locate their spawning ground: the Sargasso Sea near Bermuda, saltiest spot in the North Atlantic.

There, he discovered, American and European eels may descend 1,500 feet, release as many as 10 million eggs apiece, then presumably die. The larvae, flat and transparent, drift with the current and grow. Nearly a year later American eels shrink, metamorphose into a more eel-like form, and appear on our coasts 1,000 miles from their origin. Larval European eels drift in the Gulf Stream 2½ years to reach their coasts 3,000 miles away.

Female eels leave males at river mouths and ascend upstream, even to headwaters, unless stayed by dams. Feeding largely by night, they make destructive raids on gill nets; fishermen hauling in shad may find fish stripped to skull and backbone. The scavengers can writhe long distances over land. In about six years females swim downstream, rejoin the males, and make their spawning migration to the Sargasso Sea.

Early colonists, cherishing the fat delicious meat, speared 1,000 eels in a night. Today's harvest of less than a million pounds a year contrasts with an enormous European fishery. Tiny embedded scales give eels a smooth skin sometimes used for whips and book bindings.

Characteristics: long tubular body; continuous dorsal, caudal, and anal fins; no pelvics. *Range:* Mississippi Valley, Gulf states north to Labrador. *Length:* average 2 to 3 feet.

WARMWATER CURIOSITIES

Male seahorses bear young, skates hatch from "mermaid's purses," sharks casually eat tin cans. With the tropical fishes, expect almost anything.

ERNEST L. LI

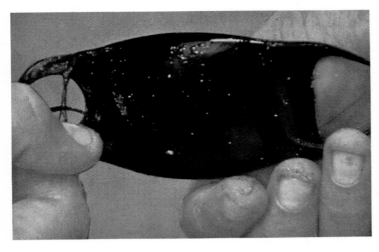

INQUISITIVE *Ken and Pat Libby find a mermaid's purse on Florida's St. Augustine Beach. Their father, the author, spent two years studying the strange birth process of its maker, the humble clearnose skate.*

Gulls, clamoring for a handout, flock around.

WITHIN *the rubbery purse, a baby skate grew like a chicken in an egg. After the embryo hatched, the sea washed the case ashore.*

"DAD, WHAT'S THIS?" my children asked. They handed me a small, dark, horned object they had found on the beach. I wonder how many youngsters, beach-combing after Atlantic storms, have stumped their dads with a mermaid's purse.

"Well, now," I hedged, "it's certainly an empty egg case. But what hatched out of it I don't know."

"Thanks anyway, Dad," said Ken and Pat, their disappointment evident.

For some years I had been photographer for the Marine Studios at Marineland on Florida's Atlantic coast 18 miles south of St. Augustine. One morning Ronnie Capo, skipper of our collecting boat, was leaving with his nets to catch candidates for our famous trained-porpoise act. I showed him the children's mermaid's purse, or sea purse, as it is sometimes called.

"I'm a father in bad standing," I said. "Catch some of whatever lays these things."

He grinned and put to sea.

Two weeks later my phone rang.

"I left some clearnose skates in the receiving tank for you," said Ronnie. "Already they're laying mermaid's purses."

In the library of Marineland's former curator, F. G. Wood, Jr., I looked up the clearnose. Science, I learned, knows this flat, mottled fish as *Raja eglanteria,* a distant but harmless little cousin of the savage white shark and the gigantic manta ray.

I had a small studio crowded with camera gear and salt-water aquariums. Into one of the photo tanks went the fresh-laid purses and my new skates.

Day after day I haunted my sanctum, watching my skates as they watched me. Soon they knew that my approach could mean tasty tidbits of fresh shrimp. Folding their wings into inverted U's, they stood hopefully on their back fins and poked their snouts out of water.

Far greedier than their husbands, the little mothers among them darted out of water like jet-propelled pancakes and grabbed my fingers. Thus one learns: Clearnoses have powerful, toothy jaws, and their mouths shoot out from their undersides when they bite.

Miracle of the Mermaid's Purse

Children's curiosity about a strange object on the beach leads to remarkable photographs of how a skate is born

EGG LAYING BEGINS. *Seen in its glass tank, this clearnose is about to shake free the horned case. Translucent patches on each side of the snout give the fish its name. Winglike pectoral fins propel it; the barbed tail helps it to steer.*

LIGHT SILHOUETTES *an 18-day embryo in its secure world. It began as a dot on the egg yolk. A gummy substance on the horns anchors the case to sand and shell.*

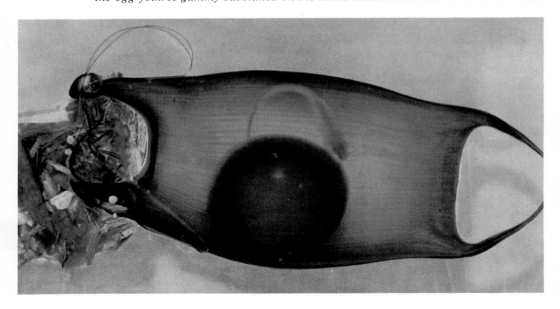

BORN PREMATURELY, *a skate sits on the egg yolk, tied by an umbilical cord to its built-in feed bag. For models to photograph, Mr. Libby freed clearnoses early from their purses. Those three weeks old or more survived the shock and thrived in his aquariums. In nature this 24-day baby would live in its case about 40 days more. Embryonic gills sprout like bushy red hair.*

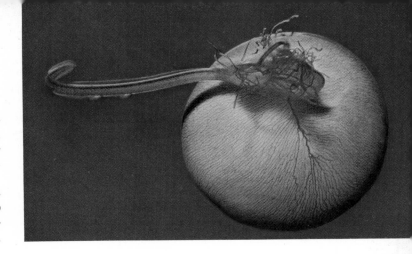

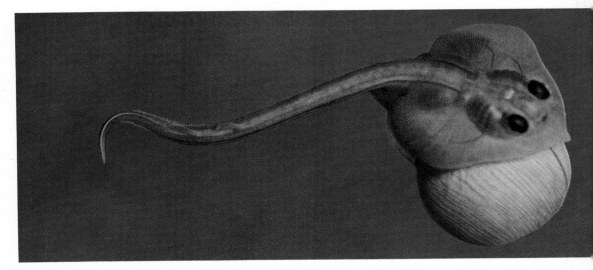

SHOE-BUTTON EYES BULGE *at 44 days. Wings now spread above the yolk.*

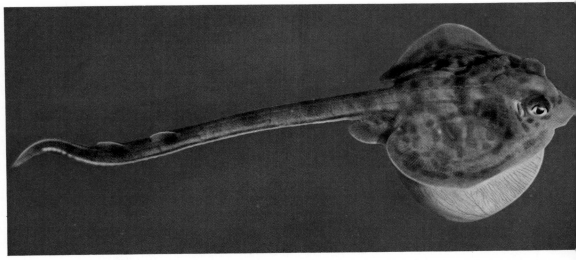

56 DAYS: *Rations almost spent, Junior faces life in a leopard coat.*

Curator Wood entered my private world.

"Let's candle a skate's egg," he suggested with a scientist's curiosity.

The dark-brown mermaid's purse is made of keratin, the basic stuff of hair, horns, and fingernails. Light came blood red through the case we chose, and we saw in silhouette a buglike embryo atop a round yolk.

"Put some time in on this, Ernie," said Woody, much interested. "Try and find a way to photograph these embryos as they develop. I think you might turn up something of real scientific value."

Ronnie Capo, whose tremendous stock of fish lore lies in the practical realm of how do you catch them and what do you do with them afterward, was greatly impressed.

"Gosh, Ernie," he said, "studying a fish as useless as a skate makes you a pure scientist, like the fellow who studies ways to cure a disease nobody's got.

"People won't eat a skate. It's a nuisance in a shrimp trawl and on a fishing bottom. You can't even show it to tourists; it hides in the sand with only its popeyes out."

Ernest Libby, pure scientist, set to work. Technical problem No. 1: how to photograph a thing that lives in a keratin suit. Indicated method: undress it.

I snipped the end from a purse and poured its contents carefully into sea water. They soon disintegrated.

At this age—a day or two—a clearnose's egg apparently cannot stand salt water; so I reasoned its case must be watertight. Tests on other fresh purses proved it. But the case we had candled was three weeks old and definitely *not* watertight; water had dribbled out when we picked it up.

Woody and I opened it and put embryo and egg-yolk anchor into a quiet aquarium. The skate-bug not only survived the abortion but grew and thrived.

Our discovery made possible my sequence photographs of a living clearnose as it would look inside its shelter from three weeks old until it emerges at nine weeks. At that time the purse seam splits and the case opens.

I learned that the twentieth day or thereabouts is a critical one for a little clearnose: Then it apparently gets its introduction to salt water. The albuminous egg white that surrounded the yolk finally disappears, probably absorbed, and this frees a tiny hole in each of the purse's four horns.

To be sure of enough oxygen-bearing sea water, the skate starts its pumps. The tip of the tail seeks one of the orifices, flutters, and sets up a current. Water comes in, exhausting through the other three holes.

The embryo by this time has developed a temporary network of external gills for extracting the life-sustaining oxygen from the current. The infant meantime is growing a permanent set of internal gills.

Now I had seen the miracle in the mermaid's purse. I had watched a tiny creature that would otherwise have fallen immediate prey to some prowler of the deep begin life protected by its own fortress—a fortress that clings to rocks with a gummy coating on the horns. I had seen how nature times matters so that her children may grow up to perpetuate their kind: The sea enters the mermaid's purse when it must, and only then, and the clearnose takes to the open sea when seaworthy, not before.

I had as yet no understanding of how the egg was given the spark of life and placed within the purse. I asked Ronnie for more skates, and he filled my tanks.

One of them I christened Abigail. Abigail laid infertile eggs. I put a likely looking male in her tank.

Hardly had the honeymoon begun when Clarence—that was Abigail's husband—sailed out of the tank and expired on the studio floor. But Abigail began laying fertile eggs and kept it up all during the laying season, suggesting that skate husbands need not spend too much time around the house.

It was Monday. Abigail was due to lay eggs the next day. I could always tell. Every four days her back humped slightly. Prowling her tank, she found a spot she liked; she hovered, and—it happened.

At such times I had only to focus my camera on the same spot and stand by for half an hour. Abigail would come back and lay another egg. Click! went the shutter.

But this particular Monday night an octopus in the next-door tank pulled down the

AFTER ONE MATING, *a clearnose lays two fertile eggs about every fourth day during a nine-month season. This one chose a rocky nook for her nest.*

EYELIKE NOSTRILS *in a ghostly face scent food; gill slits, arranged like lapels, mark the skate's breathing apparatus. Toothy, woebegone mouth pops from the underside when it bites. Diver at left searches for egg cases.*

hose that carried sea water for circulation through Abigail's tank—flooding the studio and suffocating Abigail.

Sadly I watched Cliff Townsend, our assistant curator, perform the postmortem.

"She was a factory!" he exclaimed, pointing at eggs from pea-size to thumb-size in Abigail's twin production lines.

"But here's something interesting. Look, not a sign of a case around the eggs she would have laid tomorrow. Think how fast her purse-making department must work!"

Equally wondrous is the skate's breathing system. Oxygen-laden water enters two spiracles on top of the head, and spent water leaves through slits on the underside.

So practical! Were the breath current reversed, the bottom-hugging skate would choke its gills with sand.

Paddlelike segments of the pelvic fin, looking for all the world like little paws, power the skate on the ocean floor. Wings—actually the pectoral fins—furnish the swimming drive. The long tail helps in steering.

Ridged with spines, perhaps it also discourages faint-hearted predators.

The largest clearnoses weigh little more than six and a half pounds. I have no evidence on longevity. Some of my clearnoses thrived for more than two years. Death visited my tank only through accident, not age.

Around St. Augustine, people catch skates when they would rather catch bass. Annoyed, they throw the clearnoses onto the sunseared walkways, where they quickly gasp away their small lives.

Sometimes, if it is not too late, I drop them quietly back into the ocean. Besides, a practical application for my research has already been found.

I learned about it the other evening. Young voices came through my window.

"One ole mermaid's purse isn't worth two rare conch shells," said a neighbor's son.

"This one is," boasted young Ken. "It came from the research lavatory of Dr. Ernest Libby, world's greatest authority on clearnose skates."

WINGS FOLDED *like a rolled pancake, a baby clearnose leaves the purse. Its wingspan—3½ inches—is triple the width of the egg case. Soon the wings will unfold free of the horns, leaving only the tail encased. The protecting purse always splits at the end opposite its anchored horns.*

A FINAL KICK *of the tail frees the prisoner. Now the skate must hunt for its next meal. The author found his premature infants stronger at hatching time than those born naturally, presumably because they had had more exercise.*

ERNEST L. LIBBY

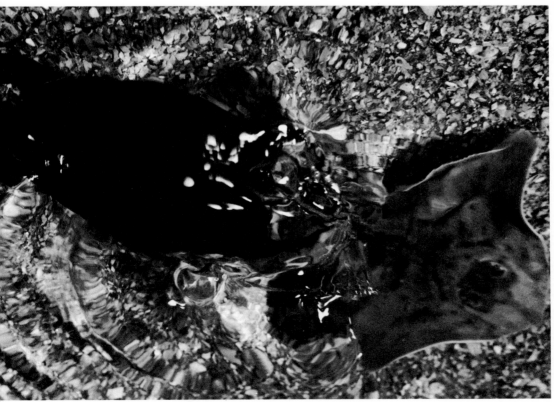

IT WAS OUR young son Paul's turn to make a little recitation at his New York City school for boys. The kindergarten teacher nodded approval as he began:

"Yesterday I watched a seahorse give birth to many babies. I saw the babies come out of the father's stomach."

The teacher, reddening slightly, cut in: "Paul, you mean a *mother* seahorse."

"No," insisted the youthful ichthyologist, "the father had the babies."

A patient smile played over the teacher's face as Paul, with quiet confidence, went on. He told how his father had set up salt-water aquariums stocked with dwarf seahorses in their apartment. And how he and his sister Eda, age 9, had watched a male seahorse delivering. One by one the babies had come out of the "stomach," usually tailfirst. Quickly they had propelled themselves off in search of a blade of grass about which to twine their tails.

Whether Paul convinced the teacher, I do not know. As she confessed subsequently, she did check his story in an encyclopedia.

There it was in black and white—the facts of a strange life cycle in which the female seahorse deposits her eggs in the male's brood pouch. Here they are fertilized, developed, and brought into the world.

Our first shipment of dwarf seahorses (*Hippocampus zosterae*) arrived one icy February day. Eagerly, the children watched as I tore open the wrappings.

One of our bulging bags was tagged "Specimens," the other, "Condensed Sea Water." This one held a gallon of soupy sludge that smelled strongly of the sea. Diluted with nine parts of tap water, it became sparkling sea water. We distributed this among four small aquariums.

Later, when the chlorine in the tap water had partially dissipated, I transferred our seahorses to the aquariums. We had ordered two dozen, but a rapid tally revealed at least 36, many so small I could barely see them. One or more pregnant males had delivered in transit!

A final package held a small vial containing the eggs of brine shrimp. Sprinkled in a dish of sea water, within 24 hours they

CHAPTER EIGHTEEN

By PAUL A. ZAHL, Ph.D.

National Geographic Senior Staff

Neptune's Little Horses

The seahorse has a colt's head, an insect's shell-like body, a kangaroo's pouch — and the male gives birth to the young

JUMBO SEAHORSE, *tethered by his tail to a sea whip in the author's aquarium, lets a miniature cousin ride his tapered back. A second dwarf* (Hippocampus zosterae) *perches at lower left. Spangled with silver and galaxies of white dots, the six-inch lined seahorse* (H. erectus) *arches his neck like a thoroughbred. He and the mimicking dwarf live compatibly in Florida waters.*

PAUL A. ZAHL, NATIONAL GEOGRAPHIC STAFF

SEAHORSE ROUNDUP: *Skin divers serve as cowboys in Florida's grassy pastures. Dwarfs the size of paper clips live by the tens of thousands in these shallows near Key Largo. They drew the author and his family for two months to observe and collect* Hippocampus *in its natural habitat. Nine-year-old Eda Zahl and Robert P. L. Straughan, a marine collector, search the four-foot depths in face masks and flippers. A net fastened to the anchored inner tube holds their finds. A trawl pulled across the bottom made most of the captures (below). Its rectangular metal frame, about four feet wide and 20 inches high, drags a bulging nylon net that collects the specimens. Swimmers ride the frame to prevent fouling on sponge masses and coral heads. A fifteen-minute run behind the slow-chugging outboard produces about 30 seahorses.*

304

PAUL A. ZAHL, NATIONAL GEOGRAPHIC STAFF

hatched into nearly microscopic larvae, fine food for captive pygmy seahorses.

Hippocampus intrigued us for months in our apartment and lured us, in early June, 1,000 miles south to the grassy shallows off Florida's famous Keys and Gulf coast. Habitat observations, agreed the National Geographic Society, might add significantly to the general fund of marine knowledge.

In a motel on U. S. Highway 1 on Key Largo, we set up quarters. Soon our two-room apartment was abuzz with aquarium aerators and cluttered with collecting gear and an assortment of tanks.

On my first collecting trip, my companion was Robert P. L. Straughan, a skillful skin diver and one of the country's principal suppliers of live seahorses. He had sent our specimens the previous winter.

One morning Bob and I rented a skiff. We were soon a couple of miles offshore in fairly clear water about four feet deep. A solid blanket of green grasses covered the bottom. Bob prepared our trawl, a metal frame about four feet wide and 20 inches high that held a bulging nylon net.

With the outboard barely chugging, we moved slowly in a large circle. After about 15 minutes of sweeping, we drew in our net. It revealed grass, sponge fragments, mud, sand, bits of shell and coral.

My eyes focused on a wriggling object no larger than a paper clip—a tiny seahorse colored a beautiful golden yellow.

Quickly we spotted others in the debris—more yellow ones, a few bright green, some chocolate brown—32 in all.

We tossed the net overboard and made another run; then another, and another. By midafternoon we had about 200 seahorses.

305

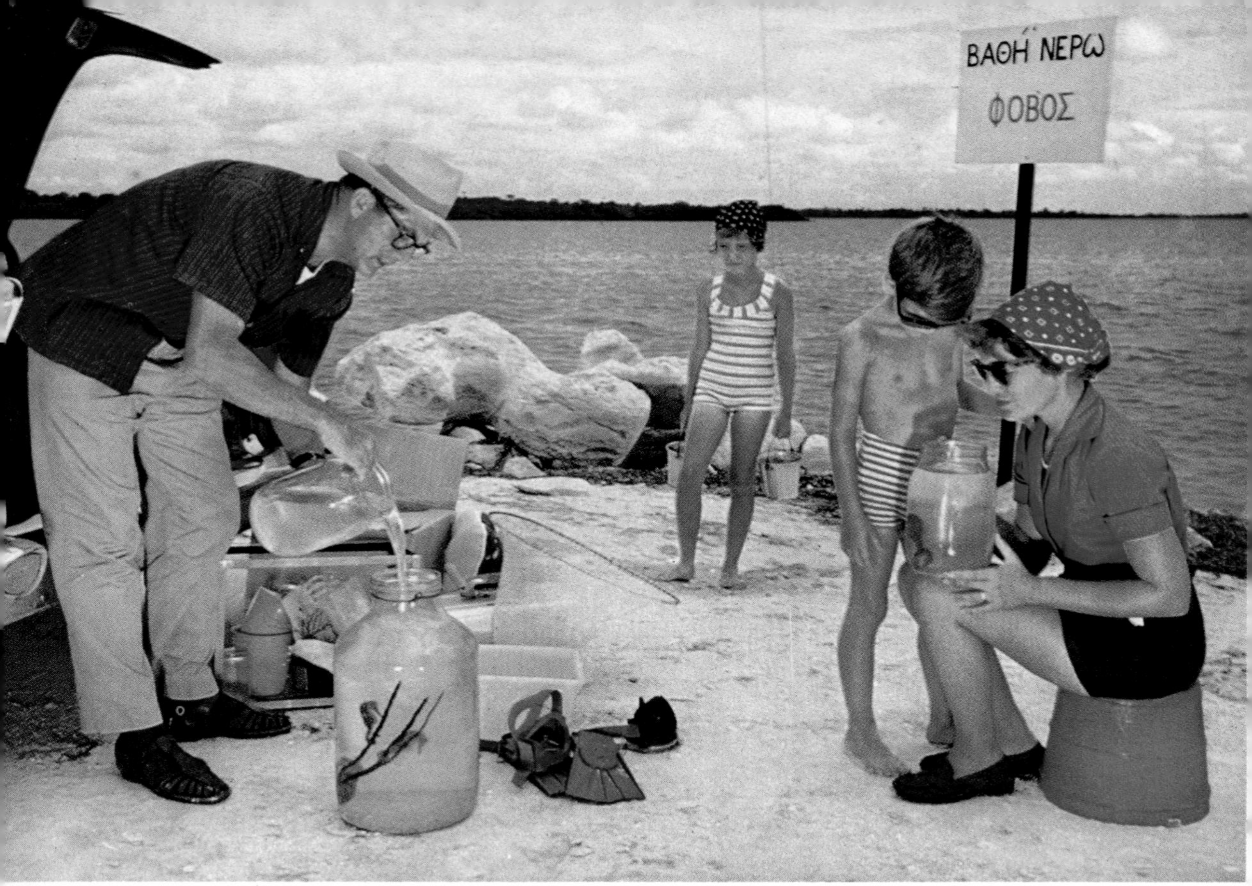
ΒΑΘΗ ΝΕΡΩ
ΦΟΒΟΣ

THE ZAHLS *pause to refresh seahorse passengers during the family quest in Florida. Carboys of living specimens rode in the back seat with the youngsters. A lined seahorse perches calmly as the author fills its jar.*

"Deep Water! Beware!" reads the sign in Greek near Tarpon Springs, home port of sponge fishermen of Greek origin.

PAUL A. ZAHL, NATIONAL GEOGRAPHIC STAFF

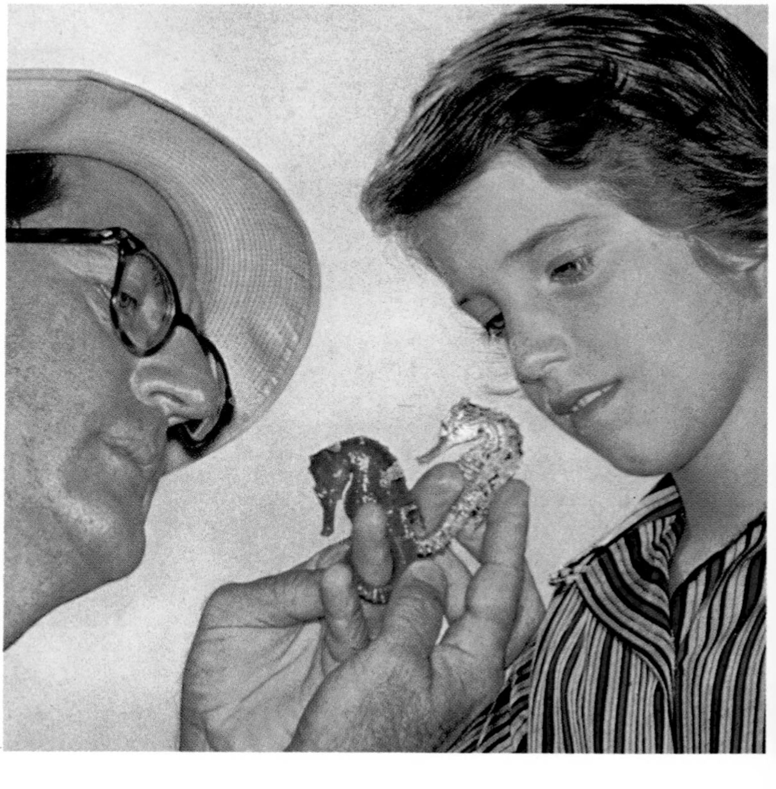

SEAHORSES CLING *to the author's fingers with the grip of a small child's. Ashen gray and a scarce brick red illustrate the wide color range of the giant* H. erectus.

Florida

Gulf of Mexico

SAFARI TO SEAHORSE COUNTRY *took Dr. Zahl and his family from Key Largo north along the Gulf to Tarpon Springs and back to Miami.*

I put the catch in my motel aquariums.

"Look at the hippocampuses!" yelled Paul as the children came in that evening, their bathing suits still dripping.

"And see the pregnant males," cried Eda, as though Paul needed any coaching on that delicate matter. "Will they give birth tonight, Daddy?"

"I'll let you know in the morning," I replied, and prepared for an all-night vigil.

Hours later, with the children and their mother sound asleep, I sat before an aquarium and watched. Soon one of the dwarf males began to twitch uneasily. His body began to sway, and at about one-minute intervals he thrust forward his bulging pouch and seemed to tense his entire system.

The pouch aperture, previously shut tight, began to open. More tensing and straining, until finally a tail poked through the opening. A two-minute rest followed, and again the father began his somewhat rhythmic "labor pains." The tail, wiggling now, got longer. Finally, following a spasmodic squeeze, a baby seahorse popped out.

For a few seconds the newborn drifted downward, writhing helplessly. Then it snapped upright, and two transparent fins on its head began to quiver. Before I could count to three, the baby swam away under its own power, and soon its tail twisted around a tendril of sea grass. There it sat and looked straight at me.

The father continued in labor. Two and a half hours later, 20 newborns were clinging to objects around the tank with their flexible tails.

That prehensile tail is one more unfish-like peculiarity of the seahorse. Another is the fact that it has no scales. It wears a strange "skin skeleton" composed of some fifty bony rings extending from neck to tail. They support a series of plates. The ultimate effect is that of a medieval war horse clad in jointed armor.

The eyes swivel independently; one can gaze astern while the other peers ahead.

The mother produces the eggs, but after that, gestation is the male's responsibility. The couple performs a mating dance, the female deposits her eggs in the father's pouch, he fertilizes them as they enter, and from then on he runs the hatchery.

His pouch expands as capillary blood vessels swell and multiply. Tissue forms around each egg, giving it a room of its own.

Species of the seahorse are found throughout the world's warmer seas and as far north as the chilly English Channel. Dwarfs measure about an inch, but Australian and Japanese waters produce seahorses a good foot long—real Percherons!

307

MOMENT OF BIRTH: *Headfirst a baby* zosterae *pops out of the pouch (opposite). The paper-clip-size father, twitching and swaying, seems to have actual labor pains as his several dozen young emerge, usually one at a time. Larger* erectus *may pour out as many as 700 in quick spurts. The female plays but the briefest part in the foaling; she merely deposits the eggs in the male's pouch and departs, perhaps never to see her children. Father then carries the embryos about 10 days before ejecting the young.*

POUCH APERTURE *fully opened reveals a mass of young (right). One black eye peers out. Another baby, ejected a moment earlier, clings to a branch. The free-floating male above has just given birth to two baby seahorses which clutch a passer-by. At this tender age their horselike snouts are pugged. Infants drift helplessly for a few seconds, then right themselves and swim away in a vertical position. Unable to return kangaroolike to the pouch, they grow rapidly on their own and mature in a few months.*

308

LASSOED PIPEFISH *serves as a roost for its seahorse relatives. Like the latter, the male* Syngnathus floridae *incubates its young in a brood pouch. Bent into the shape of a knight chessman, he would resemble a seahorse. Seiners often bag both together.*

Big or small, they do not lack a statuesque dignity, their necks so proudly arched, their gait so obstinately upright. Too fascinated to be fatigued, I sat for hours that night studying their antics.

To its prey, the mild little seahorse undoubtedly seems savage. With its tail gripping some object, it waits for shrimp larvae or other plankton to drift by. Suddenly a trap door at the tip of its snout snaps open. There is a lightning-fast intake of water, and down a seahorse gullet sweeps the hapless prey, swallowed whole.

Poor swimmers by any fish standard, seahorses avoid tidal currents. For motive power they have several little buzzing outboards: a fin halfway down the back, two delicate flaps on either side of the head, and a tiny bit of fin tissue just below the abdominal bulge. But even though its dorsal fin flutters 10 times per second, a seahorse may take five minutes to scull across a three-foot-wide tank.

When the seahorse wants to rise, it unkinks itself, straightening out like a pencil. When it wants to descend, it tucks its neck in and rolls up its tail.

In subsequent weeks Bob and I netted thousands of dwarfs. We noted that their hues—greens, yellows, browns, and even oranges—represented a protective adaptation to the grasses, corals, or sponges of their habitats.

Minute changes in the pigment cells, or chromatophores, of the skin help seahorses produce these colors. In another trick of mimicry the seahorse often displays weird branchings from its head and body that look like the arboreal growths it hides among.

"That golden-yellow dwarf," I mentioned to Bob, referring to the beautiful specimen we had taken on our first day out. "Have you seen any similar to it?"

"They're not common," he replied. "Perhaps one in a thousand. Speaking of color, you should have seen a giant lined horse I had around here a few months ago. A *Hippocampus erectus* I caught—it was bright red."

"I'd give my eyeteeth to see one," I said. "Do you think we can find another?"

From five to eight inches long, *H. erectus* is similar in structure to *H. zosterae:* tubiform snout, hard exterior armor, upright orientation, fluttering fins, prehensile tail, and pouched body of the male. Its birth process differs in that 200 to 700 young are produced at one delivery, spurting from the pouch in a veritable cloud of life.

Finding a brightly colored giant did become a matter of eyeteeth. Bob and I spent weeks on Biscayne Bay seining in sight of Miami's majestic skyline. We got a few dozen lined horses but none with brilliant color.

Then my patient family and I began a protracted seahorse roundup that led across the peninsula and along the Gulf: to Naples and Fort Myers, to Sanibel Island and Pine Island Sound, to Tampa Bay and the friendly Greek atmosphere of Tarpon Springs.

Finally, having found only one pallid specimen, I took my long-suffering wife and children back to Miami for a goodbye visit with Bob Straughan.

"Are you lucky!" Bob exploded happily as he met us. "Ever since you left I've been trawling Biscayne Bay to get a colored lined horse. And yesterday, believe it or not, I netted an orange beauty in the first trawl."

An hour later, in a Miami motel, the whole Zahl family gathered around my aquarium on the kitchen table to stare at the rare brilliant specimen Bob had presented to me.

"Isn't it beautiful!" breathed little Eda.

"Yes, it's a female—no pouch, see?" young Paul added.

"And now that you have your gay seahorse," sighed my wife, "I hope we can go home. Two months of wrangling seahorses is enough!"

DRIED LINED SEAHORSES *stand artfully on driftwood podiums at a Tarpon Springs curio shop. Bait trawlers keep up the supply. Other souvenirs include a spiny lobster and a variety of Gulf fishes, including a barracuda's gaping, toothy head.*

311

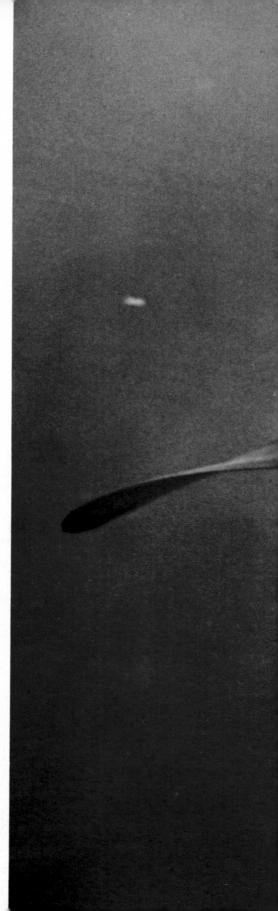

CHAPTER NINETEEN

By NATHANIEL T. KENNEY

National Geographic Senior Staff

Sharks: Wolves of the Sea

IN MASK AND SNORKEL I was diving in 15 feet of water off the western shore of North Bimini, tiny Bahama island. A jumble of coral-encrusted boulders lies on the bottom sands there; among them dwell thousands of brilliantly colored small fishes.

One moment I was surrounded by these vivid jewels of the warm salt seas. In the next I was uneasily alone, for my small friends had all dashed for shelter into crevices or to concealing jungles of grass and sea fans. Turning seaward to discover what had alarmed them, I saw a shadow in the depths grow into an eight-foot-long torpedo headed directly at me.

Some 20 feet away it turned broadside. An eye the size of a quarter inspected me from head to toe. Then, with sinuously graceful movements of body and tail, the monster returned to the open sea, never varying its serene cruising speed. Popping to the surface, I also returned whence I came—to the solid, sunny beach. I moved at something better than cruising speed.

RIPPING HAM-SIZE CHUNKS *from a dead porpoise off New York, a blue shark symbolizes the rapacity of earth's 250 shark species.*

PETER GIMBEL

312

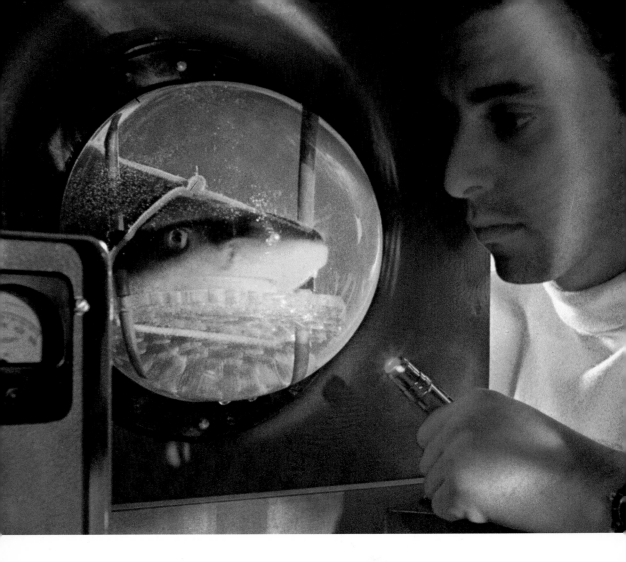

I had met a shark, and the encounter was typical: In the overwhelming majority of meetings between the fearsome carnivores and humans, the predators cruise on past.

But one must not count on it. Any moment the time may come when one of the enigmatic creatures will attack a man. And results can be gruesome. Razor-edged teeth may remove an arm or leg or cleanly take out a 10-pound piece of flesh. Hide rough as a rasp can flay, edges of fins and tails cut like swords. A shark is all lethal weapon.

And what are the odds for or against your becoming a target next time you go to the beach? The experts cannot give a completely satisfactory answer. You have only the assurance that the odds are long—perhaps millions to one—in your favor.

Since 1958 the Smithsonian Institution of Washington, D. C., has been custodian of a shark-attack file on an international scale. Dr. Leonard P. Schultz, who helps maintain the file, believes it to be far from complete.

"Faraway primitive people do not compile statistics," he explains, "and seaside resorts don't overexert themselves publicizing incidents that could bring bankruptcy."

From the evidence of the file, plus the opinions of experts to whom I talked during a year of studying sharks in many parts of the world, I would make an educated guess that in a normal year sharks kill or maim not less than 40 or more than 300 people, without apparent provocation by the victims. In times of war at sea or major marine disaster, the toll undoubtedly rises.

TESTING THE VISION *of a young lemon shark, Samuel Gruber of the University of Miami's Institute of Marine Sciences employs an ingenious apparatus that he devised. The shark is lashed down in a tank of circulating water, its nose fitting into a Plexiglas hemisphere. At intervals a lamp flashes light of varying color and intensity; at the same time a mild shock causes the fish to blink. Eventually the shark becomes so conditioned that it blinks when only the light is flashed, an indication that it can see that particular color or intensity. Knowledge of whether sharks distinguish colors could prove valuable in designing garments for ocean use.*

Shark's blink occurs with the upward movement of a nictitating membrane that serves as an eyelid (above). Infrared detector enables observation of each "wink" in a darkened testing room at the institute.

JERRY GREENBERG

HOW SENSITIVE *is a shark to sound? It can hear objects moving in the water at a distance greater than it can see them, tests reveal. Its ability to locate the source is acute—a trait vital to the predator (diagram, pages 318-19).*

At Miami's Institute of Marine Sciences a researcher puts a live lemon shark into a water-filled tube; sounds projected into the tube can be regulated by the electronic equipment in the foreground control room. Conditioning the shark with electric shocks, the scientists learn what frequencies the fish can hear, and how well it can hear them.

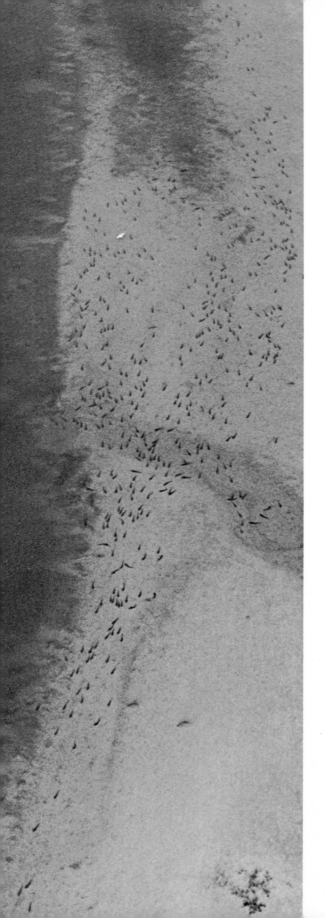

Thus you can go into the sea—any principal sea or ocean, for the shark lives in them all, plus many rivers and a few freshwater lakes—with far less risk than you run every time you take a trip in an automobile. You will also hear that lightning is a greater danger than shark bite, and figures support the statement.

You must not, of course, provoke a shark into attacking—not even the small, slow species encountered in coastal waters. If you step on one of these or tweak its tail, it can—and often will—bite hard.

Despite the odds against unprovoked attack upon us, we attach a sinister mystique to the shark. The sight of a gray fin in the surf, even the rumor that somebody has seen one, brings unreasoning panic. Add, on a more impersonal level, the shark's inroads on commercial and sport fisheries, and you have a malefactor of some consequence. But it was not until fairly recently that science organized to study sharks and seek ways of controlling them.

Blood-chilling mass attacks on survivors of torpedoed ships and crashed airplanes in World War II gave the initial impetus to the search. After the war, interest in sharks broadened as divers in unprecedented numbers began searching the depths for ways to tap food and mineral riches of the oceans.

Encounters with sharks became everyday occurrences. Plainly, more knowledge of the fish was needed. In 1958, the American Institute of Biological Sciences, Washington,

EXTRAORDINARY GATHERING *of sharks peppers Oja de Libre Lagoon in Baja California. Pacific gray whales breed in these waters, and some scientists speculate that sharks may too.*

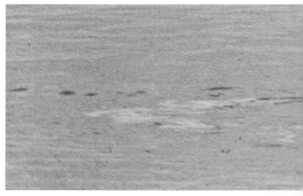

D. C., formed the Shark Research Panel to serve as an international clearinghouse and repository for shark knowledge.

Dr. Perry W. Gilbert, executive director of the Mote Marine Laboratory in Sarasota, Florida, and probably the foremost American authority on sharks, is chairman. Dr. Schultz is an emeritus member. Five other scientists serve on the panel.

The panel devotes much effort toward finding ways of protecting shipwrecked sailors or downed airmen against sharks. Obviously, you begin such a quest by noting that a shark is a predator and normally attacks for food. In a way, it is like a wolf.

"A shark is an opportunist," Perry Gilbert said. "It frequently hunts the weak, the old, the stupid, and the crippled. The prey animals often are weakened fishes. Thus a man in the sea should avoid making jerky, struggling movements that could resemble those of a crippled fish."

In tests off Florida, taped sounds of wounded fish and thrashing swimmers, played in the sea, have caused sharks hundreds of yards away to home on the source.

How else does a hurt fish tempt sharks?

"It bleeds," said Stewart Springer, biologist with the U. S. Bureau of Commercial Fisheries and a panel member. "A small amount of blood attracts sharks from afar. They have extraordinarily sensitive noses."

Following blood trail or sound, the shark approaches to within sight distance of a possible meal. It circles cautiously, gradually narrowing the circles. Eventually, if still alone, it bumps the object with its snout. A bite comes next, delivered with a savage shaking of the head. The rest is mayhem.

This is the normal feeding pattern of a lone shark. If other sharks appear, all may short-circuit the pattern, attacking in a competitive rush without the preliminaries. As feeding continues and blood and flapping stimuli increase, the sharks become wildly excited and snap at anything they encounter.

Sharks do have their uses. Scientists believe them to be resistant to cancer and less prone than humans to heart diseases and other ailments. Sharks synthesize serum antibodies like the ones the human infant produces to protect itself against disease, and they show less reaction to brain injury than mammals. A host of scientists across the Nation investigate these phenomena, knowing that explanations could help man.

Shark livers, huge organs making up as much as a quarter of the owner's weight, abound in vitamin A, although a synthetic now dominates the market. Dried shark fins flavor sharkfin soup, fancied by Oriental gourmets. Fresh shark meat is widely eaten; anyone who has ordered scallops or "steakfish" in a cafe may very well have had shark.

Shark hide makes tough, good-looking leather. With the scales on, it forms an abrasive called shagreen, once used as sandpaper. Oddly the scales are in reality crude teeth, known as placoid scales, or dental dermicles. They cover nearly all the body.

PURSUING AN ELUSIVE MEAL, *a young shark—possibly a white—broaches in San Ignacio Lagoon, Baja California. More and more anglers recognize the fighting shark as one of the world's best game fish. The sport of shark fishing began in Australia in the 1920's, and an Australian holds the record for the biggest fish landed by rod and reel—a 2,664-pound white.* 317

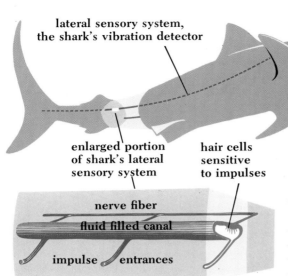

lateral sensory system,
the shark's vibration detector

enlarged portion
of shark's lateral
sensory system

hair cells
sensitive
to impulses

nerve fiber
fluid filled canal
impulse entrances

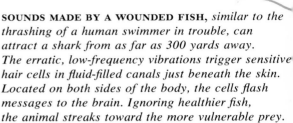

erratic impulses

smooth rhythmic impuls

SOUNDS MADE BY A WOUNDED FISH, *similar to the thrashing of a human swimmer in trouble, can attract a shark from as far as 300 yards away. The erratic, low-frequency vibrations trigger sensitive hair cells in fluid-filled canals just beneath the skin. Located on both sides of the body, the cells flash messages to the brain. Ignoring healthier fish, the animal streaks toward the more vulnerable prey.*

"SURVIVAL SACK" *holds its designer, Dr. C. Scott Johnson, above a lemon shark at Lerner Marine Laboratory on North Bimini. Attached to a life jacket, the plastic bag inflates quickly.*

In the shark's mouth the teeth grow in rows at the front of the jaws. From 20 to several hundred teeth, depending on the species, form a fearsome armament. Five or six more sets—in some species as many as 15—wait in reserve behind, continuously moving forward so that when front teeth drop out, new ones take their place.

Of the more than 250 shark species known at present, only a dozen can be listed as proven eaters of man. These are the white, which also bears the name "man-eater"; shortfin mako; bull; lemon; tiger; dusky; blue; blacktip; Pacific Ocean gray; Australian whaler; the largest hammerheads; and the oceanic whitetip. All these sharks have attacked living humans as well as corpses.

In addition to the proven man-eaters, there is a category of sharks best characterized as "reasonable suspects." The sandbar, or brown is one. So is the silky, named for its relatively glossy skin. Some others may be dangerous but usually live in waters too deep or cold to pose a threat to man.

Every shark—and every other marine creature as well—gives sea room to the white shark. Here is the real lord of the sea.

More than most sharks, they prefer a mammalian diet—whales, seals, sea otters, and so on. The inference is obvious. Man is a mammal too, and in a rubber diving suit, a man looks like a seal. Also, according to Perry Gilbert, neither whites nor any other sharks see things in clear detail.

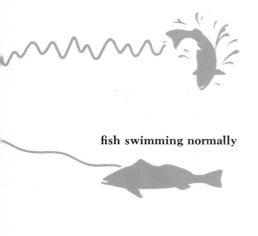

fish in distress

fish swimming normally

In 1916 a shark or sharks attacked five swimmers along the New Jersey coast. Four died of savage injuries. The fifth lost a leg. There was panic and publicity. Shortly afterward a fisherman caught a white shark with human remains in its stomach.

As the years passed, fishermen from Maine to Nova Scotia reported occasional encounters with whites. In most cases the huge fishes attacked their boats.

In 1964, off the Farallon Islands, in cold California waters, scuba diver Jack Rochette survived serious bite wounds. The surgeon found a tooth fragment in the victim's leg. It had belonged to a white shark.

Two years before, Leroy French, Al Giddings, and other members of a Marin County scuba club had been diving in the same area.

"I was in the water near our boat," Giddings recalled. "Leroy surfaced from a dive 75 yards away. Suddenly he screamed for help and went under. I swam to him fast as I could. The water was red. Leroy came to the top. So did a large shark.

"I towed Leroy to the boat without interference from the shark. The Coast Guard flew him to a hospital, where he eventually recovered from dreadful bites.

"From my father, a California fish and game warden, I had learned to recognize all our local species of sharks. I saw this one quite well. It was a white."

Happily, white sharks seem rare. Few people have seen more than two together.

Not until the comparatively recent development of scuba gear did anyone meet pelagic sharks face-to-face in the open ocean and come back to tell what happened. Captain Jacques-Yves Cousteau, co-inventor of the Aqua-Lung, may have been the first man to face the oceanic whitetip in its own element and live to describe the encounter. In 1951, in the open Atlantic off the Cape Verde Islands, he and his companions were harassed by one of these marauders.

The fish exhibited a pattern of curiosity, increasing boldness, and eventual attack. Captain Cousteau drove it off finally by banging it over the snout with his camera.

Chuck Henderson, a Washington, D. C., diver, told of a similar experience he had with a pelagic shark off Delaware. From the description, it could have been a blue.

"I had a dead tautog on the end of my fish spear," Chuck said, "and this attracted the shark. I backed up against the plates of a wreck in 30 feet of water and fed the tautog to the shark, hoping it would go away.

"It didn't. It kept returning, each time coming a little closer to me until I was pushing it away bodily with the spear. I pushed gingerly, you can be sure. I didn't want to make this fellow mad.

"When I began running low on air, I knew I had to take a chance on sterner measures. I stabbed the shark in the eye, and it rushed off, shaking its head.

"I could have killed this fish, but I didn't have an underwater gun."

Used skillfully, this weapon, nicknamed "bangstick," is probably the diver's best close protection. Triggered by jabbing against a target, it will kill a shark instantly if fired close to the brain. But it is bulky, a menace to other divers, and can give a nasty concussion if the shell used is too large.

The U. S. Navy has tried long and hard to develop a shark repellent to protect drifting seamen. During World War II scientists learned that sharks, though cannibals, shun decaying shark flesh. They developed a repellent containing copper acetate, an organic acid like those in decayed shark meat.

"To this we added nigrosine dye, which forms a dense cloud in the water," said

Stewart Springer, who helped develop the repellent. "It raises a man's morale to believe he is hidden. Moreover, the shark's final visual attack may be hindered."

Although its efficacy is limited, the services still issue the repellent. Another device, an electronic repellent, has been tested with inconclusive results. One of the most promising innovations is a six-foot-long plastic survival sack called Shark Screen. A seaman or airman carries the buoyant bag on his life jacket and quickly inflates it around him when necessary.

One of the puzzles facing experts is why a shark in one part of the world harasses humans while its brother of the same species in another place does not. Stewart Springer feels that entire shark populations living in less than ideal natural conditions may be dangerous to man.

"Principal populations of sharks establish themselves, quite naturally, in areas where food is abundant and other conditions are good," Stewart said. "The area may be large: Some species of sharks migrate over regular ranges, like African big game.

"Around the edges of the principal area you will find an accessory population that includes congenital weaklings, cripples, or possibly neurotics—animals that can't compete with the others and drift away.

"Life is harder for these peripheral sharks, and they may be the dangerous ones. As you might expect, they take whatever food comes along. This could be man."

One day I stopped by to see Cliff Townsend at Marineland of Florida, where I had earlier helped the collecting crew add a pair of lemon sharks to the main fish tank.

"What became of my friends the lemon sharks?" I asked Cliff.

"One is the nicest, calmest shark you ever saw," he said. "It's the only large lemon we've had that never gives the divers a moment's worry, and it eats the food we give it, not its tank neighbors.

"The other killed every fish it could catch, bit chunks out of the coral rocks we put on the bottom for background, and nearly got a couple of divers before we could get it out of the tank.

"I don't know why these sharks were so different; no one else does. They did, however, prove one of the few things we know for sure about shark behavior: The animal is unpredictable. Never trust a shark."

No better advice could be given a man about to enter water where sharks may lurk.

POWER OF A SHARK'S BITE *measures in tons, not pounds, as Dr. Perry W. Gilbert discovers at the Lerner Marine Laboratory. A leading shark authority, Dr. Gilbert uses a "bite meter," a cylinder containing an aluminum core of known hardness enclosed by four steel quadrants. Twelve stainless-steel bearings separate the two layers.*

Bait wrapped around the device (below) attracts sharks like the 8½-foot dusky opposite, which clamps down. Knowing the force needed to dent the aluminum core, Dr. Gilbert estimates the dusky's bite: about 18 tons per square inch!

CHAPTER TWENTY

Gallery of Sharks and Hawaiian Fishes ▶

SIDE BY SIDE through warm seas the delightful reef fishes and the somber sharks swim in grim contrast. Each fascinates man in its way. Reef tropicals gladden the soul with their exquisite beauty. The sharks, powerful of body and fearsome of visage, symbolize evil and cruelty.

Sharks worked a macabre spell on primitive man, who wove them into his beliefs. Pacific Islanders made human sacrifices to appease shark gods. Japanese mythology enshrines a "shark man" as god of storms. Ancient Hawaiians pitted native gladiators against starved sharks in underwater pens. Many mariners even today dread sharks in their wake as omens that men will die.

Tropical reefs and their gay residents bring delight to skin divers, riders of glass-bottomed boats, and aquarium lovers everywhere. But Hawaii's fishes are unique among the Nation's species. For the islands sit at the eastern edge of oceandom's most teeming faunal area, the Indo-Pacific system that extends past Australia and Asia to Africa. Oddly, Hawaii is shy of fresh-water species; it boasts mainly gobies that long ago migrated from salt water, and a few bass, trout, and catfish introduced recently.

FEROCIOUS YET FASCINATING, *the 27 sharks in this rogue's gallery include ten known man-eaters; white, bull, tiger, great hammerhead, lemon, oceanic whitetip, blacktip, shortfin mako, dusky, and blue. Oddly, the two giants of sharkdom, the whale and basking sharks, dine on plankton and small fish. The possibly dangerous porbeagle, Greenland, sixgill, and sevengill usually live in waters too deep or too cold to endanger man. Sizes are average adult lengths.*

OPPOSITE PAGE
FOLDS OUT

WHITE SHARK
18 FEET

TIGER SHARK, 15 FEET

GREAT HAMMERHEAD SHARK
15 FEET

BULL SHARK, 9 FEET

SPINY DOGFISH
4 FEET

LEOPARD SHARK
4 FEET

GREENLAND SHARK, 18 FEET

North American Sharks

EARTH'S APPROXIMATELY 250 SHARK SPECIES remain true prehistoric monsters; for more than 300 million years they have terrorized the seas—with little need to make evolutionary changes. Their skeletons of cartilage predate bone. Brains are tiny. Air bladders are lacking, hence many sharks must move constantly to keep from sinking. Powerful mouths bristle with ugly teeth, and behind these lie rows of new teeth, ready to rise escalator-fashion to replace ones lost. Male sharks have grooved fin appendages that help transfer sperm to fertilize females internally; most females bear live young.

COW SHARKS
Family Hexanchidae

Even among the ancient order of sharks, cow sharks are primitive, unorthodox creatures. While their cousins standardized eons ago with five gill slits on each side of the neck, the cows retain variations that inspire their names: sixgill (*Hexanchus griseus*) and sevengill (*Nortorynchus maculatus*).

Giants that exceed 17 feet in length, sixgills have been hooked at depths of more than a mile.

They also haunt both Atlantic and Pacific shallows. A female of these live-bearers carried a reported 108 embryos.

Smaller sevengills patrol the Pacific coast, swimming constantly and effortlessly. San Francisco Bay, a sevengill nursery, once yielded an albino—a trait rare among sharks.

Similar to the Hexanchidae is the frill shark, family Chlamydoselachidae. A Pacific six-footer, *Chlamydoselachus anguineum*, has six gills with the first slit running continuously around the underside of the neck—the frill.

HAMMERHEAD SHARKS
Family Sphyrnidae

A spearfisherman rises from a reef, his impaled fish oozing blood. The faint spoor reaches the nostrils of a great hammerhead (*Sphyrna mokarran*), and the beast zeroes in as if drawn by a magnet. Suddenly fear seizes the diver, for before him looms a proven man-killer.

Known to reach 20 feet, great hammerheads (right) luckily are few in number. Ranging warm seas north to California and the Carolinas, they resemble the abundant, slightly smaller smooth hammerhead (*S. zygaena*), found world-wide in warm and temperate waters. In summer streams of smooths migrate north to New England, fouling fish nets. A third species, the scalloped hammerhead (*S. lewini*), wears the handlebar head, but with indentations or scallops on the snout.

Powerful swimmers, hammerheads clamp underslung mouths on swift mackerels and sluggish skates, other hammerheads, even beer cans. Anglers find the predators pull like tug boats and at times fight until dead of exhaustion. Female smooth hammerheads bear up to 37 pups whose head lobes fold back for easy birth.

Another hammerhead, the abundant bonnethead (*S. tiburo*), has a head shaped like a shovel instead of a hammer.

LADY AND A MAN-EATER: *A Florida diver approaches one of the few safe hammerheads: a stunned one. Peculiar head, with nostrils near the lobe tips, helps in "homing in" on prey.*

WALTER A. STARCK II

HORN SHARKS
Family Heterodontidae

Unobtrusively mild in the violent world of sharks, the tiny-toothed horn sharks number only about 10 species. The sole North American representative is the Pacific horn *(Heterodontus francisci)*. Occurring from central California to Baja California, this five-footer grows an oddly flattened snout that earns it the name pig shark. Males proclaim their courtship by repeatedly biting their mates, who deposit cylindrical, four-inch eggs wound by a spiral flange. Incubation takes seven months. Female horn sharks in aquariums often attack the eggs and crush them in their teeth, though whether a female destroys her own eggs is not known.

A stout spine at the front of each dorsal identifies all horn shark species.

CAT SHARKS
Family Scyliohinidae

Shine a light on a member of this numerous family, and the eye pupils form vertical slits like a cat's. Most renowned North American cat is the three-foot Pacific swell shark *(Cephaloscyllium uter)*, which, when hauled on deck, gulps air and inflates to twice normal girth. Tossed back, some struggle for days to deflate, meantime floating helplessly.

A two-foot cat shark with a canine name—chain dogfish *(Scyliorhinus retifer)*—dwells near bottom along the Middle Atlantic states; trawlers scoop up many. The Atlantic false cat shark *(Pseudotriakis microdon)* is a giant among pigmies, reaching 10 feet. African waters harbor the shy-eye cats, which "hide" by curling their tail over the head, thus hiding their eyes.

SAND TIGER SHARK

WHALE SHARKS
Family Rhincodontidae

World's mightiest fish, awesome whale sharks grow so enormous that man can seldom weigh them. A Florida 38-footer, relatively small as whale sharks go, weighed 26,000 pounds. Full grown specimens, exceeding 45 feet, could double that amount.

Docile as they are colossal, the warm-water sharks let swimmers ride them. An Australian diver boarded one, took pictures from its back and from alongside as he leisurely swam with it, even knelt on the unprotesting animal's head and looked down into its mouth. Numerous ships have collided with whale sharks as they basked alone or in schools.

The shark's tiny eyes peer from tough, spotted hide four to six inches thick. Small teeth grow in 310 rows and number about 7,200 in a mouth located at the tip of the head instead of underslung like most sharks'. Horny capsules encase the leviathan's eggs.

Roaming the seas for delicate plankton, sardines, and anchovies, *Rhincodon typus* often assumes a vertical position with head uppermost when feeding on schooling fish. A specimen dissected in the Philippines yielded 47 buttons, 3 leather belts, 7 leggings, and 9 shoes—items probably swallowed accidentally as the great fish sucked in nutriment.

Abounding nowhere, whale sharks occur most often in the Caribbean, Gulf of California, Red Sea, and off the Philippines. Strays wander as far north as New York.

SAND TIGER SHARKS
Family Carchariidae

As if bent on her own destruction, a diver swims alongside a fanged sand tiger and pats its coarse flank (above). Surprisingly, little danger exists in this scene in an Australian aquarium: Once regarded with dread, the wicked-looking sand tiger is now believed to enjoy a clean record as a harmless companion to swimmers.

And companion it is, for sand tiger sharks (*Odontaspis taurus*) abound in Florida waters year round, and in summer flock along shores from Delaware to Cape Cod.

Embryo sand tigers, pre-natal cannibals, devour other embryos while still in the uterus. Australians call the sand tiger a grey nurse, while South Africans call it the ragged-tooth and once accused it of attacks on humans.

DOGFISH SHARKS
Family Squalidae

Scourge of fishermen around the world, swarming spiny dogfish (*Squalus acanthius*) clean fishing banks of cod and hake, gobble lures, shred nets, and devour seined fish even as they are being drawn in. Boated dogfish, thrashing in the net, imperil fishermen with venomous spines that bristle before each dorsal. Though Europeans savor the four-footers, Americans shun them, losing out on a potential protein bonanza that saw 27 million dogfish netted in 1913 off Massachusetts alone.

A family of some 60 species, the Squalidae include one of the smallest sharks, the 12-inch Atlantic *Etmopterus hilianus,* and the massive 18-foot Greenland shark (*Somniosus microcephalus),* which devours seals and even reindeer.

MACKEREL SHARKS
Family Lamnidae

Swift and powerful predators, mackerel sharks include the sea's most malevolent killer, the white shark, or man-eater *(Carcharodon carcharias)*. Thick of body and bristling with saw-edge teeth, whites are leading culprits in attacks on bathers and challenge even boats. In addition to human remains, the brutes' stomachs have yielded—intact—such mouthfuls as a 100-pound sea lion and a seven-foot shark. A record 2,664-pound white caught on rod and reel in Australian waters measured 16 feet; the longest specimen reliably reported had a length of 21 feet. Fortunately, man-eaters seem to be rare and usually prowl the open sea in warm and temperate zones.

White-shark ferocity is shared by a smaller cousin, the shortfin mako *(Isurus oxyrinchus)*, another documented man-killer. Its teeth curve clawlike at the front to hold fish, grow knifelike behind for chopping. One of the few enemies of the swordfish, makos attack from the rear, slashing off massive portions of the fish with a single bite; the stomach of a 730-pound mako produced a 120-pound broadbill intact with sword.

Hard-fighting makos delight fishermen with frequent leaps, and reward them again at table with their delicious flavor. Makos roam the temperate seas world-wide.

Another mackerel shark, the Atlantic porbeagle *(Lamna nasus)*, is regarded by shark experts as potentially a man-eater. It and the similar Pacific salmon shark *(L. ditropis)* vigorously pursue mackerel and other schooling fishes, but show little fight when hooked.

THRESHER SHARKS
Family Alopiidae

Flailing elongated tails that form half their total length, swift thresher sharks *(Alopias vulpinus)* circle schooling fish along both coasts and herd them into compact masses. Then they race through, scooping up mouthfuls. A dissected 13-footer had consumed 27 mackerel.

Threshers, temperate and warm-sea dwellers, may exceed 20 feet and 1,000 pounds. Females bear two or four pups, with tails even longer in proportion to their bodies than the parents'.

NURSE SHARKS
Family Orectolobidae

Fleshy barbels and thick-lipped mouth lend a look of innocence to the nurse shark *(Ginglymostoma cirratum)*, although the languid giants have been known to bite when grabbed by foolhardy bathers. Clustering lazily in Florida shallows, often three dozen to a school, nurses root the bottom for crabs, shrimps, and squids and delight in gobbling toadfish. Unlike many sharks, they thrive in captivity. Found in warm waters of the Atlantic and eastern Pacific, the livebearers reach 14 feet in length.

Australian nurse sharks, known as wobbegongs, rest on bottom by day and hunt by night.

Along with identifying barbels, members of the nurse shark family share such features as a conspicuous groove running from the mouth to each nostril, and a tail that instead of jutting upward extends in line with the rest of the body.

NURSE SHARK

LIKE A LIVING BATTERING RAM, *a white shark splinters a dory off Canada's Cape Breton Island. The 1953 attack re-created in this painting smashed an eight-inch hole that swamped the craft. As the shark swam away, lobsterman John MacLeod clung to the wreckage until rescued; John Burns drowned. Despite the experience, Mr. MacLeod returned to fish the same waters, locale of several shark attacks on boats. The shark's length was estimated at 12 feet, its weight at more than 1,000 pounds. Eliminating doubt about identity, the planking was embedded with the unmistakable serrated, triangular tooth of a white shark, such as those that arm the 12-footer at right.*

LLOYD D. DAVIDSON (OPPOSITE) AND RON TAYLOR; PAINTING BY PAUL CALLE

REQUIEM SHARKS
Family Carcharhinidae

These dread sharks earn their haunting name from victims "whose dying shrieks serve as their requiem or dirge of last repose." So wrote a 19th-century ichthyologist about sharkdom's largest family—a notorious band of 50 species that includes six convicted man-eaters: the tiger shark, bull, lemon, dusky, blue, and oceanic whitetip.

Tiger sharks *(Galeocerdo cuvieri)* eat everything—lumps of coal, garbage, turtles, sea lions, fellow sharks, and bony fishes. But porpoises team up to pummel tigers to death with their snouts, and with good reason: The sharks eat porpoises, too. Recorded at 18 feet and possibly reaching 30, tigers move sluggishly except when killing. Found in all warm seas, in summer they venture north to New York and California.

Scientists studying shark attacks on humans write an ever-more devastating indictment of bull sharks *(Carcharhinus leucas)*. Found worldwide, the aggressive 10-footers have colonized fresh-water Lake Nicaragua and lakes in Guatemala and New Guinea. They often travel in groups, ranging as far north as Chesapeake Bay; mouths of the Mississippi are a favorite nursery.

Abundant, shallow-water lemon sharks *(Negaprion brevirostris)* poke blunt snouts about reefs and bays in warm waters of both coasts, gobbling fishes and occasionally attacking bathers. They do well in aquariums, and often serve as experimental specimens for ichthyologists.

The dusky shark *(C. obscurus),* a giant that probably reaches 14 feet, has a rounded snout which gives it the name shovelnose. Duskies are often confused with the sandbar shark *(C. milberti),* a nemesis of flounders and mackerel, that abounds off New York and New Jersey.

Slender blue sharks *(Prionace glauca)* trail ships plying warm and temperate seas, gleaning scraps and haunting superstitious seamen. Tuna

OCEANIC WHITETIP SHARK

fishermen watch helplessly as blues materialize from nowhere to make mincemeat of a catch.

The dangerous oceanic whitetip *(C. longimanus),* a 13-foot wanderer of the open seas, harasses Pacific set-line fishermen by tearing great chunks from hooked tuna. The smaller blacktip shark *(C. limbatus),* a speedy six-footer along Gulf states, will leap like a porpoise. Coloring on fin tips gives these sharks their names.

An unusually smooth skin names the pugnacious silky shark *(C. falciformis),* which vies with the oceanic whitetip for depredations on tuna lines. Its range is confined to a 1,200-mile-wide band straddling the Equator, where silkies are probably the most abundant shark.

The Pacific soupfin *(Galeorhinus zyopterus)* is the shark so cherished by Oriental gourmets. California coastal fishermen find similar fine flavor—though dull sport—in the five-foot leopard shark *(Triakis semifasciata).* San Francisco Bay is a nursery for leopard pups.

ANGEL SHARKS
Family Squatinidae

Wing-shaped pectorals, not a sweet disposition, inspire the name of the 11 species of angel sharks. Though harmless to swimmers, angels grow testy when netted, audibly snapping toothy jaws that can inflict a serious bite.

The Atlantic coast angel *(Squatina dumerili)* ranges close inshore from New England south to the Caribbean, the Pacific species *(S. californica)* from Alaska to Baja California.

Broad, compressed bodies identify the angels as links between the other sharks and the flattened rays. Usually only four or five feet long, they sprout two whiskers from each nostril. Because angels live mostly on bottom, thus exposing the gills to clogging debris, they "inhale" through holes behind each eye and expel the water through the gills. They show a preference for shallows, often bury themselves in sand.

SILKY SHARK

RAVENOUS SILKY SHARK *charges diver Donald Nelson, who frantically pushes away the six-foot attacker with one hand and with the other aims an underwater gun. An instant later the would-be killer thrashed out its own death agony.*

SINISTER OCEANIC WHITETIP, *a proven man-eater, patrols its domain off Florida with pilotfish and a solitary almaco jack* (Seriola rivoliana).

Other Cartilaginous Fishes

Flatten a shark, enlarge its pectoral fins, move the gill clefts under the body, and you have a ray or skate. These sluggish, pancake kin of the sharks usually prowl coastal bottoms, often with the gills buried; hence most of them inhale through holes atop their heads called spiracles and use gills only for expelling water. Lacking sharks' formidable fangs, many of the world's 340 species of skates and rays arm themselves with electric shock organs, located in the pectoral fins or along the tail. Others grow elongated, saw-edged snouts, or venomous tail spines they can drive through arms and legs, even the planking of boats. Docile guitarfishes lack any such defenses, and they promptly surrender when hooked.

RAYS GLIDE GRACEFULLY *through both water and air. A squadron of cownose rays (above) cruises the Gulfarium at Fort Walton Beach, Florida. Studies by Dr. Frank J. Schwartz of the University of North Carolina reveal that great flotillas of cownoses* (Rhinoptera bonasus) *make amazing migrations, summering in Chesapeake Bay and wintering off Venezuela—a 2,400-mile trip.*

Spotted eagle ray (opposite) at Florida's Marineland flaps behind a pair of French angelfish. Aetobatus narinari *decimates tropical Atlantic clam beds as it roots for food.*

Like bats out of the deep, a trio of Pacific mantas (Manta hamiltoni) *flush off Panama (left).*

335

ATLANTIC MANTA

ATLANTIC MANTA
Manta birostris

Capable of crushing boat or man, mantas trustingly permit approach; they fight only for freedom. But their enormous size and hornlike cephalic fins cast them as villains in countless sea stories: clamping cephalic fins to close off a diver's air hose, or wrapping huge bodies about a victim in a smothering grip. Fact may father fable, for the cephalic fins close on whatever they touch, and the fish have incredible power.

Mantas cruise slowly at or near the surface, flapping oversize pectoral fins. Occasionally the flattened giants leap, a ton of fish awesomely erupting from the sea; then they crash back with a thunderclap that shatters tropical quiet.

Ages ago warm-water "sea bats" forsook the bottom-dwelling habit of most rays to hunt at the surface for planktonic crustaceans and small fishes. Small teeth lining the lower jaw—4,800 in an 11½-footer—have no function with so dainty a diet. Most rays take in respiratory water through spiracles on the back, but mantas are believed to inhale through the mouth.

Females apparently carry a single pup which at birth measures four feet across and weighs 20 pounds. Reports tell of a harpooned manta that cartwheeled above the surface and ejected a cylindrical fetus. Unfolding its "wings" in midair, the newborn vanished into the sea.

Characteristics: fleshy pectoral fins that make the body twice as wide as long; two earlike fins projecting from head; back reddish brown, greenish brown, or black. *Range:* tropical western Atlantic, straying to New England. *Weight:* tops 3,000 pounds. *Width:* to at least 22 feet.

PACIFIC ELECTRIC RAY
Torpedo californica

Though slow moving, flabbily muscled, small toothed, and weak eyed, this shark-tailed pancake of a fish sits on the sea bottom unperturbed. Let a Pacific bather step on it, and its 75 volts send him leaping with pain.

Early Romans "cured" gout with shocks from electric rays. Greeks closeted them with pregnant women, believing they eased delivery. Today scientists study their batteries—stacks of tiny gelatinous disks that sit honeycomblike on each side of the head. Discharges stun prey, repel enemies, and perhaps serve as sonar. Successive shocks grow weaker, but a ray with exhausted batteries soon recharges.

Characteristics: black-spotted gray back; flat body; electric organs. *Range:* Vancouver Island to San Diego. *Length:* to 3 feet.

PACIFIC ELECTRIC RAY

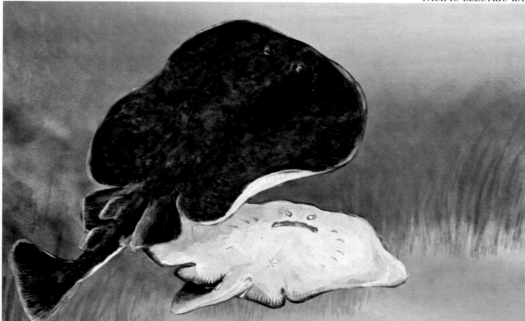

SMALLTOOTH SAWFISH

SMALLTOOTH SAWFISH
Pristis pectinata

Sea yarns credit the sawfish with slashing humans in half and slicing whales like salami. But this member of the ray family really uses the sawlike snout only to stab and stun schooling fishes and sometimes to stir bottom mud for small prey. Oceanarium attendants, dropping food in the great ray's finely toothed mouth, merely guard against an accidental saw swipe.

Plentiful in the Gulf area, smalltooth sawfish often shred nets and rip captive fish. Anglers hooking them in shallow waters face strong, sluggish adversaries who put up wearisome, hours-long fights.

Characteristics: cartilaginous snout with 25 to 32 pairs of teeth. *Range:* both sides tropical Atlantic, strays to New York. *Weight:* rod and reel record 890 pounds. *Length:* to more than 16 feet.

ATLANTIC GUITARFISH
Rhinobatos lentiginosus

Flat in front like a ray and slim behind like a shark, the guitarfish seems undecided what to be. An underside view shows gill clefts, which tag it as a ray; nostrils open like inquisitive eyes above the expressive mouth.

Southern anglers loathe the guitar-shaped fish because it chomps blunt teeth on baits, then languidly surrenders. Skin divers catch it by the tail. A similar Pacific guitarfish (the shovelnose, *R. productus*) surprisingly nipped a swimmer's leg.

About 45 guitarfish species inhabit warm waters world-wide, feeding on bottom-dwelling crustacea. The adaptable live-bearers often ascend rivers; they thrive in aquariums.

Characteristics: back gray to brown, white dots except on Texas-area specimens. *Range:* North Carolina to Yucatán. *Length:* to 30 inches.

ATLANTIC GUITARFISH

ERNEST L. LIBBEY (ABOVE) AND RALSTON PRINCE; PAINTING BY HASHIME MURAYAMA

Hawaiian Fishes

BRILLIANT FISHES FLASH like living jewels in the lotus land that is Hawaii. From tidal pool to three-mile abyss, amid water of unusual clearness, approximately 585 species sparkle along the 25-island chain.

Hawaii's coral belles show a temperamental streak, nagging, pecking, eating each other. Some are viciously armed: Scorpionfishes bristle with venomous spines; wrasses grow canine teeth; surgeonfishes wield razor-sharp scalpels. Moray eels shoot from coral lairs to slash trespassing swimmers' arms or legs.

A third of Hawaii's shallow-water fishes are unique to the Aloha state and to Johnston Island, an isolated U. S. atoll 800 miles southwest of Honolulu. Wrasses and morays rank first in number of species; butterflyfishes, goatfishes, squirrelfishes, and surgeonfishes boast huge populations. The sprightly reef dwellers encounter an increasingly frequent visitor: man. Skin divers come sightseeing, aquarists come collecting, and fishermen come with hook and net, mindful that Hawaiian reef beauties can taste as good as they look.

BLACKSPOT WRASSE (left) and CLOWN WRASSE

WALTER H. CHUTE

Straight snouted while young but round nosed as an adult, the **BLACKSPOT WRASSE** (*Bodianus bilunulatus*) has a particularly bad reputation for eating aquarium neighbors. Weighing two pounds—large for the wrasses —it finds popularity in Honolulu markets. Lines around eyes of the 10-inch **CLOWN WRASSE** (*Novaculichthys taeniourus*) give gill covers the look of cracked china. Like most of Hawaii's 48 wrasses, it changes colors at different growth stages.

Buck teeth of the 16-inch **BLACKBANDED WRASSE** (*Coris flavovittata*) belie a peaceable nature that distinguishes it from most of the irascible wrasses. Bands streak only upper sides in adults, all the body in young. The brightly decorated **UNICORN FISH** (*Naso lituratus*) browses among shallow reefs for algae. The 15-incher carries sharp paired spines at the base of the tail.

338

ORANGELINED WRASSE (top), POOU (lower left), and SADDLE WRASSE

Hawaii's plentiful wrasses are never conspicuous: Shy and solitary, they swim close to bottom and retreat into coral hideaways. At night some of the toothy carnivores sleep burrowed in the sand. About 450 wrasse species (family Labridae) inhabit the earth's warm waters. They range from three-inch midgets to six-foot giants.

The somber young **ORANGELINED WRASSE** *(Thalassoma lutescens)* will turn yellowish green at maturity but keep its dark pinstripes. Anglers catch the **POOU** *(Cheilinus unifasciatus)* over deep coral reefs. A brown collar marks the **SADDLE WRASSE** *(T. duperreyi)*, a testy aquarium inhabitant that mutilates even its own kind.

BLACKBANDED WRASSE (left) and UNICORN FISH

The orange and white **CLOWN ANEMONE** (*Amphiprion percula*) participates in one of fishdom's most pernicious partnerships. Wearing a protective coat of mucus, this gaudy damselfish lures other fishes to the waving tentacles of the sea anemone. The tentacles' poison paralyzes the victims, then the partners share a grim banquet.

The **BLUEGREEN DAMSELFISH** (*Chromis caeruleus*), an abundant three-incher, darts among Pacific corals gobbling copepods. The **THREESTRIPE DAMSELFISH** (*Dascyllus aruanus*) inhabits Pacific islands to the south and west of Hawaii. Damselfishes (family Pomacentridae) include America's garibaldi and sergeant major.

The male of the **BLACKSTRIPE CARDINALFISH** (*Apogon novemfasciatus*), huge eye hidden by a streak of black, incubates eggs in its mouth. Teeming cardinalfishes (family Apogonidae) provide important forage for larger fishes.

Spotted patch at lower left marks a skulking **POLKADOT MORAY** (*Gymnothorax meleagris*), a three-footer common at depths of 30 feet.

From top: BLUEGREEN DAMSEL, THREESTRIPE DAMSEL, CLOWN ANEMONE, BLACKSTRIPE CARDINALFISH

Black-barred twins at first glance, the **LONGFIN BUTTERFLYFISH** (*Heniochus acuminatus*) and the **MOORISH IDOL** (*Zanclus canescens*) belong to different families. Black tail and long snout of the idol (family Zanclidae) help tell the seven-inchers apart. Pacific islanders see moorish idols swimming conspicuously in shallows. Fish fanciers prize the graceful fish but find them pugnacious and susceptible to sickness.

The **BLUESTRIPE BUTTERFLYFISH** (*Chaetodon fremblii*), a common five-incher, occurs only in Hawaii. The islands claim about 25 kinds of butterflyfishes and angelfishes, which belong to the family Chaetodontidae. More than 150 species ornament tropical reefs around the world.

Seldom a foot long, the butterflyfishes poke their usually elongated noses into crevices and seize small invertebrates with flexible, bristlelike teeth. A few species never venture closer than 100 feet to the surface. Most butterflyfishes are solitary in habit and gaily splashed with color, though they apparently lack the pigment green.

LONGFIN BUTTERFLYFISH (left), MOORISH IDOL (center), and BLUESTRIPE BUTTERFLYFISH

From left: LONGNOSE BUTTERFLYFISH, RECTANGULAR TRIGGERFISH, YELLOW TANG, WHITELINE SQUIRRELFISH

Pinocchio snout and tiny mouth of the **LONG-NOSE BUTTERFLYFISH** *(Forcipiger longirostris)* probe for food in rock and coral crevices. The nine-inch **RECTANGULAR TRIGGERFISH** *(Rhinecanthus rectangulus)* shares the Hawaiian name humuhumu-nukunuku-a-pua'a with the triggerfish pictured below. Lee sides of islands appeal to the **YELLOW TANG** *(Zebrasoma flavescens),* a numerous eight-incher. The **WHITELINE SQUIRRELFISH** *(Holocentrus diadema),* like most squirrelfishes, hunts on the reefs at night.

HUMUHUMU-NUKUNUKU-A-PUA'A, introduced to millions by a hit song, liltingly labels the brainless-looking *Rhinecanthus aculeatus,* a nine-inch member of the triggerfish family. Needlelike dorsal spine and piggish grunting noises prompt the name; the Hawaiian words translate "fish that sews and grunts like a pig."

The armament triggerfishes bear can kill a predator that bites down: Clan members erect a sharp first dorsal spine or "trigger," then move the second spine forward to lock it in place.

HUMUHUMU-NUKUNUKU-A-PUA'A

Morays and skin divers exercise a mutual distrust around Hawaii's reefs. When swimmers intrude, the moray eels strike like snakes. Scattered reports tell of unprovoked attacks on man. Their needle teeth lack venom but often cause infection.

Morays (family Muraenidae) lurk worldwide on tropical and subtropical reefs, their numbers usually underestimated as they hide in cave and crevice by day. Though the flesh of some is poisonous, they are widely eaten.

All eels lack pelvic fins, and morays also lack pectorals. The spotted **TIGER MORAY** (*Uropterygius tigrinus*) speared at left has no fins at all. Those in the photograph below wear fleshy, ridge-like dorsals, indicating they belong to the genus *Gymnothorax*. Only minute anatomical variations distinguish many confusing species.

Morays constantly open and close their sinister mouths to force water back through tiny, round gills.

Zoologist Vernon E. Brock (left) once wounded a monster moray estimated at 10 feet long. He nearly lost an arm in the Johnston Island encounter; pursuing Brock, the speared eel mangled his elbow with a crushing bite.

Nine moray species inhabit warmwater reefs along the Atlantic coast; one, the **CALIFORNIA MORAY** (*Gymnothorax mordax*), haunts Pacific shores.

MORAY EELS (tiger, above, and *Gymnothorax* specimens)

THREADFIN (top) and SANDFISH

Fin lengths identify this **THREADFIN** *(Alectis ciliaris)* as an adult; on juveniles the dorsal and anal fins stream behind like those of the related young African pompano (page 111). Fifteen-inch threadfins abound in Hawaii's bays. The tapering, foot-long **SANDFISH** *(Malacanthus hoedti)* appears frequently on Hawaiian tables. Armed with a sharp spine on each gill cover, it closely resembles its Atlantic kin, the slightly larger **SAND TILEFISH** *(M. plumieri).*

The sinuous, three-foot **PUHI-UHA** *(Conger cinereus)* abounds in shallows and tidal pools. Less temperamental than the moray, the puhi-uha and other conger eels grow teeth that form a continuous cutting edge. Dorsal, caudal, and anal fins are connected. A smaller Hawaiian conger *(Ariosoma bowersi),* unable to spawn in aquariums as in the deeps, swells with eggs until it explodes. North America's east coast harbors eight conger species; its west, one.

PUHI-UHA (conger eel)

PAUL A. ZAHL, NATIONAL GEOGRAPHIC STAFF (OPPOSITE), WALTER H. CHUTE (TOP), AND JOHN TASHJIAN

SPOTTED HAWKFISH (lower left), LONGFIN RAZORFISH (center), and MEMPACHI

Fond of rough water, the 10-inch **SPOTTED HAWKFISH** *(Cirrhitus pinnulatus)* hides in the surf waiting to pounce on passing prey. Occasionally the nocturnal feeder meanders to a new ambush point, then resumes its vigil. The world's 34 hawkfish species (family Cirrhitidae) occur mainly in the Indo-Pacific.

A knifelike dorsal fin marks the **LONGFIN RAZORFISH** *(Iniistius pavoninus)*. This high-browed, 15-inch wrasse is a common food fish.

Spear fishermen seeking delicacies comb reef crevices for the **MEMPACHI** *(Myripristis berndti),* a squirrelfish that brings premium prices in Hawaiian markets. A nocturnal feeder that holes up by day, it bears a large spine on each cheek capable of dealing painful wounds. Its bright red coloring typifies most of the world's 70-odd squirrelfish species (family Holocentridae).

PACIFIC FLYING GURNARD

Black spine sprouts like an Indian headfeather from the **PACIFIC FLYING GURNARD** *(Dactylopterus orientalis).* Credited with flying on winglike pectoral fins, in reality the fish is grounded by a bony, boxlike body. It walks on the bottom, using its separated pectoral spines as legs and as feelers for food. The **ATLANTIC FLYING GURNARD** *(D. volitans),* like its Pacific cousin, gorges chiefly on small crustaceans and mollusks.

A folding, fanlike tail and file-edged dorsal spine christen the **FANTAIL FILEFISH** *(Pervagor spilosoma)*. The five-inch reef fish abound some years, grow scarce others.

Equipped with minute mouths, filefishes steal bait adroitly but sometimes starve in aquariums when competing with faster feeders. They lack pelvic fins and wear scaleless, velvety skins. Some species are believed poisonous. They form the warmwater family Balistidae.

Both sportsmen and commercial trollers seek out the high-browed jacks, three-foot fishes found beyond the reefs. Black spots appear on the **BLUE CREVALLY** *(Caranx melampygus)* when it reaches about 10 inches. The **BLACK-BARRED JACK** *(C. speciosus)* when young wears an all-gold coat and swims as a pilot for other fishes. Its jaws contain toothless plates.

The rough-scaled **GLASSEYE SNAPPER** *(Priacanthus cruentatus)* is not a true snapper but one of the nocturnal bigeyes (family Priacanthidae). Ranges of the glasseye and the two jacks extend to America's west coast.

The spiny, reef dwelling **NOHU** *(Scorpaenopsis cacopsis)* wins esteem as a food fish.

FANTAIL FILEFISH

BLUE CREVALLY (top), BLACKBARRED JACK (center), GLASSEYE SNAPPER (lower left), and NOHU

SAILFIN TANG (top), CONVICT TANG (right pair), RED GOATFISH (far left), and WHITESPOT GOATFISH

The yellow-banded **SAILFIN TANG** *(Zebrasoma veliferum)* schools among coral shallows in search of succulent sea lettuce. The 16-inch **RED GOATFISH** *(Parupeneus pleurostigma)* and similar **WHITESPOT GOATFISH** *(P. porphyreus)* detect bottom foods by groping with a pair of barbels. Feelers tuck under the chin when not in use. Goatfishes (family Mullidae) and the nine-inch **CONVICT TANG** *(Acanthurus sandvicensis)* rank as important Hawaiian food fishes.

Like Mata Haris with knife in garter, many of the treacherous surgeonfishes carry a sharp-edged spine that folds into a groove on each side of the caudal peduncle. Frightened, they snap out the forward-pointing blade and sideswipe the enemy. Hawaii's abundant, algae-eating surgeonfishes, or tangs (family Acanthuridae) include the **STRIPED TANG** *(Ctenochaetus strigosus)*, **BLACK TANG** *(Acanthurus mata)*, and **ORANGESPOT TANG** *(A. olivaceus)*. All three wear knives.

STRIPED TANG (left), BLACK TANG (center), and ORANGESPOT TANG

A reddish-orange patch warns of the sharp caudal spine of the **REDSPOT TANG** (*Acanthurus achilles*). This 11-incher frequents surging water near exposed reefs, grazing on algae. The 15-inch **WHITESPOT WRASSE** (*Anampses cuvieri*) lives only in Hawaii. Two of its upper teeth and two lowers protrude absurdly forward.

REDSPOT TANG (top pair) and WHITESPOT WRASSE

Ribbony fins of the bizarre **LIONFISH** (*Pterois volitans*) wave beware: Sharp dorsal spines inject a poison that causes excruciating stings and can bring humans near death. The 10-incher may attack objects, jabbing them with its fins.

Lionfish, also called turkeyfish, move with stately calm, unmolested by other fishes. Exquisite aquarium attractions, they belong to the numerous mailed-cheek family of scorpionfishes.

LIONFISH

347

POACHED TO PERFECTION, *a striped bass moves from pan to platter under the author's careful guidance. Lemon, parsley, and hollandaise sauce grace the final product (right, prepared like red snapper, page 363). Wines, glassware, and utensils brighten Mr. Beard's New York kitchen. Teacher of chefs and author of numerous articles and books on cooking, Mr. Beard esteems the fish as a food. "If we Americans prepared our rich variety of fishes in all the many ways there are," he observes, "we could dine on a new fish dish every day of the year, and each would be a gourmet's delight."*

B. ANTHONY STEWART, NATIONAL GEOGRAPHIC STAFF

A Guide to Fish Cookery

I GREW UP in the Pacific Northwest where fishing excursions were common. We camped in the Cascade Range beside lakes and streams filled with bass and brook trout, cutthroats, rainbows, and Dolly Vardens. In the rivers running down to the Pacific we fished for salmon. In the bays and bayous of the Columbia we caught crappies, catfish, bluegills, and perch.

I recall times when the smelt ran in tributaries of the Columbia in such profusion that people caught them in burlap sacks, orange crates, and even bird cages. Women waded into streams and scooped them up in their skirts. Some gourmets regard smelt as the finest of edible fish.

Among my earliest gastronomic memories is the delicacy of freshly caught rainbow trout, cleaned and tossed into a pot of vinegar and water. This is *truite au bleu* served up in the wilds, enhanced by the fresh smells of forest and ferns and the rippling sound of the trout stream.

Summers we spent on the Oregon coast, where the men fished in the surf for rockfishes, surfperches, and greenlings, and netted surf smelt as they washed onto the sand to spawn. We children spent many a day angling at the mouth of the Necanicum

349

River for flat fish resembling sole and called pogies (not to be confused with porgies). These we split open, cleaned, and cooked Indian style—flattened, impaled on a stick, seasoned and brushed with oil, and held up to a beach fire to toast like a marshmallow. In a minute or so the delicate pogie, being thin, was cooked through. What juicy, flavorful eating!

Each fisherman has his own favorite way of cooking his catch. Probably the most popular is to roll the cleaned fish in cornmeal or flour and fry it in a pan over the campfire. I have no objections; I have done it myself and enjoyed it. But if you explore the many ways of cooking fish, I believe that you will find a whole new world of gastronomic pleasures opening up for you. Here are a few of my favorites, and some tips on preparing your catch and selecting fish at the market.

CLEANING

Fish are tastiest when you clean or gut them right after they are caught. If you can, toss the entrails back in the water; this way the fish will keep better and the waste will feed other fishes.

To gut a fish is not a bad job. With a sharp knife, cut along the stomach from the anal fin to the head. You can remove practically all the entrails with your finger. Any that remain can be brushed out with a piece of paper or cloth. This same operation applies to any bought fish that has not been gutted, but you will rarely find a merchant who won't do it for you.

When I was a boy in Oregon, we always wrapped the gutted fish in ferns, and this kept the flesh sweet and clean. Moist leaves work too. If your journey home is a long one, it might be well to purchase some crushed ice en route and pack the fish in an ice-filled container.

SCALING

If you buy from your fishmonger you need not be concerned with scaling. He'll do it for you if it hasn't already been done. To scale your catch, use either a dull knife or a heavy spoon. A wet fish scales more easily than a dry one, so dip it into cold water. Place it on a table and get a firm grip. Scrape toward the head from the tail.

Needless to say, if you are planning to fillet the fish and then skin it, don't bother to scale it.

RUNNING THE FINS

If you are cooking a fish whole or cutting it into steaks, running or removing the fins is a necessity. First cut out the pectoral fins, just behind the gills. Then remove the head by cutting through the flesh to the backbone. To snap the backbone, hang the fish's head over the table edge and bend it down with a quick thrust. Cut any flesh that may hold the head to the body.

Next comes the dorsal fin on the back of the fish. Don't try to cut it off with knife or scissors; you will leave the roots of the bones in the flesh. Run a knife along each side, then remove the fin and the root bones with a quick forward pull. In the same way, remove the pelvic fins—the ones on the underside. Then cut off the tail.

Now the fish is dressed and ready for poaching, baking, or broiling, if it is to be cooked whole. In the case of a large fish—a salmon, cod, or halibut—you may wish to cut it into steaks according to your idea of the right thickness. The fish also is ready to be filleted, although you can do this with fins and tail on.

FILLETING

Although small fish are usually associated with filleting, larger ones such as salmon, small or "chicken" halibut, and big bass often are treated in the same way.

You will need a sharp knife. A keen kitchen blade will do, but do not expect one made of ordinary steel to have a sharp enough edge. A true filleting knife has a 6- to 8-inch-long triangular blade of supple steel.

If the fish is still whole, place it on a cutting board or table with the backbone nearest you and the head to your left. Grip the head firmly. Cut into the flesh back of the tail and slide the knife along the backbone toward the head, leaving the fins attached to the fish itself. Cut away the whole side

MAKAH INDIANS *of Washington's Olympic Peninsula prepare salmon for a community potlatch. They strap red-fleshed fillets between cedar stakes, then drive the stakes in a circle around a roaring fire. Fish can also be cooked without heat. In Latin America a common way is to pour fresh lime juice over fish, letting the lime acid work on the flesh until it becomes a delicate tidbit called* seviche.

CAMP COOK *serves a panned rainbow trout fresh from a mountain lake in the Glacier Primitive Area of Wyoming. More rainbows fry in the skillet in the time-honored cooking technique of most outdoor fishermen. Trout on restaurant menus usually are rainbows, raised on fish farms scattered across the northern half of the United States.*

of flesh. Turn the fish and repeat the process. You now have two almost boneless fillets.

If the head, tail, and fins have been removed, just cut the flesh off along the backbone on both sides.

SKINNING FILLETS

Fillets may be cooked with the skin on but some people prefer them skinless. There are three ways to remove the skin:

● If the fish is very fresh and the flesh firm, use a knife or your fingers to loosen the skin at the tail, get a good grip, and pull the skin off. If the flesh is tender, work carefully so as not to tear it.

● Cut through the flesh at the tail and

SHOPPER INSPECTS *a red snapper at a Washington, D.C., market. Ice bin holds (from foreground) deep-bodied scup, boiled lobsters, striped bass, black sea bass, pompanos, snappers, coho salmon, American shad, and Spanish mackerel.*

then flatten the knife against the skin and cut the flesh away very slowly.

● Grip the flesh with a fork and hold the skin against hot running water. The skin will then pull away as easily as removing the peel from a ripe peach. This method works quite well for me.

Skinned fillets should be trimmed of flesh tags to make them ready for cooking. Store them in waxed paper or in foil.

In France, large fish are sometimes cut into what is termed a *filet* or *darne*. Cut the fish into 5- or 6-inch sections and then cut out the backbone in each section. You may skin this cut or not as you choose.

BUYING FRESH FISH

When you shop for fish, remember that many varieties, such as salmon and smelt, are seasonal. Like vegetables and fruits, they are often less expensive and better tasting when the fresh product is in abundance. Consult your dealer about the best times to buy your favorite fish.

When buying a whole fish, check the following points to be sure it is fresh: The *eyes* should be bright, shining and bulging. The *gills* should be pink to red, clean, and fresh smelling. The *scales* should be shiny and cling tightly to the skin. The *flesh* should be firm, and when pressed should spring back into shape.

Here are general rules for amounts:

If you are buying fish *fillets,* allow ⅓ to ½ pound for each person.

If you are buying fish *steaks* or a *center cut,* allow ½ to ¾ pound a person.

If you are buying *whole fish* complete with head and tail, buy a pound per person.

To keep the fish fresh, wrap it in moisture-proof paper or place it in a covered container and store it immediately in the refrigerator. Use within one to two days.

FROZEN FISH

Modern freezing methods have greatly increased the variety of frozen fish that can be purchased throughout the year. Store frozen fish in the freezer compartment of the refrigerator until you are ready to use it. When it thaws, use at once. Do not refreeze.

1590 ENGRAVING BY THEODORE DE BRY, LIBRARY OF CONGRESS

ALGONQUIAN INDIANS *stage a cookout, 16th-century style. "Broylinge Their Fishes over the Flame," observed the contemporary artist, "They Take Good Heed that They Bee Not Burntt." The chef tends shadlike fish; new catch includes a garfish and a small hammerhead shark.*

Frozen fillets or steaks may be cooked without thawing. Fish to be stuffed or breaded must be allowed to thaw until it can be handled easily.

Do not thaw fish at room temperature. It will become flabby. Remove from the freezer and place it on a shelf in the refrigerator. Let it thaw just enough to be readily handled.

GRILLING AND BROILING

Cooking over an open fire is undoubtedly the first method known to man and is still one of the best. Colonial cooks grilled fish by splitting them and nailing them to boards propped by the hearth. Today we have all sorts of grills for outdoor and indoor use.

Fish properly cooked over charcoal has unbeatable savor. No other method, even with the greatest chef in command, can so decisively emphasize the flavor of fresh fish.

You need a fine bed of coals, never a hot fire. Oil the grill. If you use a hinged basket grill, be particularly careful to oil it well so that the fish does not stick. Small fish or fillets will bear a little more heat than the larger, which take more time to cook. But neither should ever have a hot fire.

The same rules apply for oven broiling. Preheat the oven for about 12 minutes. Line the pan with foil and place the rack on top.

Whole fish, from a little butterfish to a medium-sized salmon, can be broiled outdoors. A basket grill is preferred, although you may, if careful, use a large regular grill.

Oil the skin and rub inside the fish with salt, pepper, and a little lemon juice. If you wish, add fennel, thyme, tarragon, or dill.

A small fish will take 12 to 15 minutes on an outdoor grill. One weighing 5 or 6 pounds requires 25 to 40 minutes. Turn it several times and brush with oil before and during cooking. You may add white wine or lemon juice to the basting oil. Don't forget to serve the crisp skin too.

To broil a whole fish in the oven, place it 3 to 6 inches from the heating unit. Turn it

353

once. Allow 5 to 6 minutes per side for a medium fish and 7 to 10 minutes per side for a larger one.

Old timers contend that a fish broiled with the head on will be juicier. You may experiment on your own and find out how much truth there is in this view.

Fillets grilled outdoors require a hinged broiler like the old-fashioned toaster, or a basket grill. The fish must be carefully handled lest it break and become unattractive to the eye. Lubricate well with oil or melted butter before and during the cooking and add lemon juice if you wish. Cook for 5 to 7 minutes. You may bring up the heat for a minute at the end of the broiling period.

For oven broiling, flour the fillets lightly. Oil the rack and place it about 2 inches from the heating unit. Do not turn the fish. Cook 5 to 8 minutes. Overcooked, the fillets will become crumbly.

Fillets may be marinated and broiled with the marinade as a baste.

Fish steaks cut 1 to 2 inches thick may be broiled easily outdoors. Brush with oil or butter as you do with fillets. A 1-inch steak should take about 5 or 6 minutes to broil while a thick steak may take 10 to 14. When done the steak will flake easily.

To broil steaks in the oven, dust them with flour before you brush with oil. Place 2 to 4 inches from the flame or unit, depending on the thickness of the steaks. Brush with oil or butter once or twice during the cooking. Salt and pepper well.

Split fish may be cooked with the backbone left in. Broil skin side up for 4 minutes 3 or 4 inches from the heating unit. Turn carefully, brush the flesh with butter or oil, and continue broiling until it flakes easily when tested with a fork. This should take from 5 to 10 minutes depending on size and thickness of the fish. Season to taste.

SAUTÉING

I have always been a great believer in the simple foods, carefully prepared. A delicacy I could never get enough of as a child in Oregon was salmon cheeks *sauté meunière*. To gather these tiny morsels we often drove to the salmon canneries at Astoria, where friendly Chinese workers would go through the pile of cast-aside fish heads and extract the cheeks. What a treat when they were quickly sautéed in butter and served up with a bit of lemon.

The simple sauté is an excellent way to prepare small fish—trout, sole, flounder, sanddabs, or perch, for example. Simply cook quickly in a little butter or a mixture of butter and oil until the fish is delicately browned and flaky tender. Add salt and pepper to taste and a touch of lemon juice if you wish. Serve with additional butter and slices of lemon.

Some people like to dust the fish with flour to make it brown more easily, but this is not at all necessary.

There are several delicious variations of this simple basic dish. The portions below apply to servings of four small fish:
- When the fish are done, add a pat or two of butter and two tablespoons of chopped parsley to the pan. Turn the fish in the parsley butter before removing them to a hot platter. Then pour the parsley butter over the fish.
- When the fish are half done, add 4 pats of butter and ½ cup of shaved blanched almonds and let them cook with the fish. Spoon them over the fish when you serve. This is called *sauté amandine.*
- With a heavy fork, knead together 2 ounces of butter, 1 tablespoon of chopped parsley, and a good squeeze of lemon juice. Add this to the fish when they are removed to a hot platter.

The classic companion of sautéed fish is plain boiled potatoes with butter and freshly ground pepper and salt.

FISHERMAN'S WHARF *in San Francisco serves seafood in sight of the fleet that caught it. Family at Tarantino's Restaurant enjoys marine delicacies including local crab and lobster, shrimp from Louisiana, and oysters from Chesapeake Bay.*

DAVID S. BOYER, NATIONAL GEOGRAPHIC STAFF

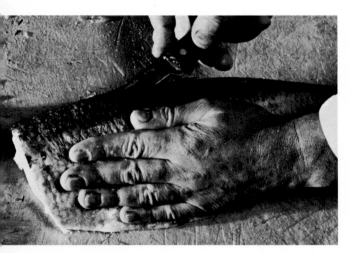

SHAD FISHERMEN *on the Hudson River boat a catch in the shadow of the George Washington Bridge and New York City towers. Each spring, when shad swarm from the ocean to spawn, men string gill nets from the banks. On the slack of the flood tide they haul in the prized fish. Lantern on net pole alerts river craft.*

The shad's six rows of small bones nearly defy filleting, giving rise to professional shad boners. Skilled and rare, they spend years learning the art. The boner at left slides a knife along the backbone. Below, from left: He cuts the halves from backbone and ribs, pulls out a row of bones loosened by the knife, then cuts under a row hidden near the tail. He processes 25 an hour, a novice perhaps four.

PANNED FISH

This method often serves campers. In England it is particularly popular. Throughout the American hinterland, especially in the West and South, panning is the favorite fashion of cooking small fish or fillets.

For 2 pounds of fish or fillets, use a fork to beat 2 eggs with a couple of tablespoons of water. Prepare 1½ cups of bread crumbs with a grater or blender. Now melt 6 tablespoons of butter and 2 of oil in a large, heavy skillet. Heat to the bubbling stage but do not let burn.

Dip fish or fillets in flour, then in the egg, and press into the crumbs. Sauté in the hot fat until nicely browned, then turn and repeat the process. Allow 3 to 6 minutes per side, depending on the size of the fish. Salt and pepper to taste.

Caution: Fish so cooked are delicious unless they are overcooked. Then they resemble fried sawdust.

Serve with lemon wedges or a tartar sauce (recipe page 362). Again, boiled potatoes, perfectly cooked, are as fine an accompaniment as you can choose.

DEEP FRYING

Patrons of the old fish-and-chips houses that still abound in England tote home or eat on the road their deep-fried fish and chip potatoes, usually wrapped in newspaper. The tidbits often are eaten with a touch of vinegar—don't ask me why. Deep frying is not my favorite way, but it is enormously popular.

Again let me caution against overcooking.

To fry in deep fat, heat oil or shortening in a deep-fat fryer at 375°.

The pieces of fish or small whole fish should be dusted with flour, then dipped in a mixture of beaten eggs and water (2 eggs and 2 tablespoons of water beaten with a fork will suffice for about 2 pounds of fish). After the egg dip, press the fish into bread crumbs, corn meal, corn flake crumbs, or sesame seeds. Place 2 or 3 pieces of fish in the frying basket and lower into the hot fat for 3 to 5 minutes. Drain on absorbent paper and season with salt and pepper.

BRAISING

This French process is thoroughly rewarding, even though it takes a little more time than most other methods. It is a great favorite at the Brasserie des Catalans, a notable restaurant in Marseille.

For a 5-pound whole fish, cut in matchstick pieces 3 carrots, 2 stalks of celery, 3 onions, and a clove of garlic, and add a few sprigs of parsley. Heat 3 tablespoons of butter in a fish cooker, large Dutch oven, or heavy pot, and add the vegetables. Cook for about 4 minutes over a brisk flame. Reduce the heat.

Place the fish on the vegetables and top with a few strips of bacon. Add a teaspoon of salt, a few grinds of pepper, and 2 cups of white wine. Cover the pan very tightly and let the liquid come to a boiling point.

Now reduce the heat and simmer for 25 to 30 minutes, or place in the oven and bake

357

at 325° for 35 minutes or until the fish flakes easily when tested with a fork.

Remove the cooked fish to a hot serving platter, and, if you wish, put the vegetables through a blender with the liquid in the pot and make a sauce. Or merely serve the fish with the cooking liquid either thickened or not, as you wish. Fish cooked in this manner is also delicious when served cold with mayonnaise.

If you wrap the fish in cheesecloth, or arrange it in a hammock of loose foil, it is much easier to remove from the pot.

POACHING

In your grandmother's day this was called boiling. But long experience has proved that results are much more satisfactory if the fish is cooked at a feeble ebullition called simmer—a point just under boiling. Hence poached fish.

Sometimes fish are poached in a *court bouillon,* which is a mixture of water, a little wine or sometimes beer, and seasonings such as onion, garlic, thyme, carrot, and herbs. Cook the spiced mixture at a boil for 15 to 45 minutes to blend the flavors thoroughly before the fish is added.

If you do not wish to use a court bouillon, it is perfectly good practice to poach the fish in salted water. In either case the cooking time is 6 to 8 minutes per pound. If the fish is not entirely covered by the court bouillon, it is wise to baste with a dipper or ladle during the cooking process.

If you do use a court bouillon, you can make a sauce for the fish with a reduction of the broth, which has become deliciously fla-

SKEWERED MACKEREL, *resembling lollipops stuck in the sand, roast over coals on a Mexican beach. Munching one like an ear of corn, a boy from Puerto Vallarta smiles "bueno." The baked tidbits cost about two pesos—roughly 16 cents.*

Tackling a fish with the hands like this at the table might draw frowns. But there's a polite and easy way of deboning a fish served whole. With the fish on its side, cut down to bone along the lateral line (page 15). Turn back the flesh, hinge-fashion, on both sides of the cut. Use a knife to lift the backbone free at the tail, then, with fingers, strip toward the head and remove.

vorful by the time the fish is cooked. Add cream, eggs or thickening, and wine.

The sauce is often garnished with parsley, hard-cooked eggs, and sometimes tiny shrimp or mussels. You may also spike the sauce with a liquor such as cognac, armagnac, brandy, dry vermouth, Madeira, sherry, or whiskey.

As with braising, the fish is more easily lifted from the pan if wrapped in cheesecloth or arranged in a loose foil hammock.

BAKING

The first baking was probably done in a pit dug in the ground. Early bakers lined their pits with hot rocks, wrapped the food in leaves and put it in to cook, and covered it all with soil. Men still cook fish this way in Pacific islands and in some areas of the Caribbean. Praise be to our modern oven.

Years ago a woman named Evelene Spencer, a fish cookery expert with the U. S. Department of the Interior, developed her own way of baking fish. The Spencer method calls for short cooking at high heat. It is still the best way to bake fish.

Modern modification of this method calls for lining a baking pan with foil and placing the fish either directly on the foil or on a rack above it. A whole fish should be brushed with fat, butter, or oil, or stripped with slices of salt pork or bacon. If the fish has a heavy skin, it is wise to slash it in two or three places.

A whole fish of about 4 pounds will take 30 to 35 minutes to bake; a larger one takes about 4 to 5 minutes more per pound at a reduced temperature. Start the fish in a 425°

SEVEN APPETIZING WAYS *of preparing fish parade in these classic dishes. Ranging downward from the top: baked stuffed bass, breaded haddock fillets, broiled porgy, poached salmon with hollandaise sauce, trout meunière, rolled sole in white wine sauce, and deep-fried smelts.*

to 450° oven, and if it is a large fish, reduce the temperature after 30 minutes to 350°. Test with a fork or toothpick to see if the flesh flakes easily.

If a recipe calls for basting with butter or wine or a mixture of both, place the fish on a rack over the pan so that the basting and pan juices mix and so that the fish does not lie in liquid.

You can stuff fish with bread crumbs or with flavor-giving vegetables such as thin slices of onion, pepper, tomato, or garlic.

Or you may want to stuff the fish with butter, pepper, salt, and your favorite herb combined with parsley and a sliced onion. This, of course, imparts a delicious flavor to any fish, and with the addition of melted butter and lemon offers an appetizing dish.

Certain herbs rank high for fish. Fennel is one; the dried stems of this bulb are used. Dill is popular in the Scandinavian countries. Tarragon and oregano have long been favored in the Latin countries. Parsley blends with any of these.

Fish Recipes

If you have always cooked your catch in the same old way, why not experiment? Try various seasonings, flavorings, and sauces. Create your own specialties. Cooking your fish may then become as much fun as catching it. Here are a few recipes to give you a start.

PIKE AND PICKEREL

Our inland waters offer a rich variety of pike, pickerel, and muskellunge. You may catch a pike weighing 25 pounds, but those sold in markets weigh from 2 to 10. The French value the delicacy of this fish and prepare it in many delightful ways. Among the most flavorful:

BRAISED STUFFED PIKE

5-pound pike
½ cup of chopped onion
½ pound of ground smoked ham
2 cups of dry bread crumbs
½ cup of chopped parsley
½ teaspoon of thyme
3 eggs and 2 egg yolks
1 teaspoon of salt
1 teaspoon of freshly ground black pepper
4 tablespoons of melted butter
strips of salt pork
white wine
lemon juice
beurre manié (2 tablespoons of butter
 kneaded with 3 tablespoons of flour)

Clean the fish and prepare it for stuffing.

Sauté the chopped onion in butter until tender. Combine with the 3 eggs, the smoked ham, bread crumbs, chopped parsley, thyme, salt, pepper, and melted butter. Stuff the fish with this mixture and sew it up.

Place the pike in a shallow baking pan with enough white wine to cover the bottom of the pan thoroughly. Top the fish with strips of salt pork and bake in a 350° oven for 45 minutes. Baste occasionally, and cover the pan after the first 15 minutes of cooking. When done remove the salt pork and arrange the fish on a platter.

Strain the pan juices and thicken them with the beurre manié. Stir a little of this hot combination into the 2 egg yolks slightly beaten. Add this mixture to the remainder of the sauce, stirring constantly over a very low flame until well blended and smooth. Do not let it boil.

Taste for seasoning and add salt and pepper if needed. Add a dash of lemon juice and a generous amount of fresh chopped parsley. Pour the sauce over the stuffed pike.

TROUT

Many people who like to eat their trout right beside the lake or stream feel that the only way to cook them is to dip them in flour or cornmeal and sauté in butter or bacon fat. This can be tasty, but I am certain that if you prepare live trout in the classic manner of the Swiss or French, you will find it far superior:

TRUITE AU BLEU

The trout must be alive. Slit and gut them just before you plunge them into the broth.

Prepare the broth of 3 parts water to one part vinegar. Add 6 peppercorns, a piece of bay leaf, and a teaspoon of salt to each quart of liquid. Bring to a boil. Plunge in the trout and poach them just long enough to cook through—about 4 minutes for the average fish.

Serve them hot with melted butter and boiled potatoes, or chill them and serve cold with mayonnaise.

The vinegar in the water turns the skin of the trout a vivid metallic blue; hence the name *truite au bleu*.

CATFISH

Most fishermen have caught catfish at one time or another, and nearly 20 million pounds are sold commercially every year. It is a great favorite in the South, where roadside stands selling fried catfish and hushpuppies often outnumber hamburger stands.

For all methods of cooking, catfish must be skinned. Draw a very sharp knife around the fish just in back of the gills. Then strip off the skin with your fingers, or with the aid of tweezers.

Catfish is usually fried, and here is the most popular recipe:

DEEP-FRIED CATFISH

Use the fish whole or cut it in pieces. Heat the fat in the deep fryer to 370 degrees. Put out a bowl of flour, a bowl of 2 lightly beaten eggs, and a bowl of rolled cracker crumbs, fine bread crumbs, or cornmeal. Dip the fish in the flour, in the egg, and then in the crumbs or meal, and fry in the hot fat for 3 to 5 minutes, depending on the size of the fish. Drain and season to taste with salt and pepper. Serve with tartar sauce (see recipe below).

HADDOCK

The haddock is a close relative of the cod, but it is much smaller, usually weighing 2 to 3 pounds. It is found in our northeastern coastal waters and is popular in New England.

BAKED STUFFED HADDOCK

Select a 3-pound haddock. Split the fish without cutting clear through and clean it. Leave the head and tail intact.

Prepare the following stuffing:

½ cup of finely chopped onion
¼ cup of butter (½ stick)
2½ cups of bread crumbs
3 tablespoons of chopped parsley
salt and freshly ground black pepper
   to taste
2 eggs, lightly beaten

Sauté the onions in the butter until soft but not brown. Add the rest of the ingredients except the eggs, then toss well. Finally blend in the beaten eggs.

Stuff the fish with the bread crumb mixture and sew it up. Strip it with salt pork or bacon and place it on heavy foil or on a rack over foil. Bake for 30 to 35 minutes in a 400° oven.

Remove the fish to a hot platter. Serve it with tartar sauce and tiny new potatoes boiled in their jackets.

TARTAR SAUCE

1 cup of mayonnaise
2 tablespoons of chopped onion or scallion
2 tablespoons of chopped parsley
1 tablespoon of chopped fresh dill weed
   or 2 tablespoons of chopped dill pickle

Blend well and allow to mellow for an hour or two before serving.

RED SNAPPER

This is one of the great fish of our country. It is found on both the Atlantic and the Gulf coasts and is considered a delicacy wherever it is caught. Its flesh is juicy and sweet, and the brilliant red of its skin is appealing to the eye. To bring out the best of its flavor and texture, try this recipe:

POACHED RED SNAPPER

First, prepare a simple court bouillon.
2 quarts of water
2 tablespoons of salt
½ cup of wine vinegar
1 teaspoon of peppercorns or
  ½ teaspoon of pepper
1 bay leaf
2 carrots
1 onion stuck with 2 cloves
1 stalk of celery
2 sprigs of parsley

Put all the ingredients in a long fish cooker or a kettle large enough to hold the fish. Bring the liquid to a boil, lower the heat, and cook gently for 25 minutes.

Clean the fish, leaving it whole. Cradle it in a piece of cheesecloth or foil, leaving long ends to use as handles when lifting the fish. Lower it into the hot broth and cook gently, allowing about 8 minutes per pound. Test for doneness. Remove and serve hot with hollandaise sauce and boiled potatoes. Or, cool the fish and serve it with a good homemade mayonnaise or tartar sauce and perhaps a cucumber salad.

HOLLANDAISE SAUCE

Hollandaise is a perfect sauce for many fish dishes, particularly for plain, sautéed, broiled, or poached fish.

If you have an electric blender, preparing hollandaise is simple. Place 3 egg yolks in the blender and add ½ teaspoon of salt, a dash of tabasco, and the juice of half a lemon. Turn the blender on and off very quickly.

Melt ¼ pound (one stick) of butter until it is bubbly. Start the blender on high and gradually pour in the melted butter. Blend until the sauce is smooth and thick. The entire operation takes less than a minute.

REGULAR HOLLANDAISE

Here is the method for making the sauce without the electric blender. Combine 3 egg yolks and 2 teaspoons of water in the upper part of a double boiler over hot, *not boiling,* water. Whisk until the eggs have started to thicken a little, then add ¼ pound of butter softened and cut in small pieces. You must add the butter bit by bit, whisking constantly. The sauce will thicken fairly soon. Add a few grains of salt, a dash of tabasco, and the juice of half a lemon. If the sauce gets too thick, add a little cream. If it curdles, and it sometimes does, you can usually correct this by adding a little boiling water.

Variation: Add a tablespoon or more of prepared mustard after the sauce is made.

SALMON

Salmon is my favorite fish. Probably this is because I grew up near the mouth of the Columbia River where some of the world's best salmon is caught. Of course it is a lordly fish wherever it is found and as a food it is versatile and hearty.

This is one of the ways my family enjoyed fresh salmon steaks:

SALMON STEAKS FLORENTINE

Dust 4 thickish salmon steaks with flour. Put 4 tablespoons of butter and 2 tablespoons of oil in a large skillet and heat over a medium flame. Sauté the steaks in the hot fat, turning them once to brown on both sides. Season to taste with salt and freshly ground black pepper when you turn them. They should take 6 or 7 minutes to cook. Test for doneness with a fork.

Serve the salmon steaks with chopped spinach dressed with olive oil, garlic, and lemon juice. Boiled potatoes or crisp sautéed potatoes make another good accompaniment.

WHOLE SALMON

If you are a salmon fisherman, there is an excellent way to use a whole fish and have good eating for several days. Poach it first and serve it hot with hollandaise sauce. Next day serve it cold with mayonnaise and a cucumber salad. If there is any left, cover it with three parts oil, one part vinegar, and sliced onions, and allow it to absorb the flavors for several hours. Serve this marinated salmon plain or in a salad.

MACKEREL

This is one of the most plentiful fish we have. It tastes remarkably good whether you broil it, poach it, or stuff and bake it as follows:

BAKED STUFFED MACKEREL
1 mackerel (about 4 pounds)
2 medium size onions, finely sliced
8-10 sliced mushrooms
2 tomatoes, peeled and thinly sliced
salt and freshly ground black pepper
olive oil

Clean the fish and stuff it with the sliced vegetables. Dribble olive oil on the vegetables and season to taste with salt and pepper. Fasten the fish with a skewer or sew it if necessary. Place on a rack over foil and top with a few onion slices; then cover with slices of bacon. Bake at 425° for 35 to 40 minutes, or until the fish flakes easily when tested with a fork.

Serve with crisp garlic-flavored French bread and a good green salad.

FISH STEWS

Each great fishing region in Europe, especially those along the Mediterranean shores, has developed outstanding traditional fish stews made with combinations of local fish plus wine or broth and seasonings. Some of these dishes have become internationally famous. *Bouillabaisse,*

zuppa di pesce, matelote, and *bourride* are examples. I have always felt that these stews were at their best when made with the traditional fish. However, you can make good fish stews using any catch you have.

In America, we have the popular clam and fish chowders, hearty mixtures resembling stews. The court bouillon of the Gulf region and the she-crab soup of Charleston are similar. In California, the Portuguese and Italian fishermen created fish stews of many varieties. These gradually combined to become the well known cioppino so popular in San Francisco. There are several versions of cioppino. Here I give two.

CIOPPINO I

This recipe is quite old and, I believe, one of the original cioppinos.

Cut a 3- to 5-pound fish into fairly large pieces. Save the head, tail, and bones and with them make a fish stock. Place them in a kettle and cover with salted water. Cook until the broth is flavorful. Strain and keep.

In a large stew pot, place ½ cup of good olive oil and heat it. Add 1 cup of finely chopped onions and 3 finely chopped garlic cloves. Sauté gently for about 4 minutes. Add 2 cups of peeled, chopped fresh tomatoes, or the same amount of canned Italian tomatoes. Salt and pepper well and add 1½ cups of the fish stock.

Cover the pot and cook briskly for 10 minutes. Add the pieces of fish and spoon the vegetables over them. Add 2 tablespoons of chopped parsley and a pinch of fresh or dried basil. Cover the pot and simmer until the fish is just tender. This takes about 15 minutes. Do not stir the stew. Correct the seasonings and serve in hot soup plates with garlic-flavored toasted French bread.

On the West Coast, the fish used might be lingcod, rockfish, or halibut. Easterners can use red snapper, haddock, or any favorite fish.

CIOPPINO II

This is a more modern version. Follow the directions above, but add dried Italian mushrooms and a minced green pepper to the onions and garlic. When you pour in the fish stock, add a pint of red wine. Five minutes before the fish is done add shrimp and clams. This makes a hearty stew, truly a meal in itself.

ITALIAN FISH STEW, zuppa di pesce, *tantalizes a hungry Positano fisherman. Served over croutons, it contains a medley of fishes, shrimp, squid, and other sea life cooked with olive oil, parsley, garlic, and tomato sauce. American cioppino dishes described above are variations of this Lucullan feast and the* bouillabaisse *of Marseille.*

LUIS MARDEN, NATIONAL GEOGRAPHIC STAFF

Index
Text references are indicated in roman type—000; illustrations in boldface—**000**; fish biographies in boldface and brackets—**[000]**

AQUARISTS *prize the fairy basslet or royal gramma (below) and the bluebanded goby. Often called Catalina goby, striped* Lythrypnus dalli *hides in Pacific crevices at depths of 20 feet or more. Purple-headed* Gramma loreto *brightens reefs of Bermuda, the Caribbean, and West Indies.*

WALTER A. STARCK II

HOVERING *bluehead inspects a sponge off Mexico's Yucatán Peninsula. Young and adult* Thalassoma bifasciatum *display wide ranges in markings and color; those developing bright blue heads are always males.*

FRINGED *goosefish waves a flesh-tipped dorsal spine above its cavernous mouth to attract Atlantic prey. Among the largest of the angler-fishes, gluttonous* Lophius americanus *dines on assorted fishes, crabs, even sea birds.*

ERNEST L. LIBBY

CAUTIOUS CONEY, *a half-pint grouper, peers from a conch shell hideaway. Native to Florida and the West Indies, polka-dotted* Cephalopholis fulva *seldom reaches a foot in length. Body color, usually reddish, changes at whim.*

Composition by National Geographic's Phototypographic Division, HERMAN J. A. C. ARENS, Director; JOHN E. MCCONNELL, Manager. Color separations by The Lanman Company, Alexandria, Virginia. Printed and bound by Fawcett-Haynes Corporation, Rockville, Maryland.

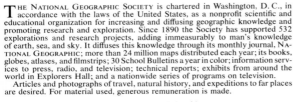

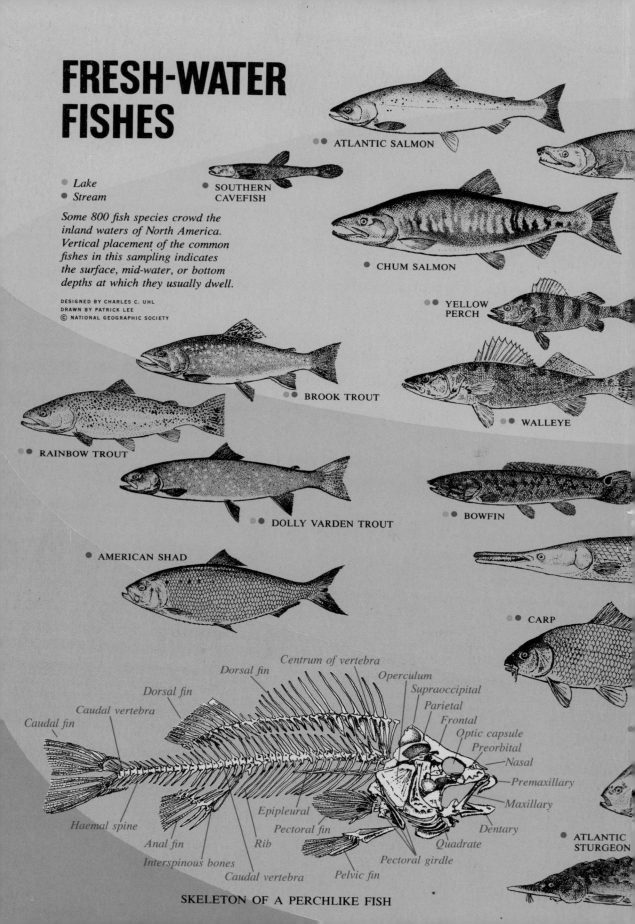

FRESH-WATER FISHES

● *Lake*
● *Stream*

Some 800 fish species crowd the inland waters of North America. Vertical placement of the common fishes in this sampling indicates the surface, mid-water, or bottom depths at which they usually dwell.

DESIGNED BY CHARLES C. UHL
DRAWN BY PATRICK LEE
© NATIONAL GEOGRAPHIC SOCIETY

●● ATLANTIC SALMON

●● SOUTHERN
CAVEFISH

● CHUM SALMON

●● YELLOW
PERCH

●● BROOK TROUT

●● WALLEYE

● RAINBOW TROUT

●● DOLLY VARDEN TROUT

● BOWFIN

● AMERICAN SHAD

●● CARP

ATLANTIC
STURGEON

Caudal fin
Caudal vertebra
Dorsal fin
Dorsal fin
Centrum of vertebra
Operculum
Supraoccipital
Parietal
Frontal
Optic capsule
Preorbital
Nasal
Premaxillary
Maxillary
Dentary
Quadrate
Pectoral girdle
Pelvic fin
Pectoral fin
Epipleural
Rib
Caudal vertebra
Interspinous bones
Anal fin
Haemal spine

SKELETON OF A PERCHLIKE FISH